OREGON FOSSILS

ELIZABETH L. ORR
University of Oregon

WILLIAM N. ORR
University of Oregon

KENDALL/HUNT PUBLISHING COMPANY
4050 Westmark Drive   Dubuque, Iowa 52002

Cover photography by Gary Tepfer, Eugene, Oregon.
Pleistocene freshwater snails mark an ancient shoreline of Summer Lake
in southcentral Oregon.

TABLE OF CONTENTS

STRATIGRAPHY AND CORRELATION CHARTS

LOCALITY MAPS

PREFACE

This book grew out of the *Handbook of Oregon Plant and Animal Fossils*, published in 1981, which in turn developed from a summer paleontology field course offered at the University of Oregon many years ago. The present treatment is not meant to be an exhaustive account of every reported fossil or locality but attempts to relate major events and people who have made significant contributions to the story of Oregon's geologic past. We have tried to highlight a few of the specimens out of the many found and the occasional locality in the midst of many thousand. Because of the vast breadth of material covered, most accounts are, of necessity, only "sketches" - which can lead to additional research if the reader so desires.

Throughout the manuscript we have, where possible, used the exquisite pen and ink drawings from the turn of the century by John Newberry, Karl von Zittel, George Sudworth, and others, whose work has yet to be duplicated by modern illustration techniques. Updating taxonomy is beyond the scope of this volume, and the faunal and floral lists are not comprehensive.

Paleontology periodically molts to appear again with all new feathers. The Golden Age of Paleontology lasted from the mid 1800s until the 1930s. The focus then was on spectacular vertebrate bones, when large-scale expeditions went forth and tens of thousands of fossils flowed back to the institutions who financed them. A period of describing and naming new species and tracing evolution followed. From the 1930s to the 1970s fossils of every description were recognized as useful tools for working out stratigraphy, especially in the petroleum industry. Later trends saw detailed interpretations of paleoenvironments based on fossils. Currently fossils are being exploited to unravel the history of exotic crustal terranes and trace their wanderings across the globe, while DNA extracted from fossilized plant and animal tissue is resolving taxonomic problems.

We would especially like to thank Ewart Baldwin for his time, marvelous perspectives, and commentaries. Greg Retallack's careful reviews, ideas, and loans of publications greatly improved the book. Because of Carol McKillip's extensive library, we were able to obtain works, which would have been unavailable otherwise. Ellen Moore's time and editorial abilities were also appreciated as were those of Arnold Shotwell and Lillian Mascall. Many more people sent fascinating vignettes and contributed photographs. Research of this sort could not go foreward without the services of librarians and archivists. Elizabeth Nielsen at the Oregon State University Special Collections was especially helpful and pleasant as were Cathy McNassor at the Archives of the Page Museum, Los Angeles, and Joe McGregor in the Geology Library at the U.S. Geological Survey in Denver. The prompt and enthusiastic response of Klaus Neuendorf from the Oregon Department of Geology and Mineral Industries greatly assisted in obtaining photographs. The science library resources at the University of Oregon, Isabel Sterling, and others who work there are outstanding.

Eugene, Oregon, 1998

Dedicated to eem

A Sunday outing to look for fossils in southwest Oregon [photo courtesy Grants Pass Art Studio and Oregon Department of Geology and Mineral Industries].

OREGON FOSSIL PLANTS

The fossil record of ancient plant life, preserved as leaves, seeds, flowers, petrified wood, and pollen grains, documents environmental settings of past ages. In Oregon, fossil plants of the Paleozoic and Mesozoic eras, 300 to 65 million years ago, are scarce and known only from the Klamath and Blue mountains. Despite their limited diversity preCenozoic floras play a key role in deciphering the complex stories of plate tectonics and paleoclimates. Early floras were brought to Oregon from some distance during the processes of crustal plate movement, and it wasn't until the Cretaceous period that plants developed as part of local environments here. Although these ancient ferns, cycads, and conifers are no longer part of the state's modern floras, similar species can be seen worldwide at tropical latitudes.

In contrast to those of older time periods, the quality and quantity of Cenozoic fossil plants is impressive. Remains of former vegetation from 40 million years ago both east and west of the Cascade Mountains reflect a wide variety of changing conditions as the landmass, which now is Oregon, emerged from the ocean. The Cenozoic also saw numerous lakes as the result of extensive volcanic eruptions when lava and mud flows dammed streams. An accompanying layering of fine ash, falling over the landscape was collected by streams that built elaborate flood plains and deltas, contributing to the preservation of a particularly fine array of plant fossils.

PRESERVATION

Unlike those of mammals and invertebrates, leaves, wood, and pollen require that special conditions be met for fossilization. While mineral-rich bone, teeth, and shells need only to be buried to earn a place in the geologic record, vegetable and woody matter is highly susceptible to decay, bacteria, oxidization, and insects. A critical factor to successful preservation of plants is rapid burial in an environment free of oxygen, such as a swamp or lake bed, to prevent destruction of the delicate soft tissue. In a quiet setting even fragile thin leaves fossilize by being pressed flat within the very fine particles of clay making up shales and muds. Coarse-grained rocks represent areas of rapid deposition where swiftly flowing streams tend to destroy leaves before they are deposited. Sand or gravel, that permit the passage of water through the sediments after burial, allow destruction of plant tissue by solution and oxidation.

Other considerations in plant preservation are dispersal and the chemical make-up of plant tissue. Because leaves and wood float, they can be carried with a minimum of abrasion to favorable burial sites. Large thick tropical leaves are more easily moved by streams and are thus more readily preserved than small thin ones, typical of temperate environments. Dispersal of needles by wind, moreover, is not nearly as thorough as it is for deciduous leaves. Pollen may be airborne or carried by water for weeks before it settles. Additionally the chemistry of plant tissues contributes to fossilization, as pollen, wood, leaves, and fruit contain a variety of organic compounds that may retard decay.

Leaves are most frequently preserved as a thin carbon layer. This type of fossilization called "distillation" is the process of removing the volatile organic material from the leaf without disturbing the fine details. What remains after distillation is a delicate carbon film displaying the leaf outline, veins, and even cell structures.

Fossil wood is preserved in a variety of ways. Wood may undergo distillation like leaves by the slow removal of most other elements except the carbon. What appears to be charcoal in sediments is usually distilled wood. Burning wood to make charcoal makes walls fuse to create a distinctive trellis-like shape in thin section. Very often wood is permineralized, which entails the infilling of all the vacant pore spaces by minerals such as calcite or silica. Compared to surface streams, water percolating through porous rock is normally rich in dissolved minerals, augmenting permineralization. Fossil wood in this condition may appear fresh and unaltered, but it is strikingly heavy because of saturation by minerals. The unaltered appearance of permineralized wood has been dramatically displayed when individuals, thinking such wood is modern, have actually attempted to run it through a sawmill, destroying the saw blade in the process. In this state wood can occasionally take a polish on a lapidary wheel, but frequently the framework of the woody tissue makes the specimen crumbly. Wood that has undergone complete replacement by minerals is "petrified." During petrification, silica, in the form of calcedony, jasper, or agate, has been exchanged for the wood tissue. This slow process permits the preservation of delicate features as annual rings and details of individual cells. Like permineralization, replaced or petrified specimens are noticeably heavier than ordinary wood, but they will usually take a nice polish.

Overall, fossil pollen and spores are unaltered. That is, pollen, as it is fossilized, undergoes little substantive change other than being flattened and darkened with burial. The waxy, resinous wall of these tiny grains are especially resistant to decay, but they may be oxidized unless they are buried rapidly.

In spite of the multiple difficulties that stand in the way of preservation, the plant fossil record is remarkably good. Plants are generally better represented than, for example, mammals, and several factors contribute to this. A mammal skeleton will produce around 100 separate bones in its skeleton as potential fossil material, whereas a typical deciduous or hardwood tree will annually contribute tens of thousands of leaves and possibly one hundred times that in its lifetime. The sum total of leaves from a needle tree exceeds even that. The amount of pollen produced by a plant in either a lifetime or on an annual basis can be estimated in the millions. This overwhelming statistical edge wins a prominent place for plants in the fossil record.

PLANTS REVEAL PALEOCLIMATES

Among the most fascinating and useful aspects of plant fossils is their role in unravelling prehistoric climates. The flora that develops in a region is the complex by-product of an interrelated series of environmental factors including, in part, rainfall, temperature, sunlight, growing season length, and soils. By understanding the growth habitat and a multitude of characteristics of modern plants, ancient habitats can be deciphered.

Quite often when fossil plants are used to correlate or determine the geologic age of a rock, it has been shown that environments, not time, are being correlated. Stated another way, two floras that are identical certainly represent the same ecological conditions, but they may represent completely different time intervals. A good fossil inventory that includes the dates of various climatic events in a given geographic area can be employed to date strata of unknown age.

Early proponents for using leaf shapes to ascertain paleo-environments were Irving Bailey and Edmund Sinnott, in the Botany departments of Harvard and Yale universities respectively. Following careers dedicated to the study of plants, both men made major contributions to the knowledge of plant evolution and botanical theory. As early as 1916 they were able to distinguish between living tropical and temperate plants by examining the margins of leaves. Bailey and Sinnott observed that leaves with entire or smooth margins are overwhelmingly dominant in lowland tropical regions, while plants having serrated or non-entire margins populate temperate areas. In the tropics, foliage with serrated-margins favors moist uplands, mild temperatures, and protected cooler environs. In more temperate habitats, leaves with smooth margins prefer arid or dry locals.

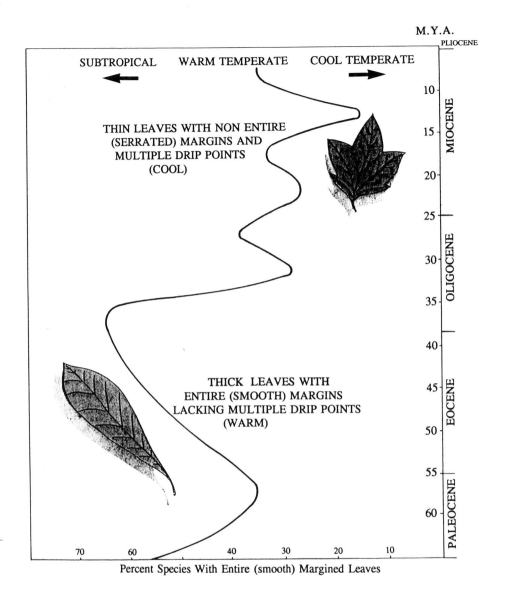

Comparing smooth and serrate leaf margins permits not only the distinction between temperate and tropical floras but allows for the tracing of climate change through time [after Wolfe and Hopkins, 1967].

One of the first to apply the technique of leaf morphology to deduce prehistoric environments in the Northwest was Ralph Chaney, of the University of California, Berkeley, who published widely on the floras and paleoecology of this region. It was Chaney who suggested rainfall also plays an important role in leaf shape, concluding that the contrast between smooth and serrate leaf margins is largely determined by available moisture, since leaves form drip points for water to run off the surface. Thus areas of high rainfall would tend to have plants that develop leaves with serrate margins.

Chaney's student Daniel Axelrod worked with regional Tertiary plant origins and distributions as a professor at the University of California. He made paleo-climate determinations by carefully comparing fossil plant species with those from modern settings. In addition to climates, Axelrod demonstrated that plants provided clues to prehistoric landscapes and physiography. By recording modern plants from different altitudes - from hardwoods in lowlands to mountain conifers at higher elevations - he was able to estimate paleo-altitudes of individual fossil floras. He surmised, for example, that in eastern Oregon the Sucker Creek flora grew in a lowland area at an elevation of only 500 feet. The Mascall flora was estimated to have developed at 1,500 feet, the Blue Mountain flora at 2,000 feet, and the Trout Creek flora around 2,400 feet.

In several recent papers, Jack Wolfe, a paleobotanist with the U.S. Geological Survey, has identified some of the problems that can arise when deriving paleo-environmental data based just on one or two parameters. He suggests the method of reconstructing ancient forests by leaf counts is flawed because of the many variables affecting preservation. For example thick, smooth margin leaves are more readily preserved than small thin ones. Therefore, a mixed living flora with few tropical leaves might appear to be dominantly tropical once fossilization has taken place because the temperate leaves didn't preserve well. Wolfe points out that there is no exact match between Tertiary and modern forests and that current knowledge of plant habitats is inadequate. He harks back to Bailey and Sinnott's method of correlating foliage characters with climate and altitude at which a plant grew to conclude that increasing cold not changes in precipitation caused changes in plant types. Serrated narrow leaves dominated in cool climates and broad smooth leaves at higher temperatures.

Interpreting paleoenvironments using pollen and spores can be far more definitive than by leaves or seeds since floras of fossil pollen grains are almost invariably more diverse and complete than those of leaves from the same rock. The richer pollen floras may provide information on temperature, climate, and even topography. Because fossil pollen and spores are rarely attached to the parent plant, in most cases they are treated and classified as separate entities. For example, an individual pollen grain may be identified as being from an oak tree, but the association of a particular fossil oak leaf species with a fossil oak pollen species is usually impossible to make. Often pollen for a given species is far more distinctive than the leaf. The presence of that pollen in a fossil assemblage will, then, confirm the identification of a questionable leaf. Unfortunately, published reports of pollen and leaves from the same locality are rare.

PLANTS AND CHANGES IN ENVIRONMENTS

Sudden or dramatic changes in the environment are invariably more prominently reflected in fossil plant sequences than are the slow evolutionary changes that take place through time. Natural catastrophies can alter the composition of vegetation, and frequently floral patterns are interrupted, slowed, or even stopped and reversed by variations in climate, fires, floods, volcanic eruptions, plant disease, or insects.

The thick layer of ash and pumice from Mt. Mazama, ejected about 6,900 years ago when the immense Crater Lake caldera formed, provide an extensive marker bed between floral changes over a wide area of the Pacific Northwest. This eruption came at the end of a warm, dry period recorded by oaks in the Willamette Valley, pines in the Cascades, grasses in eastern Washington and Idaho, and the reduction of Douglas fir in Puget Sound. Following the Mt. Mazama eruption, oaks declined in the valley, where they were replaced by Douglas Fir. In the Cascades, pines remained static or waned, while hemlock flourished in Puget Sound, and in eastern Washington pines replaced grasses.

Fire appears to have had a dramatic effect on floras in southern Washington state, where it apparently retarded hemlock expansion in the postglacial period. Elsewhere fire promoted the expansion of certain trees. In eastern Oregon and northeast Washington, the growth of white pine forests was favored by intermittent fire, and, for the same reason, lodgepole pine replaced yellow pine in the Cascades.

Some of the most detailed records of environmental change are found in the form of prehistoric floral successions. A "succession" is the slow change local plant communities undergo with time as the soils and landscapes mature. By utilizing fossil plant material, paleobotanists have been able to document three stages of succession. The initial condition or pioneer phase is usually represented by grasses. The pioneer phase, after a period of dominance, prepares the soil to the degree that it is eventually displaced by an intermediate phase of hardwoods followed by a climax community of conifers. Because successions proceed from a pioneer to climax phase in less than a thousand years, recognition of these separate intervals in the fossil record requires precise work with closely spaced samples rich in fossils.

Imaginary view of a forest 250 million years ago [from Pouchet, 1882].

ENVIRONMENTS OF THE PALEOZOIC AND MESOZOIC ERAS

The seas that covered much of the northwest during the Paleozoic and early Mesozoic between 300 and 100 million years ago were dotted by offshore volcanic island chains and submerged oceanic plateaus. Sitting atop moving pieces of the earth's crust, these projections above the otherwise smooth ocean floor were transported eastward to be permanently affixed or accreted to the western edge of the North American landmass. Geologic events surrounding continental collision brought about alterations which obscured the relationship between much of the strata, and fossils are a major tool used to unravel the history of these distorted rocks. The realization over the past 30 years that slabs of fossil-rich rocks moved freely about the earth has also required that previous conclusions about global paleoenvironments must be carefully reexamined.

PLANTS OF THE PENNSYLVANIAN PERIOD

Oregon's oldest fossil plant community, going back 250 million years, is found in Pennsylvanian age rocks from the Crooked River basin of Crook County. These fossils occur in the fine-grained mudstones of the 1,000-foot thick Spotted Ridge Formation. These strata lie between the older marine Coffee Creek Formation of the Mississippian period and the younger Permian marine Coyote Butte Formation. While the Coffee Creek and Coyote Butte contain invertebrate fossils, the Spotted Ridge has only a few shallow water shells. These and other rock formations form what is called the Grindstone terrane, and the alternating terrestrial and oceanic composition suggests a variety of ancient settings from coastal plain to a shallow sea.

In the midwest and northeast United States, floras from the Pennsylvanian period, comparable to the Spotted Ridge, are commonly found with coal layers. The contrasting lack of coal in Oregon during the same time frame may reflect a different setting where plants grew at higher elevations and not in lowland swamps more condusive to the accumulation and preservation of peat. Spotted Ridge plant material is so limited that speculations on the local paleoecology for this period involve a certain amount of guesswork, although the environment was probably not unlike the warm humid climates developing elsewhere in North America. An overriding consideration is that the Spotted Ridge flora is part of an exotic terrane not yet traced back to its point of origin somewhere along the Pacific Rim.

Plants of the Spotted Ridge were discovered in 1937 by Charles Merriam and Sheridan Berthiaume from Cornell University while engaged in a detailed mapping and stratigraphic project in the southeast corner of Crook County near Paulina. They submitted a small collection to Charles Read, a U.S. Geological Survey paleobotanist, for identification. The specimens were too fragmentary for determination, but more thorough excavations at the site the following year by Merriam and Berthiaume and in 1939 by Read resulted in a published report later listing the characteristics and species of ferns and fern-like foliage.

Charles Read and Sergius Mamay worked together on early plants of North America [photo courtesy S. Mamay].

In 1956 Read and coauthor Sergius Mamay, both specialists in Paleozoic and Mesozoic floras, more fully described and illustrated the Geological Survey's Spotted Ridge plant collection naming three new species, the horsetails *Mesocalamites* and *Phyllotheca* along with the fern-like *Dicranophyllum.* Fluent in Japanese, Sergius Mamay served as a military translator during World War II before entering the University of Washington and completing his PhD degree on late Paleozoic ferns in 1950. At that time he took a government job with the Geological Survey based in the Smithsonian Institution, where he continues to work on ferns and cycads in retirement.

Charles B. Read's career was also spent with the Survey from 1930 until retirement in 1972. Born on a Texas ranch in 1907, Read gained a love of the outdoors that carried through into the field as a geologist. An interest in ranching was reflected by his early pursuit of agriculture, however, his graduate work at the University of California in 1930 was in geology. Read's career in Washington, D.C., was also the start of a long friendship and working relationship with the famous paleobotanist Roland Brown, both sharing a small office on the 3rd floor of the Smithsonian building. During World War II, Read was transferred to the U.S. Geologic Survey's Fuels Branch in New Mexico to conduct mapping. Except for brief stints, he remained a permanent resident of Albuquerque, where, along with his long-term interest in Mesozoic plants, his efforts were directed toward fossil fuels and uranium reserves. Physical problems and ultimately Alzheimers syndrome led to his death in 1979.

Horsetails [*Phyllotheca*], *Lepidodendron* trees with diamond-shaped leaf scars, and *Cordiates,* related to conifers, represent the only Pennsylvanian plants in Oregon and are the oldest plant fossils in the state.

Pennsylvanian Spotted Ridge plants depict a lush green wetlands of seed ferns, giant horsetails with whorled leaves, exceptionally tall *Cordaites* trees that had long strap-like leaves, and the scale tree, *Lepidodendron*, an ancient relative of modern clubmosses. Distinctive diamond-shaped leaf scars that resembled scales covered the trunk of this tree. *Asterophyllites*, *Mesocalamites*, and *Phyllotheca*, all three ancestral joint grass, *Pecopteris* [fern-like], *Cordaianthus* [a cone of a conifer-like *Cordaites* tree], *Schizopteris* [fern], *Dicranophyllum* [fern-like], and *Stigmaria* [the root system of a *Lepidodendron* scale tree] characterize this interval of the Pennsylvanian.

PLANTS OF THE TRIASSIC PERIOD

No known fossil plants of Permian age have been found in Oregon, and the following period was also virtually barren of plant remains except for a unique late Triassic marine dasycladacean algae recently discovered in thin limestone layers of the Hurwal Formation in Wallowa County. Shales and siltstones of this formation are part of the Wallowa volcanic archipelago, terrane rocks that were accreted as a belt to the edge of the continent along northeast Oregon, Washington, Idaho, and British Columbia. Sediments of the Hurwal, representing a shallow ocean basin with lagoons in which limestone reefs developed, were draped over volcanic rocks that made up the archipelago.

George Stanley, of the University of Montana, who has spent years mapping and collecting in terranes of the Wallowa Mountains, described the new species of *Diplopora oregonensis*, which is the first green dasycladacean algae known from the United States during this time span 200 million years ago. Curiously, although varieties of this calcareous green algae are unknown from other Triassic terrane rocks of the eastern and western Pacific, they are common in similar tropical sediments of central Europe.

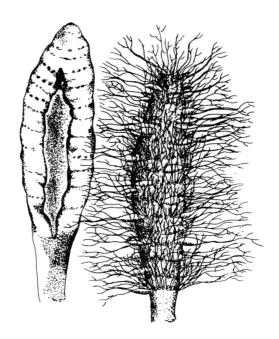

Triassic branching fossil algae from the Wallowas are the only recognized occurrence of this plant in western North America. Each specimen is one-half inch long.

PLANTS OF THE JURASSIC PERIOD

Like the Pennsylvanian floras, those from the Jurassic between 200 to 140 million years ago are preserved in fragments of exotic terranes. These fossils were part of extensive forests recorded in Mesozoic rocks. While this vast plant system was originally thought to reflect tropical conditions worldwide during this interval, the far-reaching nature of Jurassic floras may more likely represent an ancient continent broken up and dispersed by tectonic processes.

Ferns, cycad-like plants, conifers, and gingkoes were common. Most are now extinct, but descendants of cycads grow in the tropics today, and ginkgo, whose modern fan-shaped leaves are less deeply lobed, are found throughout the world. Preserved needles of a pine-like tree suggest these ancient conifers may have had some resemblance to those of the present time, but it is doubtful that any true members of *Pinus* existed back then. Although this Jurassic vegetation looks unusual, it is by no means as distinctive and archaic in appearance as that of the earlier Pennsylvanian.

In Oregon, Jurassic plants have been located in only two regions, near the town of Riddle in the Klamath Mountains and across the state in rocks of the Snake River Canyon in the Blue Mountains. The discovery of plants in the Klamaths has a curious history. As far back as 1872 a mining engineer, Aurelius Todd, accumulated several loads of plant fossils from a hard siltstone only a few feet thick near Buck Mountain in Douglas County. Of this extensive collection, a single plant specimen mixed in with some shells ultimately reached Lester Ward by way of two well-known invertebrate paleontologists, William H. Dall and Timothy Stanton. Ward, who was the head of the U.S. Geological Survey, turned the specimen over to William Fontaine who identified it as *Dryopteris monocarpa*, a dainty fern of the Jurassic.

A paleobotanist deserving special mention for his work on Mesozoic floras is William Fontaine. Growing up in Virginia, Fontaine fought for the Confederacy during the Civil War, on the opposite side to Lester Ward, with whom he later worked professionally. After finishing graduate work at the Royal School of Mines in Freiburg, Saxony, Fontaine became professor of geology and chemistry at the University of West Virginia before accepting a position at the University of Virginia in Richmond. Here he pursued his research on Mesozoic plants, contributing to Ward's *Status of the Mesozoic Floras of the United States*, 1900, which includes Jurassic and Cretaceous species from southwest Oregon. Fontaine died in Charlottesville in 1913.
[photo courtesy of the Smithsonian Museum]

More than 25 years after Todd's plants reached Washington, D.C., Lester Ward led an expedition to Buck Mountain assisted by the private collector James Storrs and mining engineer Will Q. Brown. The party included Joseph Diller, who was mapping southwest Oregon for the Geological Survey. Travelling by horse and pack animals along a mountain trail to Buck Peak, they camped for several days. The field season produced a sizeable suite of Jurassic plants from Douglas County localities such as the abandoned Nichols railroad station, Thompson Creek, and Buck Mountain. The finest specimens from this expedition were obtained by Ward and Storrs in 1899 from slates in the bed of Thompson Creek.

Todd's original fern specimen, which had earlier found its way to Ward, had been mislabelled as from the Kootenai Formation of Great Falls, Montana. In order to determine if it had really been collected from Montana or southwest Oregon, Ward and Diller needed to locate Todd, who had since moved to Dunedin, Florida. Diller persevered and finally found Todd who wrote that he had given quite a few specimens to Thomas Condon at the University, he had left others at Horn and Pain's gun store, "a sporting emporium", and he had stored boxes of specimens in the barn behind the house at 14th and Hilyard, all in Eugene. He generously offered the material to the Geological Survey, if it could be located, and his letter was accompanied by a detailed map confirming that the correct locality was in Douglas County. It isn't known what happened to the boxes of Jurassic plants that Todd left behind. The day of discovery was memorable to Todd, as he related in his letter, because he came across the fossil bed "during the early seventies [when] my older brother was killed [by a horse] in Lookingglass".

These Jurassic plant locals were described at the turn of the century by Fontaine, Diller, and Knowlton, but since that time the floras have not been reexamined in light of paleobiogeography and modern plate tectonics, which played such a dominate role in the early geologic history of the Klamath Mountains. Sediments of the Riddle Formation, in which these plants are found, are part of the Snow Camp terrane. The package of conglomerates, sandstones, and siltstones that make up the Snow Camp is believed to have been moved by faulting processes as much as 200 miles northward from the vicinity of the Sacramento Valley in California. Associated with the plants here, rare invertebrate shells of *Buchia piochii* [*Aucella*], a mussel- like Jurassic clam, occur in fragmented condition. In some regions of the Klamaths, reef-like mounds of *Buchia* are indicative of ancient nearshore settings.

It wasn't until 1991, that interest in Oregon's Jurassic floras was rekindled by the discovery of similar plants at the opposite side of the state in the Snake River Canyon. Sidney Ash, of the Geology Department at Weber State University, was able to demonstrate that fossil plants from the Coon Hollow Formation in Wallowa County could be used to help decipher the tectonic history here. Initially discovered by Tracy Vallier of the U.S. Geological Survey, Coon Hollow fossils turned up in rocks of the exotic Wallowa terrane exposed in vast tracts along the Snake River Canyon.

Poorly preserved petrified wood along with leaf and seed impressions make up this 175 million year old flora, dominated by ferns, conifers, and ginkgoes. Broad leaf plants are lacking. Ferns include *Dicksonia, Adiantites,* and *Cladophlebis.* The seed fern *Sagenopteris* is rare, but several conifers, resembling modern junipers, *Pagiophyllum, Brachyphyllum,* and *Podozamites* are plentiful. All of the fragmentary fossil wood recovered to date is similar to the conifer *Mesembrioxylon.* Specimens up to a foot in diameter and six feet long were dispersed and broken, suggesting transport some distance by streams before burial. A new fern *Phlebopteris tracyi*, which has fronds up to 18 inches in length, and the quillwort *Isoetites rolandii*, also newly discovered here, have not been found in the Riddle flora from the Klamath Mountains.

Deeply-lobed ginkgo, fine-leaf ferns as *Cladophlebis*, and the conifer *Podozamites* typify Oregon Jurassic floras.

Coon Hollow plants were deposited in fine-grained sandstones and conglomerates during uplift and erosion of the surrounding region. Volcanic debris in this strata points to eruptions near the coastline. In the moist-temperate climate, turbid, sediment-laden streams spread into deltas and flood deposits. Swampy lowlands supported ferns and quillworts, while drier hills were populated by conifers.

PLANTS OF THE CRETACEOUS PERIOD

By the Cretaceous, more than 100 million years ago, most of the major exotic terranes that form the foundation the Pacific Northwest had already merged or been accreted to the West Coast. During this period much of what is now Oregon was covered by a shallow seaway extending from British Columbia to northern California with shorelines across eastern Idaho, Washington, and Vancouver Island. A tropical rainy climate persisted through the Cretaceous interval.

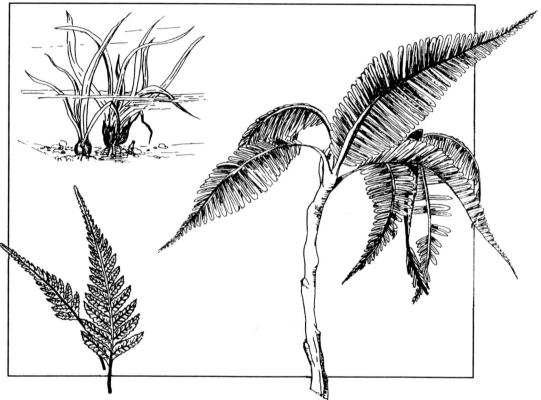

Large-leaf *Phlebopteris* along with the smaller fern *Dicksonia*, water-loving horsetail, and quillwort [*Isoetites*] depict the landscape along the Snake River over 150 million years ago.

Cretaceous floras are rare in Oregon, but, in contrast to those of the Pennsylvanian and Jurassic, these were probably native to the region. Like those of the previous periods, floras of the Cretaceous are found in the southwest and northeast regions of Oregon where land, perhaps as small islands, dotted the shallow seaway. To date no in-depth work has been done on Oregon's Cretaceous plants, and early studies of the few preserved remains give an incomplete picture of late Mesozoic life.

In southwest Oregon, floral remains along Elk River in Curry County occur in rocks of the Rocky Point Formation, a 1,000-foot thick layer above the Humbug Mountain Conglomerate. Both are part of the Elk terrane, a tectonic fragment moved northward from California by faulting. Remnants of specimens from here were sent to Lester Ward by Joseph Diller, both of the U.S. Geological Survey, but the leaves were in such poor condition that they defied identification. In order to gather better specimens, Diller sent James Storrs, "who has been the special collector of fossils in my field party for a number of years" to the Elk River in October, 1907. Here Storrs sucessfully acquired a small number of poorly preserved plants and shells from a shale layer of the Rocky Point. *Dicksonia,* the most common fern, was the only one from this local that was also found at Buck Peak and elsewhere in Douglas County. The ferns *Thyrsopteris, Cladophlebis,*and *Dicksonia,* cycads *Ctenis* and *Ctenophyllum,* as well as the conifers *Podozamites* and *Taxites* were positively identified by William Fontaine, who received the material in Washington, D.C. Fossil shells, scattered throughout the bed, included the Cretaceous clam *Buchia crassicollis.*

At the turn of the century, these collections were mentioned in publications by Diller, Ward, and Fontaine, but it wasn't until 1967 that John Stewart Lowther produced an abstract listing six species of ferns, cycads, and ginkgoes from along the Elk River. On the staff at the University of Puget Sound since 1956, Lowther had worked in the Cretaceous since he was a student at the University of Michigan. Directed to the plant local by Professor Ewart Baldwin, Lowther returned several times, completing his collection from the dark shales.

Cretaceous plants from the Blue Mountains are even more sparce. In 1958 a palm seed, encased in a concretion with an ammonite, was found by Portland resident, Mark Copeland, near Mitchell in Wheeler County. Copeland turned the seed over to Ewart Baldwin, professor at the University of Oregon, who shipped it to U.S. Geological Survey paleobotanist Roland Brown. Brown's letter of reply stated that the seed belonged to the genus *Attalea,* and "so far as I am aware this specimen is the first plant record from the late Cretaceous of north central Oregon. As such it is important to paleobotanical science and ... I would like to keep it for the U.S. National Museum collections."

One of the most unusual Cretaceous plants from the Northwest is the tree-fern, *Tempskya.* Living only during early Cretaceous intervals, this curious fossil may be related to several fern families, but its exact affinity has yet to be determined. *Tempskya* fossils are primarily trunk-like structures, formed from a ropy mass of stems and roots of a climbing plant. In cross-section the fossil displays distinctive crescent-shaped irregular bodies of the stems arranged in a radial pattern around a central core. The concensus seems to be that the false stem grew upright and not horizontally, tapering upward into a conical shape. Fossils are typically oxidized to a yellow color and occur as single, extremely hard, silicified and rounded buds averaging 30 pounds. The heaviest found was 135 pounds. The association of land plants as *Tempskya* with marine shells as ammonites suggests the presence of islands dispersed along a Cretaceous shoreline.

The most thorough look at *Tempskya* has been by Roland Brown, Charles Read, and Sidney Ash. These paleobotanists discuss the habitat and characteristics of this plant throughout North America. Sidney Ash is a relative newcomer to northwest paleobotany. Born in New Mexico, where he completed a Masters degree, Ash was associated closely with the Geological Survey office, Charles Read's influence stimulated his career in Triassic paleobotany. In 1961 he began working in Read's laboratory sectioning and photographing the tree-ferns, but the work was delayed and publication of the monograph on *Tempskya* in North America took over 15 years to complete. Ash left New Mexico in 1964 to take a PhD at the University of Reading, and Read's interests were temporarily diverted. After completion of his graduate degree, Ash accepted a teaching position at Weber State University in Utah.

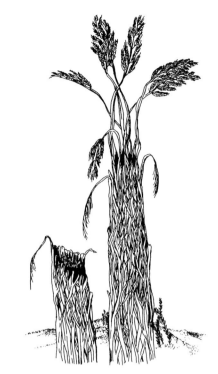

**The tree-fern *Tempskya*
[from Orr, Orr, and Baldwin, 1992]**

The oldest microfloras in the state are Cretaceous to early Tertiary marine spore and pollen [palynomorphs] from Texaco Oil Company bore hole samples near Mitchell in Wheeler County. Four commercial exploratory petroleum wells in the Ochoco Basin reveal the presence of a wide Cretaceous tract lying beneath the Tertiary volcanic cover here. Drilled to depths of almost a mile into thick marine and non-marine sediments, the cores yielded 18 fossil spore and pollen genera dominated by ferns.

PLANTS OF THE PALEOCENE EPOCH

Oregon Paleocene floras are comparatively rare, but they appear in two localities on opposite sides of the state. Microfossil floras [pollen] from Curry County in the Coast Range and megafossils [leaves] from Umatilla County in the northeast region make up the total accumulation. As offshore volcanic islands constructed a platform of lavas and sediments that became the underpinnings of the Coast Range, sedimentary layers of the Roseburg Formation retained small numbers of fossil spores and pollen. In Curry County, this distinctive tropical Paleocene to Eocene microflora was located on the West Fork of Floras Creek County by Ewart Baldwin, professor at the University of Oregon. Baldwin's 1974 survey of southwestern Oregon geology listed ferns, conifers, and dinoflagellates that point to the limited circulation and brackish water of a swamp.

Paleocene megafossils of eastern Oregon were described ten years later when a small collection of leaves from an ancient lake near Denning Spring in Umatilla County was identified by Ian Gordon, a geology student at Oregon State University. Strata at Denning Spring are similar to Clarno sediments, but only five of the 33 plant species from Denning Spring occur in the Clarno, and only two dicotyledonous plants, *Dryopteris* a fern, and *Hydrangea* are common to both. Because of the dramatic floral differences, Gordon concluded that Denning Spring plants reflected a cooler environment than that of the more tropical Clarno interval. For this reason he placed the Denning Spring in the Paleocene.The sedimentary layer, in which the Denning Spring plants are preserved, has yet to be named.

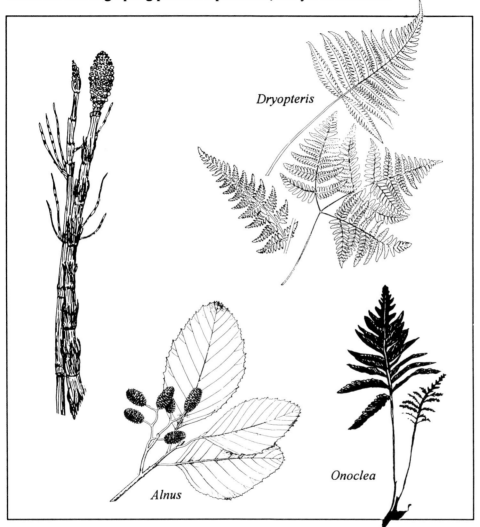

Ferns as *Dryopteris* and *Onoclea*, horsetail, and deciduous trees as alder and birch characterize the lakeside Denning Spring flora.

ENVIRONMENTS OF THE EOCENE EPOCH

The Eocene epoch in Oregon, from 55 to 38 million years ago, was a warm, tropical interval. Shorelines lay much further to the east than at present, and the landscape was dominated by volcanic activity. Clouds of ash from large stratovolcanoes fell over the low-lying coastal plain to preserve a superb representation of plant life. In the eastern part of the state, outpourings of ash from local volcanic vents mixed with water forming lahars or mud flows to entomb fossils. Streams, barricaded by lava, constructed all manner of ponds and lakes favorable for preservation.

EOCENE FORESTS OF EASTERN OREGON

Nothing reflects the Eocene landscape of east central Oregon better than the variety of plants and animal remains, and the most familiar are the leaves, seeds, and nuts found in mudflows of the Clarno Formation. Equally famous for its vertebrate fossils from the Mammal Quarry, Clarno bones and plants are confined to different levels and environments within the formation. While the seeds and leaves can be extracted intact, bones tend to be broken and crumble readily when removed.

Accompanying Geologic Survey parties to the western regions, paleobotanist Frank Knowlton was frequently in the John Day basin during the late 1800s [photo courtesy Archives, U.S. Geological Survey, Denver].

Clarno fossil floras were among the first to be studied from the state. Fifteen plant species from the Clarno, now housed at the Smithsonian Museum, were described by Professor John Newberry of Columbia University in March, 1883, and again in his *Later Extinct Floras of North America*, issued after his death in 1898. A number of other Clarno plants, presented to the University of California by the private collector C. D.Voy, were identified in 1878 by paleobotanist Leo Lesquereux. However, the most extensive early account was Frank Knowlton's *Fossil Flora of the John Day Basin* in 1902. Curator of botany at the Smithsonian, Knowlton described plants sent to him by expeditions from the University of California in 1899 and 1900 as well as those obtained by Knowlton himself in 1901 when he visited the John Day valley.

Frank Hall Knowlton, born in Brandon, Vermont, in 1860, was attracted to the study of birds at an early age. His *Birds of the World*, published in 1909, was 873 pages of detailed avian anatomy and classification. After an undergraduate degree, Knowlton went to Washington, D.C., in 1884 where his previous experience as a taxidermist landed him a job with the Smithsonian Museum. A number of years later he was appointed Curator of Botany, and, following several summers spent with surveying parties, he joined the U.S. Geological Survey as a geologist in 1907. To cope with the growing volume of literature, Knowlton produced *A Catalogue of Mesozoic and Cenozoic Plants of North America* in 1919, a testimony to his organizing abilities. He was also a prolific writer who was examining page proofs when he died on November 22, 1926.

Even though ash layers at different locals in the Clarno contain leaves and wood, plant remains from an area known as the Nut Beds, east of the town of Clarno in Wheeler County, are the most unique because of the permineralized compressions, impressions, molds, and casts of fruits and seeds found there. The Nut Beds deposit is a discrete area less than a quarter of a mile across and thirty-feet thick where the concentration of vegetative fragments has been preserved as part of stream deposits.

Since so much time has passed, pinpointing the precise discovery of the Nut Beds is difficult, but it seems to have taken place in 1930 or 1931, when the locality was visited by several persons living in eastern Oregon. An *Oregonian* newspaper article of August 11, 1931, reveals that Arthur H. Greisser, an hydraulic engineer with Portland General Electric, brought back from Clarno "silicified pecans, walnuts, and dates, perfectly formed ... Some of the nuts are perfect, with shell intact. Others ... show the nut meat inside." An unpublished account by Lon Hancock, a Portland resident who worked extensively in the Clarno region, confirms that his interest was caught by a newspaper article about "The World's Oldest Walnut", picked up by a workman on an oil rig in eastern Oregon. As a consequence of reading this account, Hancock found his first beautifully preserved walnut at the Nut Beds locality. A letter written in July, 1955, by Mrs. J.M. Harrington of Vancouver, Washington, informed Hancock that "as my husband and I were the first ones to find them [Nut Beds] as far as would could learn at that time ... we had a display box in the First street National [Bank] ... we had fourteen different kinds of nuts and leaf impressions." Mrs. Harrington was a cook and her husband was an oil driller near the site, and she thought the date was 1930 or 1931.

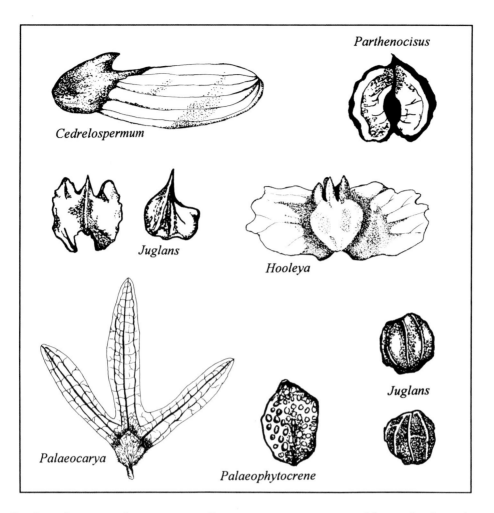

Parthenocisus

Cedrelospermum

Juglans

Hooleya

Palaeocarya

Palaeophytocrene

Juglans

Seeds as large a walnut or as small as a poppy are preserved intact in the unique Clarno strata.

Entombed in the Clarno Nut Beds over 145 genera and 173 different species are the remnants of a widespread hardwood forest which grew in the humid subtropical climate of eastern Oregon 44 million years ago. Ferns and horsetails are common, but the bulk of the material is angiosperms that comprise large thick-leafed plants such as *Cinnamomum* [camphorwood], *Ficus* [fig], *Juglans* [walnut], *Magnolia,* and *Meliosma* [sabia family]. Many are tropical vines belonging to the moonseed family [Menispermaceae]. Gymnosperms as *Pinus* [pine], *Ginkgo*, and *Glyptostrobus* [water pine] are less numerous.

During the summer of 1949 the Paleontology Museum at the University of Michigan sponsored a group under the direction of Chester Arnold, which collected 400 specimens of nuts and seeds from the Clarno. Among the group was Arnold's student Richard Scott, who ended up spending several summers in the field where he was assisted by Alonzo Hancock.

Hancock, a private fossil enthusiast, encouraged young students in paleontology. For his excellent 1954 monograph, Scott wrote to Hancock in 1951 that he "borrowed the Clarno nuts ... in the U.S. National Museum. Dr. Chaney has promised to loan me his specimens ... If you would consider loaning your specimens ... [they will be] returned to you after they are studied." When he and his wife visited Oregon in April, Scott's paper had yet to come out, and he was disappointed in not being able to present a copy to Hancock.

In the spring of 1954, Richard Scott and his wife visited collector Lon Hancock in eastern Oregon. Scott's letter to Hancock indicated he wanted to look at localities for collecting fossil woods, and he expressed the hope for a dry spring in John Day country [photo courtesy Archives, U.S. Geological Survey, Denver].

In this work Scott draws interesting parallels between sedimentation at the Clarno site and modern processes as the result of volcanic activity at Paracutin, Mexico. From his study he was able to conclude that the Clarno beds were water lain tuffs, not the product of ash falls. Both the Clarno and Paracutin regions experienced very rapid deposition of ash washed in from nearby volcanic layers, and much of the Clarno Formation is now considered to have originated as lahars or thick viscous muds of fine ash mobilized by water to move as a liquid. Scott also concluded the plants producing the nuts and fruits grew by a streambed where they may have fallen directly into the water only to be deposited downstream at a spot where the current slowed.

Born in La Grange, Indiana, in 1921, Scott received a PhD from the University of Michigan in 1952. During the academic year of 1951-1952 he was a Fulbright scholar at the University of London where he was able to compare seeds and fruits of the famous London Clay to those of the Clarno. The most interesting were the seeds, pitted on the outside, which Scott called "peach pits" although, he assured Hancock in a letter of March 23, 1952, "none of them are close to peaches." Scott went on to name a new species of the large seeds *Paleophytocrene hancockii*, the first fossil of this genus from North America. Modern relatives of this plant live in the Malay Peninsula where they form extensive jungle vines. With his usual generosity, Hancock donated his seeds to the University of Michigan museum because he had "duplicates for each one."

Returning from London, Scott filled the position of instructor at Harvard University from 1952 to 1955 while continuing his Clarno work. Here he encountered Jack Wolfe, a freshman and former Camp Hancock student, who showed him some Clarno seeds collected a year earlier. After examining the fossils, which included *Nyssa* [tupelo] and *Meliosma* [sabia family], Scott remarked "This ties the London Clay to the Clarno even more." From 1955 onward Scott worked on Mesozoic and Tertiary woods, fruits, and pollen for the U.S. Geological Survey.

A 1979 pictorial atlas of Clarno fruits and seeds by Thomas Bones supplemented Scott's work. A private collector, Bones worked with Clarno material from 1943, amassing thousands of fossil specimens, many of which are lodged in the Smithsonian Museum, at the Department of Geology, Indiana University, and in smaller displays at numerous state museums. Untrained at first, Bones could only pick out larger nuts from the matrix. As he became more skilled he discovered that even those as small as a poppy seed could be recovered by breaking the rock and shaking the material through screens. Looking at one spoonful at a time through a magnifying glass, he extracted the smallest seeds with tweezers. Bones estimated that he had mined over 10 tons of

[photo courtesy E. Baldwin]

seed rock over the years by packing out 50 pounds at a time to his car until 800 pounds were accumulated. Growing up in Texas, Bones had been stationed in the Northwest with the Army, and, once discharged, he remained there to work professionally in printing processes with photography and engraving. Because of his knowledge of photographic techniques, he was able to produce and enlarge sharp detailed photographs of his fossil finds that were published in his *Atlas of Fossil Fruits from North Central Oregon.*

Probably one of the most prolific paleobotanists studying the Clarno is Steve Manchester at the Florida Museum of Natural History, University of Florida. A Salem native, Manchester became interested in fossils at an early age and has worked on Clarno fossils since he was a student at the summer camps organized by the Oregon Museum of Science and Industry. He later directed the same programs from 1976 to 1989. Manchester noted that "I knew from that time [as an OMSI student] that I wanted to get a doctorate in paleobotany." This he accomplished in 1981, with a PhD from Indiana University on the fossil history of Juglandaceae, the walnut family. Today his focus is on the evolution of modern angiosperms along with paleobotanical investigations of fossil wood, leaves, fruit, and pollen. Based on his 1994 research, he emphasized that there was a more complex mixture of tropical and temperate plants in the Clarno interval than previously noted.

Manchester's 1996 *Fruits and Seeds of the Middle Eocene Nut Beds Flora...* treats all known fruit and seed species from this locality. In this publication he demonstrates that in the Clarno over 40% of the vegetation consists of vines, lianas, or other climbing plants. The Menispermaceae family of vines is the most widely represented. At least 60% of the leaves are large and unserrated, pointing to a warm paleoclimate and evidence that the coastline was approximately seventy-five miles distant.

From the age of 10, Steve Manchester was engrossed by fossil plants [photo courtesy M. Ashwill].

Publishing from the 1970s, Manchester has examined the the composition, environment, and families of the Clarno Nut Beds as well as listing several new species. He reviewed in depth specific members of the living and fossil Platanaceae (plane tree family), the winged fruit of *Cedrelospermum* (elm family), the fruits and seeds of individual members of the Fagaceae (beech family), and his extensive monograph on the Juglandaceae (walnut family) serves as a guide to their evolution and biogeographic history. *Juglans* dominated the Clarno landscape, and the oldest tropical walnut yet recorded is *Englehardioxylon nutbedensis*. Seeds of the temperate *Tapiscia* [bladder nut family], preserved as quartz casts, are also recorded for the first time in North America. More common in the Eocene of Europe, *Tapiscia* was widely distributed in the nothern hemisphere as late as as 40 million years ago, but its range was reduced because of late Eocene cooling.

In 1993 Manchester further demonstrated the tropical nature of the Clarno interval when he recorded a fossil banana from this formation in Wheeler County. The specimen, collected several years earlier by Ian Gordon, a student at Oregon State University, was donated to the University of Florida. Preserved as an intact mold of a banana fruit and seeds, which had been buried and flattened, it is similar to that of the modern non-domestic equivalent of the Muscaceae (banana) family - since domestic bananas have been carefully selected to eliminate all but the smallest seeds.

Focusing on preserved wood in the 1980s and 1990s, Manchester used the xylem, or woody tissue, of fossil and modern wood to demonstrate that plants readily adjust to the climate in which they live. Fossil xylem of a new genus *Triplochitioxylon oregonensis* [Sterculiaceae family] shows adaptations to the warm moist Clarno climate, so that the woody parts are distinct from those of the modern equivalent found today in the drier African

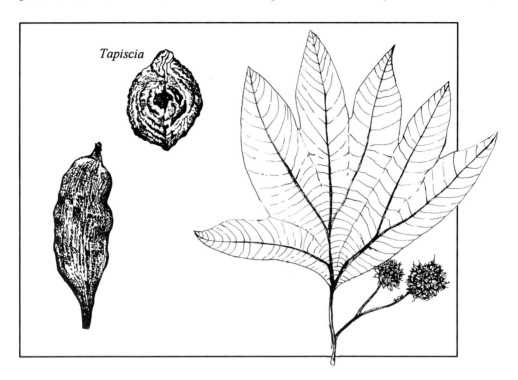

Tapiscia

Tropical bananas and temperate *Tapiscia* as well as sycamore provided a mixture of plants in the Clarno forests [after Manchester, 1993].

environments. A similar adaptation is shown to have taken place in comparing the xylem of the Eocene *Chattawaya* with that of the living *Pterospermum*, both members of the Sterculiaceae family. Even though most woods of the Nut Beds are well-preserved, they are waterworn reflecting considerable transport before burial. Since it is more durable and represents widespread parts of a large watershed, fossil wood may provide a broader picture of an ancient forest than the vegetative parts of plants.

In addition to yielding nuts and seeds, the Clarno Formation commonly contains large fossil palm leaves, *Sabalites*, as part of the prolific subtropical flora. Irene Gregory, a botanist and authority on fossil wood, summarized information on palm leaves [*Sabalites*] and wood [*Palmoxylon*] from Oregon in 1969. She listed nine Eocene locations, one Cretaceous, and two from the Oligocene.

The use here of "form genera" *Sabalites* for palm leaves and *Palmoxylon* for palm wood is a common taxonomic strategy in paleobotany where the various plant elements such as leaves, wood, and fruit have become separated in the fossil record. Palm wood fragments of the Eocene are almost exclusively found in northeast Oregon where they were limited to tropical settings of that time span. Later, occurrences of palm in Oregon are restricted to the Miocene Eagle Creek flora along the Columbia River of 13 to 16 million years of age.

A two-foot long palm leaf *Sabalites* from the Eocene Clarno Formation [photo courtesy Oregon Department of Geology and Mineral Industries].

Throughout the history of Oregon paleontology, there have been many people whose efforts sometimes have gone unacknowledged, but whose research contributed to the depth of knowledge on the state's geologic past. One of these was the botanist, Irene Gregory, whose articles on fossil wood cover many areas of the state. Instead of focusing on leaves, Gregory looked at the structure of fossil wood in cross-section as a way of identification. To obtain specimens, she, her husband James, and five children sought out localities where they camped and, as she wrote to Mel Ashwill in 1985, she hoped "to acquire the most comprehensive and detailed overview of the scope, location, and composition of the fossil wood and plant assemblages of the Pacific Northwest." Receiving a Bachelors degree from the University of Minnesota, Gregory took subsequent graduate work on native plants, which indirectly led to an interest in fossils. Arriving in Portland in the 1960s, Gregory worked as a private consultant until the family moved to Prineville where she died in 1990.

Chester Arnold not only sponsored work on the Clarno Formation by students at the University of Michigan, but he published close to 10 papers himself on fossil plant remains from eastern Oregon. He reviewed the many Clarno fern families in 1964, noting that because they preserve well and frequently have the reproductive parts attached to the leaves, ferns are often better known than the deciduous plants where the seeds separate from the parent plant.

Paleobotanist Chester Arnold in the rock lab at the University of Michigan [photo courtesy University of Michigan, Bentley Historical Library].

Arnold's career focused on preTertiary plants reflecting an interest which he pursued as a professor at the University of Michigan until his death in 1977. Born on a Missouri farm in 1901, Arnold's family moved to New York where he enrolled as an undergraduate at Cornell University. His studies culminated with a PhD from the University of Michigan in 1930 on Devonian plants of central and western New York. Arnold went on to describe several new species, providing an important link between Devonian plant foliage of *Archaeopteris* and its stem *Callixylon*. His textbook, *An Introduction to Paleobotany*, remains a standard reference. A large man physically, Arnold was somewhat shy, but willing to express definate opinions when called upon. He generally didn't show much emotion, and, for example, when he was informed that *Callixylon* and *Archaeopteris* represented parts of the same plant - an area where he had done much work - Arnold replied laconically "Well, I had always thought that might be the case."

Fossil soils preserved in the Clarno Formation also embody ancient environments. Called paleosols, these layers have undergone characteristic modification by plants, warm temperatures, and chemicals before being compacted and covered. Working in this region for several years, Greg Retallack and his students at the University of Oregon completed a comprehensive report in 1996. By trenching, field observations, petrography, and chemical analysis of the fossil soils, they reconstructed different paleoclimates and vegetation. Their studies demonstrate the subtropical environment of the Nut Beds, where the annual temperature averaged 80 degrees Fahrenheit, comparable to southern Mexico today. This landscape gave way abruptly to cooler temperatures and well defined rainy and dry seasons in the early Oligocene.

Greg Retallack's trademark drawings show fossil soils of the Clarno Formation [courtesy G. Retallack].

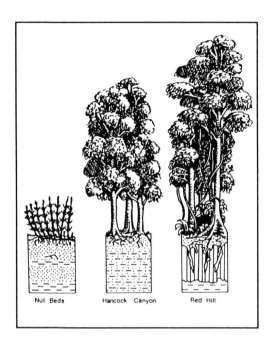

Less than a mile northeast of the Nut Beds, the Hancock Mammal Quarry, known for its vertebrate remains, contains a small flora of Eocene plants as well. Field notes dated July 4 and 7, 1955, by University of California student, Bert Coombs, note "a soft purple-black 'carbonaceous layer' ... is full of plant material..." On July 4 "Mr. Rough [Lloyd Ruff of the Oregon Department of Geology] was at the mammal bed ... He dug holes and trenches about the bottom of the quarry ... into a conglomerate and a 'carbonaceous' layer. Considerable plant material ... some whole leaves ... were in the 'carbonaceous' layer."

However, it wasn't until 1969 that an Oregon Museum of Science and Industry summer camp participant, Thomas McKee, and a team of eight students began to collect plants from the quarry. Recently graduated from high school, McKee developed a floral list based on the 204 specimens of fruits and seeds recovered. Much of the material was in such poor condition that only 39 specimens were identified, and 31 of these were *Diploclisia*, a tropical to subtropical vine of the Menispermaceae family.

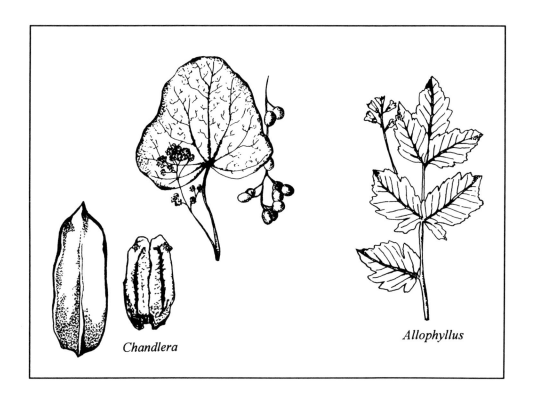

Chandlera

Allophyllus

Tropical plants of the moonseed [Menispermaceae] and soapberry [Sapindaceae] families, twining vines and trees once inhabiting eastern Oregon, are cultivated today for their attractive leaves and berries.

EOCENE FORESTS OF WESTERN OREGON

Eocene floras in western Oregon were distributed along an ocean shoreline of swamps, estuaries, and highlands that were part of a broad forearc marine trough adjacent to the ancestral Cascade volcanoes. Plants, reflective of these conditions, are scattered throughout the Coaledo, Fisher, Cowlitz, and Keasey formations.

Near Coos Bay at Riverton both fossil leaves and pollen have been recorded from the Coaledo Formation. During the late 1800s a sampling of these plants was collected by Joseph Diller during his explorations of the west for the U.S. Geological Survey, but no recorded account was forthcoming. In 1967 Coaledo pollen received a brief treatment in an article by William Hopkins. Pollen in the Coaledo, Bastendorff, and Tunnel Point formations exposed on beach headlands at Cape Arago and Coos Head was collected by Hopkins, who received a PhD in palynology from the University of British Columbia in 1966. While employed by Pan American Petroleum in Tulsa, Hopkins reported that the samples contained pollen of *Ficus* [fig], *Juglans* [walnut], *Laurus* [laurel], *Magnolia, Rhamnus* [buckthorn], and *Sabalites*

28

[palm]. The microflora records a climate that was substantially warmer and more humid than today. This subtropical environment with 50 to 60 inches of rainfall annually and a temperature that rarely fell below freezing was characterized by highlands surrounding a coastal basin. Coal seams in the immediate Coos Bay region formed from peats in an open marine embayment and adjacent low swampy delta plain.

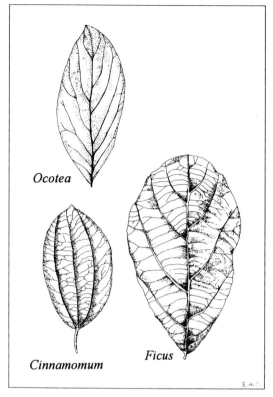

Large thick leaves with smooth margins grew in tropical conditions of the Eocene [from Orr and Orr, 1996].

Along the Eocene coastline northeast of Coos Bay warm and moist conditions are also illustrated by the Comstock and Goshen floras. These plants occur within volcanic ash of the Fisher Formation. Coastal proximity is indicated by the presence of marine molluscs mixed with the plants. At the turn of the century, Joseph Diller sent a number of Comstock fossils to Frank Knowlton at the Smithsonian for identification. However it wasn't until 1937 that Professor Ethel Sanborn issued a comprehensive publication on plant material she and students at Eugene had obtained from this local southwest of Cottage Grove. In characterizing the Comstock flora, Sanborn noted that *Cinnamomum dilleri* [camphorwood] comprised nearly one-fourth of the specimens, with diminishing percentages of *Aralia, Magnolia, Astronium* [cashew family], *Lonchocarpus* [legume family], *Allophylus* [soapberry family], and *Cryptocarya* [laurel family].

A professor of Botany and Paleobotany at the University of Oregon and Oregon State University, Ethel Sanborn was one of the early contributors to knowledge of botany in the state. Born in Goodwin, South Dakota, in 1882, she completed her undergraduate work there but took a PhD at Stanford University in 1928. That same year her mentor Ralph Chaney wrote to Earl Packard at the Geology Department in Eugene "I have been talking with Miss Sanborn today about the possibility of her giving a course in paleobotany at the University of Oregon next year and during succeeding years. From the abundance of fossil plants in Oregon

... it seems especially appropriate." Packard forewarded these remarks to the Dean, who agreed, for Sanborn was hired.

Paleobotanist Ethel Sanborn kept a huge stack of folders on her desk, all dealing with *Quercus*. When Ewart Baldwin asked and was told every one concerned varieties of oak trees, even he was intimidated [photo courtesy Archives, Oregon State University].

Initially Sanborn's research focused in modern mosses and algae, publishing on mosses of the Willamette Valley and marine algae of Coos Bay and Cape Arago while at the Oregon Institute of Marine Biology, Charleston. Subsequently working with Chaney, she completed monographs on fossil plant communities from Goshen, Scio, and Comstock in western Oregon. When science departments were forced to shift to Corvallis from Eugene during the depression, Sanborn hated the move but found it necessary to go or loose her job. At the time of her death in 1952 she was compiling information on plant material from Pilot Rock in Umatilla County.

Also in Fisher Formation strata, fossil leaves of the Goshen flora of Lane County have been intensely examined since they were initially collected by Thomas Condon in 1876. Condon was only one of many who later visited this popular site. A small florule was reported in 1914 by Chester Washburne of the U.S. Geological Survey. A few years later Earl Packard and his students observed Goshen fossils unearthed during construction of the Pacific Highway. There large slabs of rock, rich in plant fossils, which had been neatly stacked on the nearby slope, were collected by Berkeley paleobotanist Ralph Chaney in 1920. Leo Hertlein secured material for Stanford University, and Ethel Sanborn quarried plant fossils for the University of Oregon. The enthusiastic collector J.B. Winstanley, one of Condon's students, had even discovered a new, if poorly preserved, florule of the Goshen nearby.

The first definitive work on the Goshen paleoenvironment and flora was by Chaney and Sanborn in 1933. They listed 49 species, the most common of which are *Allophyllus* [soapberry], *Aristolochina* [liana vine], *Ficus* [fig], *Meliosma* [sabia family], *Nectandra* [laurel family], and *Tetracera* [liana vine]. These are typical of a low latitude, tropical to subtropical rain forest. Shallow water marine molluscs, associated with the plants, confirm the low elevation and nearby shoreline.

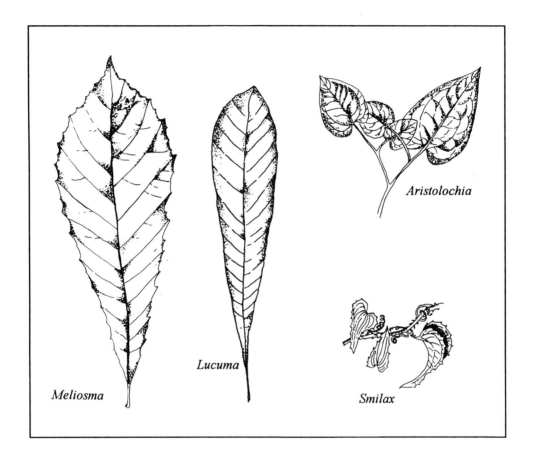

The narrow leaves of *Meliosma* and egg-fruit [*Lucuma*] trees and heart-shaped leaves of birthwort [*Aristolochia*] are tropical components of the Goshen flora, whereas the twining *Smilax*, in the lily family, grows in temperate areas.

Middle and late Eocene plant fossils from the northwestern corner of the state include a scant number of leaves from the Cowlitz Formation near the town of Timber in Washington County and an equally meager amount from Keasey sediments in Columbia County. Both formations are predominantly marine, and the leaves are mixed with invertebrate shells. In the nearshore shallow waters of the Cowlitz, large thick tropical leaves of the genus *Aralia* are particularly well-preserved as are *Equisetum* [horsetail], *Nymphoides* [floating heart], and several ferns. Fine volcanic ash layers of the Keasey at Mist yield a flora that grew on a coastal plain where freshwater merged into brackish, then marine, conditions. In Raymond Moore's paper on crinoids, paleobotanist Roland Brown identified leaves of *Quercus* [oak] and *Myrica* [bayberry] as being "tough enough to resist complete destruction while being swept out to burial in the sea." To this short list, Victor Zullo, an invertebrate paleontologist, was able to add only one specimen of *Ocotea* [lancewood] and a few fragments of *Thuja* [arborvitae] in his 1964 paper on Keasey echinoids.

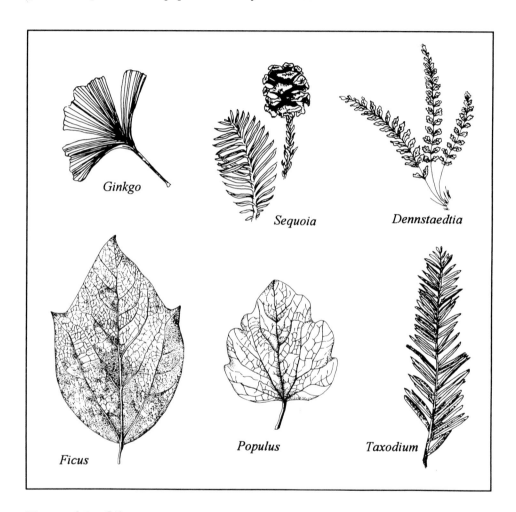

Plants of the Oligocene

ENVIRONMENTS OF THE OLIGOCENE EPOCH

The Oligocene epoch spanning the interval from 38 to 25 million years ago, saw the development of a low wide coastal plain reaching to what are now the Cascade Mountains. Shallow marine waters covered most of the western part of the state, and the landscape, plants, and animals were profoundly influenced by the early Cascade volcanoes beginning about 40 million years ago. As the Farallon plate was being subducted beneath North America, a chain of volcanoes began to rise immediately east of the shoreline. Ash and debris from this archipelago destroyed but ultimately preserved the local biota as the climate underwent dramatic changes. The steady elevation of the Cascade barrier through the late Oligocene and Miocene epochs brought increasingly drier conditions to eastern Oregon when moisture from the Pacific Ocean fell as rain and snow on the newly emerging range.

On a global scale, the Eocene-Oligocene boundary is marked by a transition from warm subtropical conditions to a cooler more temperate realm 39 million years ago. As the result of major ocean circulation changes in the southern hemisphere, sea temperatures dropped profoundly, and climates cooled correspondingly. This climatic evolution is characterized by episodic modifications in vegetation as increasingly temperate conditions continued into the late Oligocene and early Miocene. These changes gave rise to hardwood and conifer forests when an overwhelming proportion of Oregon plants were adapted to moderate temperatures and seasonal rainfall.

Cumulative research and refined dating methods have enabled present-day paleobotanists to evaluate and draw far-reaching conclusions about climate and vegetation changes across this boundary. An outstanding example of one such publication is Jack Wolfe's 1992 paper in the monograph *"Eocene-Oligocene Climatic and Biotic Evolution."* In this synthesis as well as in an earlier 1981 paper on Tertiary floras from the Pacific Northwest, Wolfe concluded that a wider seasonal range of cooler temperatures was responsible for the dramatic changes in vegetation during the early Oligocene.

Oregon Oligocene floras are numerically as rich as those of the Eocene. Forests of this time were dominated by broad leaf deciduous hardwoods such as members of the Aceraceae [maple], Betulaceae [birch], Fagaceae [oak, beech], and Taxodiaceae [redwood] families. These fossil remains are found scattered throughout a wide range of formations in the Willamette Valley and Cascades as well as in sediments from the Bridge Creek and Crooked River areas of eastern Oregon. Of the truely significant floras from this time span, the Bridge Creek flora is the only representative from the eastern part of the state, while the Rujada, Willamette Junction, Lyons, Scio, and Thomas Creek are situated in the Western Cascades along what was the coastal plain.

OLIGOCENE FORESTS OF EASTERN OREGON

During the Oligocene in central Oregon long serene periods were punctuated by volcanic episodes as Cascade stratovolcanoes violently expelled thick clouds of ash that settled over the landscape. Accumulating in streams, lakes, and swamps, these sediments were responsible for preservation of bones and plants in the John Day Formation. The John Day was divided into three layers on the basis of color - the older reddish, the middle pale green, and the younger cream to buff sections - in 1901 by John C. Merriam of the University of California. In 1972 these divisions were formally named by Richard Fisher and John Rensberger, graduate students at Berkeley, as the older Big Basin, the middle Turtle Cove, and the youngest Kimberly members. Within the formation, plant and animal fossils are unevenly distributed. The Big Basin contains a wealth of plant remains, while mammals are richest in the Turtle Cove and Kimberly intervals. This distribution doubtless reflects prehistoric environments. While lakes of the Big Basin landscape trapped and preserved leaves, streams and floodplains of the Turtle Cove and Kimberly time were optimum for preservation of bones but lacked the thin, flat laminae ("book page deposition") necessary for leaf fossilization.

The Bridge Creek flora is dominated by deciduous leaves of alder, maple, oak, beech, as well as the conifers dawn redwood and pine [from Knowlton, 1902].

34

The Bridge Creek flora is found at several locals in Big Basin shales. These plants were part of a large inland forest that lacked tropical species, although diversity was amazingly high. Preserved mainly as impressions, deciduous leaves are the most prolific. A 1997 summary by paleobotanists Herbert Meyer and Steve Manchester identifies 91 genera and 110 species from leaves, of which 34 species are new. *Metasequoia* [dawn redwood] essentially characterizes this temperate flora that takes in the more familiar conifers such as *Pinus* [pine] and *Abies* [fir]. The most abundant broad leaf angiosperms are *Acer* [maple], *Alnus* [alder], *Paracarpinus* [hornbeam], and *Pteleaecarpum* [hop tree]. Along with leaves, permineralized wood is also plentiful in the Big Basin Member. Large logs, probably *Metasequoia*, were burned black and crushed in John Day ash flows before the cells were filled with silica.

Climates of the Bridge Creek flora were warm to temperate with only a limited temperature range and about 40 inches of rainfall annually. Drier conditions had progressively developed in eastern Oregon as the barrier of the Western Cascade range rose. Bridge Creek forests covered hillsides and deep valleys, which were drained by mature stream systems interspersed with lakes. Some lake basins were at least two miles across and perhaps even wider.

Even though the Bridge Creek, dated at 33 million years, is one of the oldest of the Oregon Oligocene floras, it has long been considered much younger because of the more temperate floral characteristics. The overriding assumption that Pacific Northwest tropical environments invariably gave way to temperate climates automatically makes temperate plants seem younger, demonstrating one of the difficulties of geologic dating with plant fossils. In this case, the Bridge Creek, which appeared far inland, well beyond the mild oceanic influences, appears more temperate than other floras from the western part of the state. Coastal assemblages, although younger, appear to be from older, more tropical intervals because of higher rainfall and moderate temperatures near the ocean.

Plants of the John Day Formation have been the object of considerable interest since the middle 1800s when they came to the attention of pioneer geologist Thomas Condon, who was then living at The Dalles. He accompanied soldiers escorting a supply train across the John Day Basin to Harney Valley along "the road [which] followed Bridge Creek for several miles, and it was probably on this trip that the first of the cinnamon-colored fossil leaves were found," according to his daughter Ellen Condon McCornack. These leaves were passed on to William Blake, mineralogist and professor at the University of California, who was visiting The Dalles in May, 1867. Blake wrote to Condon in June of that year "I have had the plants from Bridge Creek, Oregon, examined by ... Dr. Newberry, now of Columbia College ... who recognized a *Platanus* and an Oak." Blake wanted a complete suite of fossils and offered to send $75 or $100 for a quantity of material to be collected. Because of hostile Indians, Condon was unable to visit the fossil beds for a year, so he boxed and sent Newberry part of his own collection in February, 1869. The following year Condon sent additional fossil plants from localities throughout the John Day valley. Newberry published a brief note in 1869 and a longer 1882 paper on plants of western North America in which he described 16 specimens from Oregon, naming one *Ficus condoni*. These are still housed at the Smithsonian Museum.

John Newberry can be characterized as one of the early leaders in the fields of botany, geology, and paleobotany. Living in Ohio, Newberry's father had owned and operated a coal mine where John, as a boy of 11, was fascinated by the fossil plants in the shales. Following a medical degree in 1848, Newberry practiced only briefly. In 1855 he accepted a position as a botanist and geologist on a government exploration in the west to determine railroad routes to the Columbia River. His wanderlust took him back and forth across the west for ten years before he was appointed Chair of Geology and Paleontology at the School of Mines in Columbia College in New York. Here his private geology and paleontology collection was purchased by the college to form the basis of their museum. Newberry published prolifically, and the 1898 volume *The Later Extinct Floras of North America* is only one example of his beautifully illustrated works.

John Newberry, who served as botanist, geologist, and zoologist on an exploratory expedition in 1855, has a volcanic peak in eastern Oregon named after him [engraving from Merrill, 1924].

The largest of the early plant collections from the John Day basin was assembled in the 1870s by naturalist and taxidermist C.D. Voy, a resident of San Francisco. It's not certain whether Voy ever visited eastern Oregon to procure his own fossils, but his specimens were subsequently purchased by D.O. Mills, a regent of the University of California, where they now reside. As the result of his sale, Voy was listed in the Oakland phone directory for 1880 to 1881 as a "capitalist." Additional material was obtained by Captain Charles Bendire of the U.S. Cavalry in the summer of 1880 when he was scouting the region. Bendire's collection, primarily of plants, but with a few fish and mammal remains, was ultimately turned over to the Smithsonian Museum.

Bridge Creek assemblages were described by paleobotanist Leo Lesquereux in 1888, but the most comprehensive publication was Frank Knowlton's *Fossil Flora of the John Day*

Basin, Oregon in 1902. Knowlton considered the earlier collections of Lesquereux and New-berry along with those acquired by the U.S. Geological Survey and the University of Califor-nia. Ralph Chaney's reports followed from the 1920s, and Roland Brown's from 1935 on-ward. Chaney was the first to consider the Bridge Creek flora as a separate ecologic plant community. Among Lesquereux's new species were *Acer bendirei* and *Hydrangea bendirei*.

Animal remains are rare in Bridge Creek shales of the Big Basin Member, but occa-sional salamanders, frogs, birds, and even bats turn up. One of the first bats mentioned was discovered by Roland Brown in 1959.

Roland Brown's paleobotany work in the Northwest stretched over 30 years and many summer visits. During the late 1950s, for example, he and Jack Wolfe toured plant locals across Oregon. Brown or "Brownie", his nickname, was quiet, studious, and knowledgable in many aspects of natural history, but his primary interest was botany and Tertiary plants. Born in Weatherly, Pennsylvania, Brown received his doctorate in Forestry in 1926 from Johns Hopkins University. After several brief assignments at the Pennsylvania Survey and Forestry Department, he began with the U.S. Geological Survey, a job that lasted until his death in Mauch Chunk in 1961. A loner by choice, Brown remained a bachelor throughout his lifetime,

Roland Brown, known for his varied interests, not only wrote on paleobotany, but brought out *Materials for Word Study* and *Composition of Scientific Words* - both dealing with entymology [photo courtesy Archives, U.S. Geological Survey, Denver, showing Brown on the left and J.C. Reed on the right].

leading a very spartan existance, even picking up small coins from the sidewalks of Washing-ton, D.C. He once said that "in a good year he would pick up $1.25." His parsimonious habits were reflected by his shabby attire, and, on occasion, he was mistaken for a camp la-borer when doing field work. Survey geologist Dallas Peck called Brown "Whistler's father" because of his many patches. Brown had a penchant for the unusual and was fascinated by the origin of scientific words. Every afternoon at 4:15 he would put down his work on fossil plants and begin on his dictionary of scientific words. His varied interests led him to publish on fossil bats, an evergreen cherry, and the tree fern, *Tempskya*.

Over the past several years, middle Tertiary paleoclimates and fossil soils [paleosols] of the Clarno and John Day Formation have been investigated by Greg Retallack and his students from the University of Oregon. Much of this work was summarized in a report on the geology and paleoenvironments of the Painted Hills strata of the John Day Fossil Beds National Monument in 1996. Retallack used paleosols, responsible for the colorfully banded sedimentary beds exposed in the area, to reevaluate local environments. At least 435 separate local paleosol layers have been defined in the Painted Hills, although only 12 yield fossil plants or animals. Humid Eocene conditions are reflected by thick deep maroon to reddish clay paleosols, whereas somewhat drier climates are evident in the red and green layers of the Oligocene. Thin brown fossil soils are indicative of the drier cooler climates of the late Oligocene and Miocene. An important result of this work on paleosols, which could not be judged from fossil plants, is evidence for an abrupt climate cooling and drying at the Eocene-Oligocene boundary.

An enthusiastic field geologist, Greg Retallack was characterized by one of his students - "when he gets in the field, his veneer of civilization is extremely thin" [photo courtesy G. Retallack].

Building on the evidence of paleosols, Retallack proposes a solution to the problem that two distinct environments seem to be primarily represented in the John Day Formation. Noting that the presence of hoofed mammals points to open grassy woodlands, while the plants signify a thick forest cover of tall trees, Retallack suggests the mammals and plants occurred in different localities and in different climatic periods. Additionally some environments are conducive to preserving vegetation while others clearly favor bones. Leaves, for example, require low oxygen situations as in the very fine sediments of a lake bottom or swamp, but fossilization of mammal remains is enhanced by alkaline carbonate soils.

Born in Hobart, Australia, in 1951 Greg Retallack is the only paleopedologist   conducting research in Oregon and one of the few in the United States. Focusing on fossil soils and paleoenvironments, he finished a doctorate in 1978 and accepted a position in the Geology Department of Northern Illinois University. Before becoming a faculty member at the University of Oregon, he travelled around the United States by car, lecturing at universities and doing field work. Retallack's interests are highly eclectic, encompassing the evolution of soils through geologic time and dispersal of Cretaceous angiosperms as well as worldwide Permian extinctions.

Large leaves of magnolia, smaller oak, sycamore, and fig are all Oligocene plants of western Oregon [from Newberry, 1898].

Along what would later become the eastern margin of the Willamette Valley, a diversity of coastal dunes, swamps, marshes, river estuaries, and sporatic rocky headlands mark the middle Tertiary coastline. Repeated lava flows and ash of Little Butte eruptions from fissures and cones throughout the Western Cascades were largely responsible for the rapid burial and preservation of coastal floral communities. The oldest and most southerly of these are the Rujada and Willamette Junction localities in Lane County, followed by those of a similar age near Sweet Home, Scio, Lyons, and at Thomas Creek in Linn County. Early Miocene Collawash and Eagle Creek floras, further north in Clackamas and Hood River counties, were also trapped by the Little Butte eruptions. These floras are temperate to tropical indicating coastal influences with precipitation of 50 to 60 inches evenly distributed throughout the year. Moderate temperatures from 30 to 40 degrees Fahrenheit in winter and 70 to 80 degrees in summer were due to the ocean proximity. Topography was probably irregular and well-drained.

The Rujada flora northeast of Cottage Grove at Lookout Point Reservoir and the Willamette Junction flora near Goshen both have a high percentage of conifers and a rich broadleaf mixture typical of the early Oligocene. First discovered in 1934 by Warren D. Smith, professor and chairman at the University of Oregon, Rujada plants were named for an old camp here when the names of two local loggers, R. Upton and Jack Anderson, plus USDA were combined. The most definitive publication to date is by Rajendra Lakhanpal, a member of the Birbal Sahni Institute in Lucknow, India, who worked here while a UNESCO fellow at the University of California. Lakhanpal based his study on collections made by Ralph Chaney and his own fossils collected during the summer of 1952. These are all stored at the University of California, Berkeley. This flora has a high percentage of conifers and deciduous trees as *Alnus* [alder], *Exbucklandia* [witch hazel family], *Halesia* [snowdrop], *Quercus* [oak], *Platanus* [sycamore], and *Sequoia* [redwood]. Lakhanpal concluded the flat laminated nature of the preservation indicated gradual accumulation in a calm water setting.

Plant remains on U.S. Highway 99 just north of Goshen were analyzed and termed the Willamette Junction flora by Richard Lewis in his Masters thesis from the University of Oregon in 1950. Discovered when the Highway Department was excavating for fill, the locality was initially examined by Warren Smith, who secured several slabs for the Condon Museum. Smith informed Ralph Chaney at Berkeley "hoping you can get up before the hill is completely removed." But it was years later that Lewis distinguished these plants from those of the nearby Goshen because each flora occupies a separate stratigraphic level and because there are floral differences, which show marked changes in climate between the two intervals. In contrast to the tropical Goshen, temperate Willamette Junction plants resulted when ocean waters withdrew westward.

Since he had fought in World War II and had been so badly wounded, Lewis was discouraged from the strenuous activities required for a geology degree. However, he persevered and persuaded the government to pay for his education, switching his field area from eastern Oregon to the Coburg Hills because of health problems. After graduation, Lewis worked for the U.S. Geologic Survey in Kentucky.

Richard Lewis has produced
the only in-depth study of
the Willamette Junction
flora [photo courtesy
Archives, U.S.
Geological Survey,
Denver].

Leaves from near Sweet Home in Linn County are characteristic of stream-bank bottomland environments. Petrified stumps at the local were shown to Hibbard Richardson by Professor Lloyd Staples, who suggested the area for a Masters thesis from the University of Oregon. Richardson spent the year from 1948 to 1949 doing field work, primarily on the geology near Sweet Home, but secondarily on identification of leaves and wood. He considered the plants to be preserved in volcanic tuffs of the Eugene Formation, but in Dallas Peck's classic paper on the geology of the Western Cascades, paleobotanist Jack Wolfe surmised that leaves of this flora were actually part of the Little Butte Volcanics. Irene Gregory, who specialized in the study of fossil wood, recorded over 50 separate species that were unmistakably tropical in nature between Sweet Home and Holley. Gregory speculated that wood of Asiatic affinity may have been transported to the West Coast as drift logs carried by ocean currents. It should be noted, however, that many of the trees in this remarkably rich flora were still upright *in situ*, even though others were float wood. There are no associated marine fossils.

Petrified wood at Sweet Home contains quartz pseudomorphs in the cubic crystal shape of the mineral halite. In this case, salt (halite) crystals have been replaced by the more stable mineral quartz. Mineralogist Lloyd Staples has interpreted the presence of halite as an indication of a highly saline environment, which may have developed when an arm or inlet of the Eocene ocean was cut off or isolated from the open sea. After this restricted water body had substantially evaporated, halite crystallized in the water-soaked wood.

The temperate to subtropical Lyons, Scio, Thomas Creek, and Bilyeu Creek floral localities are all found within 20 miles of each other in exposures of Little Butte Volcanics. Plants of the Lyons grew around a placid lake that enhanced their preservation. Examined by Herb Meyer, a former student affiliated with the Oregon Museum of Science and Industry, the Lyons does not have as many broadleaf plants as the Rujada and is more temperate than the Scio. A 1972 winner in the Westinghouse science talent search, Meyer went on to finish a PhD from Berkeley in 1986 on methods for estimating paleoaltitudes of Tertiary floras from Colorado and New Mexico. He often collaborated with paleobotanist Steve Manchester and eventually took a job with the National Park Service at the plant fossil Florissant Beds in Colorado in 1990.

In the same vicinity of Linn County, Oligocene plant localities along Thomas Creek and Bilyeu Creek present a diverse array of over 20 families and 43 species. Among the 10 most abundant are the fern, *Dennstaedtia, Dillenites* [tropical tree], *Metasequoia* [dawn red-wood], and *Phoebe* [laurel family]. Among the tropical to subtropical plants in this suite are the earliest known fossil occurrence of the genera *Amyris* [rue family] and *Tripterygium* [staff tree family] in North America. One of the most interesting features is the high number of vines and climbing plants. Approximately 33% of the angiosperms are climbers in contrast to an average of 10% in other floral communities. The size of individual leaves is very impressive with single specimens over a foot in length.

Originally from Minnesota, the Kluckings have been at Central Washington University for 30 years [photo courtesy E. Klucking].

Edward Klucking's 1964 PhD thesis from Berkeley offers the most comprehensive coverage of the Thomas Creek and Bilyeu Creek floras. Shown the sites by Jack Wolfe, a contemporary of his at Berkeley, Klucking gave an account of the difficulty in reaching and collecting fossils here. Access to the site could only be accomplished during several weeks in September and October when water levels in the creeks are very low, and then, because the shale was so fine-grained, the slabs cracked into small fragments measuring about 1/4 inch. By wrapping the slabs in wet newspaper, the cracking could be delayed.

Benefitting from discussions about leaf venation with Wolfe, Klucking went on to study and photograph modern leaf vein patterns for 25 years while pursuing a teaching career at Central Washington University at Ellensburg. A meticulous worker, he developed a remarkable method of bleaching then staining leaves to make venation stand out before mounting them between glass. The research and beautiful photographs in his book *Leaf Venation Patterns* proved a significant tool for identifying fossil leaf remains.

Fig, Oregon grape, oak, and sycamore in the bottom right show the diversity of Miocene forests [plate from Newberry, 1898].

The cooler drier trend that began during the Oligocene epoch continued into the Miocene and Pliocene. Short winters and humid summers characterize the early Miocene, but later more severe dry conditions in the eastern region of the state were brought about as coastal moisture was cut off by progressive elevation of the Western Cascades.

East of the Cascades the most profound event of this time frame was the eruption of flood basalts triggered by crustal tension that began around 17 million years ago. As tectonic plate movements during this interval severely stretched and thinned portions of the northern Great Basin, volcanic fluids were released over wide areas of eastern Oregon, Washington, and Idaho. Sheets of lavas spread across the Columbia plateau just as similar flows in Steens Mountain and the Owyhee uplands were taking place. In an excellent paper in 1990, Martin Lockley, at the University of Colorado, Denver, discusses in detail how volcanism significantly modifies paleo-environments and the role it plays in burying and preserving plants and animals. Heavy falls of ash and volcanic material, lahars, or thick muds formed by water-saturated ash and the construction of lakes all profoundly impact the biota.

An analysis of spores and pollen by Ralph E. Taggart and Aureal T. Cross at Michigan State University reached similar conclusions as Lockley. Their results showed that the quality of Miocene floras preserved here were the result of extensive local volcanic eruptions. Lava and ash blocked waterways to create lakes, deltas, and swamps that facilitated preservation of plants, while water, percolating through the fine ash layers, was enriched with silica and other minerals, enhancing the fossilization of vegetable and woody material.

Coincident with local volcanism in eastern Oregon, the Willamette Valley was experiencing eruptions of Cascade volcanoes. Here clouds of ash and volcanic debris mixed with marine and terrestrial sediments along the ancient Pacific ocean covering the northwest part of the state. The volume of this erupted material overwhelmed the existing network of streams to obstruct valleys and create a mosaic of swamps and lakes that were filled by heavy summer rain blown in from the ocean. Thickly forested slopes of the Western Cascades contributed prodigious amounts of leaves, pollen, and wood, which accumulated in the wetlands, where much of it was ultimately preserved.

Of the many fossil floras in Oregon, probably the best known are from the Miocene epoch, spanning the interval between 25 to 5 million ago. Compared to modern plant communities, Miocene floras are strikingly varied, representing a diversity of prehistoric climates, environments, and physiographic settings.

During the early and middle Miocene in Oregon, *Metasequoia* [dawn redwood] was the characteristic tree, even making up three-fourths of the flora at Twickenham in Wheeler County. The title "dawn redwood" is somewhat misleading since the plant is neither ancestral to cypress or redwood. The distinctive feature of *Metasequoia* is its "oppositeness" - branches, needles, and cone scales are all distichous or opposite each other in two symmetrical rows, easily distinguishing *Metasequoia* from *Sequoia* [redwood] or *Taxodium* [bald cypress].

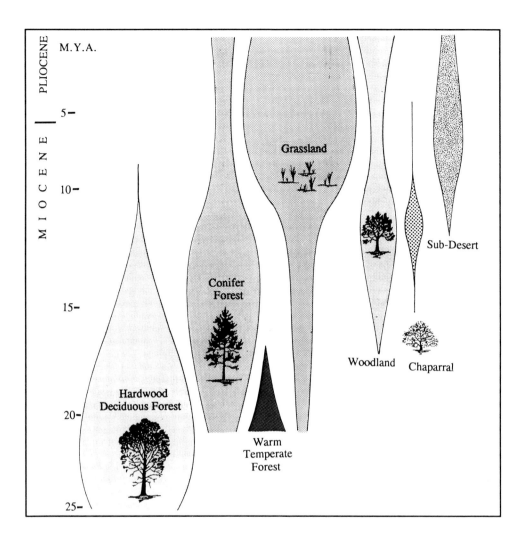

A synthesis of Tertiary vegetation from the Northern Great Basin shows clear drying trends during the late Miocene [after Axelrod, 1950].

This unique quality led to the discovery of living *Metasequoia* trees, long thought to be extinct. A Chinese forester Tsang Wang came across a grove of modern *Metasequoia* in Szechuan Province and brought these trees to the attention of Chinese paleobotanists. Some specimens were sent to Elmer Merrill at Harvard University, who wrote a brief technical report. When this stunning news became known, expeditions were organized in 1947 and 1948 to confirm the existence of the trees. Among those funded was Ralph Chaney whose journey to the remote Valley of the Tiger in central China was a true adventure. Accompanied by armed guards and a reporter Milton Silverman of the San Francisco Chronicle, Chaney and his entourage had to elude bandits and rely on local villagers for assistance and guidance. There was no road so they hired "seven coolies to carry our baggage ... and a dozen men to carry us in sedan chairs ... On the second day we acquired an escort of soldiers - a few ragged straw-sandled youths equipped with antique carbines - who cost us $60,000 [in Chinese] a day apiece, about 18 cents in U.S. money." Chaney took photographs and specimens and measured the dawn redwoods, which were up to 100 feet tall. Since the trees in this stand were being cut by local farmers for timber, he appealed to the government in Nanking to protect the stand before leaving China.

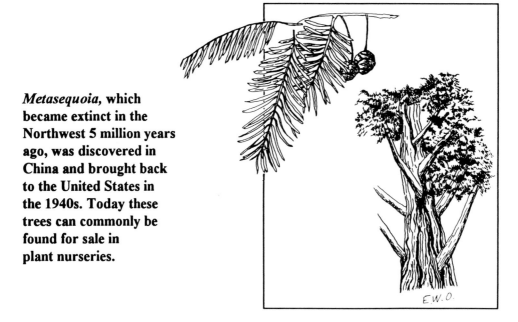

Metasequoia, which became extinct in the Northwest 5 million years ago, was discovered in China and brought back to the United States in the 1940s. Today these trees can commonly be found for sale in plant nurseries.

Once the *Metasequoia* seeds were planted, the seedlings which grew from them were the first such trees in North America in almost 10 million years. Today these trees thrive throughout the northwest, and a thick copse can even be found at the National Arboretum in Washington, D.C.

While working in the Arctic in 1986, scientists from the University of Saskatchewan and the University of Adelaide excavated stumps of *Metasequoia,* which had been preserved in an astonishing mummified state. They could saw and burn the wood and even heated water for tea over burning fossil debris. The composition of the forest would indicate the Arctic climate 45 million years ago resembled that of North Carolina today.

By late Miocene the incidence of *Metasequoia* in the northwest was greatly diminished due, in all probability, to the increasing climatic effect of the Cascades. As the Miocene progressed, taxodiaceous plants such as *Sequoia* [redwood], *Metasequoia,* and *Taxodium* [bald cypress] were gradually replaced by those adapted to cooler and drier conditions such as *Abies* [fir], *Picea* [spruce], and *Pinus* [pine]. Simultaneously, herbaceous plants of the mallow and parsley families, as well as composites and grasses expanded, apparently owing to the severity of winters over this time frame.

46

Ralph Chaney was the premier western paleobotanist for almost half a century. Born in Chicago in 1890, he became interested in natural science, and especially in birds, when young. At the University of Chicago he began studies in ornithology but shifted to botany and geology to finish his PhD in 1919 on the Eagle Creek flora of the Columbia gorge. After teaching several years at the University of Iowa, Chaney was appointed to a position at the University of California, Berkeley, where he remained for 49 years.

Ralph Chaney, who spent his first field season in Oregon in 1916, became a renowned paleobotanist and conservationist by the time of his death in 1971. Chaney is standing by a large slab of fossil poplar leaves at Vanora Grade near Madras [photo courtesy University of Oregon, Archives].

A thorough knowledge of Tertiary plants in North America enabled the innovative Chaney to develop methods for viewing fossil floras as part of an entire ecological system. Using leaf shapes and habitat, he was able to reconstruct paleotopography and climates on a broad scale and his monumental series on Tertiary floras in the west documented environmental changes based on floral sequences. In addition to his creative research, Chaney was a respected teacher, who was known to have a good sense of humor even if somewhat parsimonious in his habits. On field trips he would take time to bicker over the cost of over-ripe bananas and even go to the extent of picking his own cherries rather than pay for them at a roadside stand. His long tenure at Berkeley produced innumerable outstanding paleobotanists who influenced the direction of the science for the next several decades.

For the most part, Miocene plants in the eastern part of the state are localized in three separate regions - on the Owyhee plateau, in the Blue Mountains and Columbia plateau provinces, and in the Deschutes River basin. On the Owyhee uplands, the oldest plant remains are the early Miocene Alvord Creek and Sucker Creek floras followed by those of the middle Miocene Trout Creek and Stinking Water floras. All are preserved in thick layers of volcanic ash.

On the Owyhee plateau, ash layers followed by a voluminous basalt eruption covering over 6,000 square miles from a low shield cone in Steens Mountain was responsible for preservation of fossil leaves and pollen of the Alvord Creek Formation. Dated at 21.3 million years before the present, the flora was thoroughly investigated by Harry MacGinitie in 1933 as part of his paper covering the plants at Trout Creek. His collections, in addition to plant material from the locality in Harney County, formed the basis for Daniel Axelrod's publication on the Alvord Creek flora in 1944. Axelrod suggested the flora was deposited in a small lake surrounded by moderate topography and distant volcanoes. Rainfall, heaviest in the winter months, was only 20 to 23 inches, and seasonal temperatures were more moderate than today, probably averaging 10 degrees warmer per year.

Daniel Axelrod examining fossils in Mel Ashwill's yard at Madras [photo courtesy M. Ashwill].

Originally from Brooklyn, New York, Axelrod received his PhD in paleobotany from the University of California in 1938, studying under Ralph Chaney. Teaching for over 20 years at UCLA, he transferred to the Botany Department at the University of California, Davis, in 1968. Axelrod, known as "The Axe" to his students and friends, focused on Tertiary paleobotany, plant evolution, paleoecology, and paleoclimates. His interests and career paralleled that of Chaney, with whom he frequently worked. Axelrod was a prolific writer, and his many publications deal with regional floras such as the Alvord Creek, Rattlesnake, and Copper Basin in Oregon and Nevada. He died in 1998.

Represented by leaves as well as pollen, deciduous plants as *Acer* [maple], *Amelanchier* [serviceberry], *Juglans* [walnut], and *Rhus* [sumac] populated the Alvord Creek lake shore and slopes, while *Abies* [fir], *Pseudotsuga* [Douglas fir], and *Tsuga* [hemlock] grew at higher elevations. Remarkably, only pollen, but no leaves, of *Quercus* has been found in the flora, and pollen of *Quercus* and *Abies* are the most frequent. Climatologically, the fossil pollen of the Alvord Creek strata supports a Pliocene designation, although radiometric dates indicate a Miocene age.

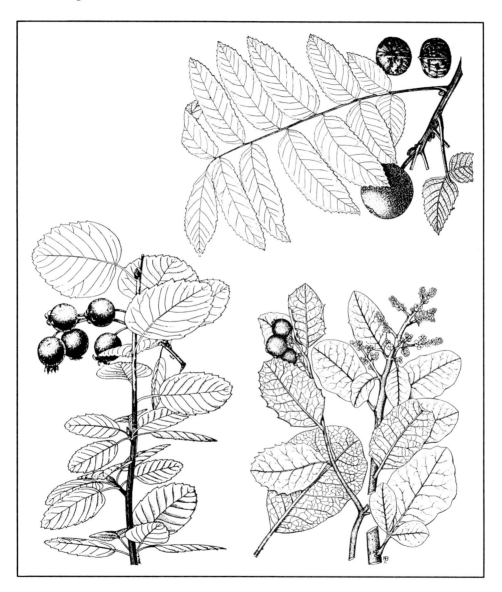

Left to right, leaves of serviceberry, sumac, and walnut are typical of cool Miocene environments [from Sudworth, 1908].

Of all the Miocene floras from Oregon, the Sucker Creek in Malheur County is perhaps the most famous. The volcanic ash that buried these plants has been officially named the Sucker Creek Formation, whereas the stream in the same vicinity was changed to its earliest designated popular name, Succor Creek, by the U.S. Board of Geographic Names. A geologic formation retains its official name even though local geographic places may change, hence the two different spellings. Ash and lava of this formation were expelled during the middle Miocene in what was probably the state's most explosive volcanic episode resulting in spectacular calderas up to 22 miles in diameter across the Owyhee plateau.

Collected in 1898 by Waldemar Lindgren of the U.S. Geological Survey, Sucker Creek material was sent to Frank Knowlton at the Smithsonian Museum for study. In 1935 the University of Michigan's Chester Arnold drew up a contract with Percy Train, a commercial paleontologist, to collect from Rockville and Sucker Creek. To the 750 plant specimens at Michigan amassed by Train, more were added later by paleobotanists Helen Smith, and Alan Graham.

The initial formal study of the flora was Helen V. Smith's Masters degree from the University of Oregon in 1932. This was the culmination of her early interest in fossil plants, aroused when, as a child, she visited the Sucker Creek leaf beds near her home with students from Boise College. After several summers of field work from 1931 to 1934, collecting at three locals, Smith recognized 15 families, 19 genera, and 30 species. She went on to teach in the Department of Botany at Ann Arbor.

Smith's thesis on Succor Creek was followed by Betty Brooks' publication in 1936 and by Ralph Chaney and Daniel Axelrod's landmark *Miocene Floras of the Columbia Plateau* in 1959. As the basis for her paper, Berkeley student Brooks used several hundred specimens collected in 1923 by Horton Hinshaw. Hinshaw, who had a zoology teaching fellowship in California at that time, went on to become a medical doctor at the Mayo Clinic in Minnesota. Hinshaw's material is housed at the Carnegie Institute, Washington, D.C.

Alan Graham's PhD thesis from the University of Michigan in 1962 dealt with several aspects of both the Trout Creek and Sucker Creek floras. Graham, now at Kent State University, examined the pollen, leaves, fruit, and flowers, recording 47 separate families, 60 genera, and 69 species. He concluded that Sucker Creek plants grew around an upland lake basin set in uneven topography. The presence of slope plants mixed with those from lowlands supports this environmental picture, and Graham estimated the lake to have been around 2,000 feet above sea level. The minimum winter temperatures did not fall below freezing as indicated by the presence of large leaf *Oreopanax*, which has a modern equivalent in South American forests. In this flora *Quercus* [oak] is the most prevalent leaf fossil.

Sucker Creek pollen from high altitude plants such as *Abies* [fir] and *Picea* [pine] reflect a similar climate and environment as that of the vegetative remains. Fossil pollen, as a rule, represents much wider environmental conditions because it is easily transported thus covering considerable distances. Several papers by Ralph Taggart, a professor of Botany and Plant Pathology and Geology at Michigan State University, have dealt with this formation. Taggart examined the composition and dynamics of Tertiary plant communities to determine environmental changes. In 1974 and 1990 papers he demonstrated, by use of both pollen and leaves from sites along the Oregon-Idaho border, that Miocene temperatures here were cool throughout the year. Freezing periods were rare, and the climate was much like that of Savannah, Georgia, before the advent of cooling later in the Miocene. Taggart and his students also uncovered evidence that the local forests were periodically smothered by volcanic ash and destroyed by forest fires.

One of the vexing problems that arises when comparing multiple fossil floras is determining whether different plant localities are part of the same age and environmental setting or whether they represent totally separate communities. A good example of this is the Rockville flora found in the Sucker Creek Formation near the Rockville post office in Malheur County. Although sometimes considered as a separate flora, angiosperms from here are similar enough to those at Succor Creek that this locality is generally considered as part of the Sucker Creek floral horizon.

Continued volcanic destruction and subsequent preservation of the biota in the late middle Miocene 13.1 million years ago is reflected by the Trout Creek flora in Harney County. Buried in an ash layer from local volcanic vents, many of the plants are comparable to those near Succor Creek. The first identifications of the flora made by Frank Knowlton of the Smithsonian appeared in Gerald Waring's 1909 paper on *"The Geology and Water Resources of the Harney Basin, Oregon."* Vertebrate paleontologists Chester Stock and Eustace Furlong of California Institute of Technology made small collections that were eventually listed in Ralph Chaney's 1925 contribution on Miocene floras.

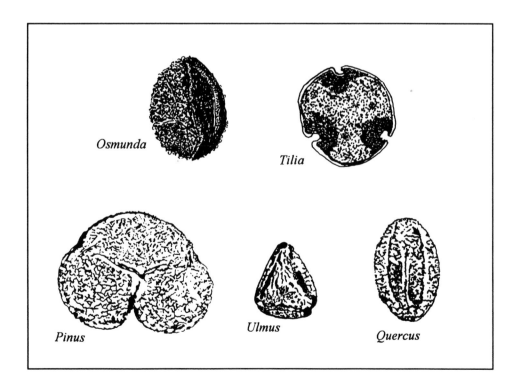

Fossil pollen of the Sucker Creek Formation

In 1932 Percy Train, under contract with the University of Michigan, Museum of Paleontology, made collections from the Trout Creek locality numbering 10,000 specimens, adding 1,000 more the following year. These were from several sites a few hundred feet apart on the same hillside in Harney County. A commercial paleontologist, Train and his wife supplied American and European universities with thousands of leaf and fish fossils from an old lake bed on their property near Denio, Nevada, close to the Oregon border. The entrepreneur Train sent out brochures advertising his products. A complete set of fossil plants consisting of 20 species of "leaves and winged seeds - half of which are new to science..." from Trout Creek went for $20. Train, who supplied museums internationally, commented in an *Oregonian* article of 1932 that "Despite the depression Germany is buying more educational material now ... France and Italy are spending little on such exhibits, however."

When working on his 1933 *"Contributions to Paleontology"* Harry MacGinitie made a thorough examination of these collections. He produced a complete floral list, habitat, climate, and associated diatoms of the Trout Creek - comparing it to other plant communities in southcentral Oregon. MacGinitie's paleobotanical studies began as a Berkeley student in 1932 where his PhD research, *Flora of the Weaverville Formation,* was completed in 1935 under Chaney. Born in 1896 in Lynch, Nebraska, MacGinitie resided for his career in Arcata, California, where he taught at Humbolt State College until retirement in 1960. Following that, he accepted an appointment at the Berkeley Museum of Paleontology, continuing to do research until his death in 1987. His careful systematic approach and innovative ideas on the vegetational significance and history of western Tertiary floras were largely substantiated by later workers in the field.

Harry MacGinitie's treatment of the Trout Creek flora in 1933 was the first comprehensive account of an upland Miocene plant community on the Columbia plateau [photo courtesy of the Archives, U.S. Geological Survey, Denver].

Train's fossils generated a list of new species from Chester Arnold in 1937. This was followed by an assessment by Ralph Chaney and Daniel Axelrod in their 1959 monograph on Miocene floras. Thirty years after MacGinitie's work, Alan Graham studied both Train's original specimens as well as later additions to the Sucker Creek and Trout Creek floras in the Botany Department at Ann Arbor, Michigan. Graham supplemented these 13,000 specimens with an examination of 40,000 pollen grains - giving an idea of the scope of his 1962 work. He surmised that Trout Creek plants represented a landscape featuring upland lakes adjacent to steep, well-drained slopes at elevations as high as 4,000 feet. Here rainfall was 50 inches per year, minimum winter temperatures were 35 to 40 degrees Fahrenheit, and maximum summer temperatures rarely exceeded 90 degrees. Surrounding the lakes was an extensive marsh as shown by *Equisetum* [horsetail] and *Typha* [cattail] and beyond that a forest of *Acer* [maple], *Amelanchier* [serviceberry], *Quercus* [oak], and *Salix* [willow]. Of the 45 species here, only five are coniferous. *Pinus* [pine] and *Thuites* [cypress family] were especially common producing a mixed forest. Fossil material consists of leaves, pollen, fruit, stems, some roots, and occasional flowers.

Presently a botany professor at Kent State University, Alan Graham was born in Houston, Texas, in 1934. A Bachelors degree at the University of Texas preceeded a PhD from at Michigan. His current research focuses on Tertiary plants of Latin America, palynology, and taxonomy.

Alan Graham doing field work in the Costa Rican jungles [photo courtesy A. Graham].

Intense volcanism and falling ash in lakes of the Juntura basin in northeast Harney County preserved leaf and fruit impressions as well as diatoms of the temperate Stinking Water and Beulah floras. Although remnants of these floras are similar to those found in the more westerly Mascall Formation, low grade lignitic coals and wetlands, common to the Mascall, are absent here.

The presence of fossil plants of the Stinking Water was brought to the attention of Ralph Chaney in 1940 by a local resident and fossil enthusiast, Alfred L. Brown. Brown, assisted by Henry Griffith, guided Chaney on a visit to a petrified stump location. Collections were made the following summer by a field party directed by Carlton Condit, a graduate student of Chaney's, who became chair of the Geology section at the Illinois State Museum in 1950. In the resultant 1959 publication on Miocene floras of northeast Oregon, Chaney and Axelrod depict the overall Stinking Water paleo-landscape as one of good drainage, broad valleys, and minimal volcanic sediment blocking waterways. The dominance of dry [semi-xeric] leaf fossils such as *Quercus* [oak] suggests rainfall as low as 10 inches annually. The most abundant were the conifer *Glyptostrobus* [water pine] and the deciduous *Alnus* [alder], *Platanus* [sycamore], *Populus* [cottonwood], and *Ulmus* [elm].

The high silica content of lakes on the Owyhee plateau, resulting from the chemical makeup of volcanic material, produced conditions favorable for prolific diatom blooms. Microscopic glassy skeletons of these single-celled aquatic plants form entire layers or diatomites in the Juntura and Drewsey formations. The earliest study of these microscopic plants was by U.S. Geological Survey paleontologist Kenneth Lohman in 1937. Lohman supplied most diatom identifications, which were listed in Bernard Moore's publication on nonmetallic minerals, but did not undertake paleo-ecologic interpretations. This was provided by William Abbott's 1970 Masters thesis from Northwest Louisiana University on diatoms from near Harper. Employed at Mobil Exploration and Production in Dallas, Abbott's anaylsis of five diatomite samples pointed to a deep freshwater lake. The presence of *Melosira islandica* and similar species indicated the water was oxygen deficient, a condition which occurs often where a high amount of decaying organic matter uses up the free oxygen. Aside from *Melosira,* Lohman and Abbott both listed *Achnanthes, Cocconeis, Coscinodiscus, Cymbella, Fragilaria, Navicula,* and *Tetracyclus*. Diatomite is mined commercially at several sites in Oregon and used for a variety of industrial purposes such as in filters, for insulation, and as kitty litter.

The Columbia River basalts, that issued intermittently from long cracks and fissures in northeast Oregon, southeast Washington, and adjacent Idaho, erupted for over 11 million years during the Miocene epoch. Hundreds of separate basalt flows that were thousands of years apart had a temporary but devastating effect on local plants and animals. The relationship of volcanism, sediment basins, environments, and fossils throughout the plateau was the basis of a landmark paper in 1991 by Gary Smith. Living at the Crooked River Ranch during several field seasons, Smith mapped and intrepreted sediments of the Simtustus Formation in the Deschutes basin for his PhD from Oregon State University.

As chronicled by Smith, basins subsided and filled with sediments as waterways were disrupted by volcanic eruptions. An intricate network of streams and lakes atop the lava plateau initially attracted the biota while later serving as a medium for perservation. Ultimately the shallow depressions acted to trap and and preserve the vegetation, which was then covered by further flows. This long succession of plant growth, punctuated by intermittent destructive lavas, is responsible for the many outstanding fossil communities found in the Blue Mountains and Columbia Plateau provinces.

Blue Mountains floras have long been known from near Sumpter, Austin, Tipton, and Sparta, small towns in old gold mining districts of Baker and Grant counties. East coast paleobotanist Leo Lesquereux first mentioned plant specimens of "Blue Mountain, Oregon" in

1878 that may have been recovered during gold mining activity. Joseph Pardee and Donnel Hewett note leaf fragments in their discussion of the Sumpter Quadrangle geology, but more thorough work was provided by University of California student, Elizabeth Oliver, in 1934, and by Ralph Chaney and Daniel Axelrod in 1959. Oliver made her own collections at Tipton and Austin that she used in comparisons with other Miocene floras. Leaf and fruit impressions of both trees and shrubs point to a temperate setting around the shores and slopes of an upland lake. Of the seven conifers and 25 deciduous plants, oak [*Quercus*], beech [*Fagus*], black hawthorn [*Crataegus*], and redwood [*Sequoia*] were the most prevalent.

Oliver also sent diatom samples to Kenneth Lohman, paleontologist at the U.S. Geological Survey. *Melosira granulata* and *Tetracyclus ellipticus* were the most common of the microscopic plants, both inhabitants of freshwater lakes fed by streams with small amounts of dissolved salts. Lohman noted that Miocene lake beds in eastern Oregon were so saline that marine diatoms could have flourished in the water.

Melosira granulata **from diatom layers near Vale [photo courtesy Oregon Dept. of Geology and Mineral Industries].**

Despite the time and care lavished on fossils by private enthusiasts, superb collections are often picked over and lost once some time has passed. This was the case with the Sparta flora northeast of Baker amassed by Leslie R. Hoxie. Born in Michigan, Hoxie moved to California where he worked in a lumber mill in Ukiah. Long fascinated by fossils, upon retirement to LaGrande, Hoxie devoted his time to these interests. The Sparta local was brought to Hoxie's attention by State Department geologists, and in 1961 he produced the only account of the composition of this flora. Before he died, Hoxie gave much of his personal collection to the Condon Museum in Eugene, but the remaining leaves and rocks went to Eastern Oregon State College where the boxes were stacked on the steps to the greenhouse. Here they languished until objections were raised by the fire marshall when they were carried to the basement.

Using evidence of abundant coniferous pollen, Hoxie extrapolated a setting of mountain slopes forested by hardwoods with moderate rainfall and temperatures. In addition to pollen, the flora is made up leaf impressions, fruits, and some wood. *Quercus* [oak] was the predominant element, but *Acer* [maple], *Carya* [hickory], *Picea* [spruce], *Pinus* [pine], *Platanus* [sycamore], and *Ulmus* [elm] were also numerous.

The accumulation of stream sediments from volcanic eruptions continued during the middle and late Miocene in the John Day basin. Of these, ash and lavas of the 15-million year old Mascall Formation are known for the variety of plants and animals they contain, whereas the younger 6.6-million year old Rattlesnake Formation has few plants but numerous mammal bones. Collected by Thomas Condon in the 1870s while he was living at The Dalles, Mascall specimens were sent to John Newberry who placed them in the New York Botanical Garden. However, he never described them. In a similar fashion, the 285 specimens from the Mascall collected by Jacob Wortman and Charles Sternberg, both renowned fossil hunters, wound up in the same Botanical Garden. A large private collection of plants from the John Day basin, accumulated by C.D. Voy of San Francisco, was sent to paleobotanist Leo Lesquereux. This included nine Mascall items, which he noted in his 1878 publication on gold-rich gravels.

Leo Lesquereux was one of the earliest authorities on fossil plants in the United States. His father was a manufacturer of watch springs and his mother wanted Lesquereux to become a minister [photo courtesy Archives, Smithsonian Institution].

Leo Lesquereux, who was totally deaf for his adult life, studied fossil plants of North America for over 30 years. Arriving in the United States in 1847, he worked in Columbus, Ohio, classifying private plant collections before receiving commissions to work for several state and federal geologic agencies. In order to support his family, he also operated a watch-making and jewelry business aided by his three sons. Although his wife Sophie was the daughter of a baron, Lesquereux's impoverished surroundings and the lack of opportunity available to him because of his deafness contrasted to that of his contemporary paleobotanist, John Newberry, who appeared as more accomplished. Lesquereux, however, was probably a better botanist, and his 3 volume *Description of the Coal Flora of the Carboniferous Formation...* in 1884 was so comprehensive that Chester Arnold remarked it gave the impression there was little left to do. From 1867 to 1872 he organized the fossils at Harvard's Museum of Comparative Zoology and, after his retirement, he classified a large private collection that was bequeathed to the National Museum. He died in 1889 in Columbus.

John Merriam's 1899 and 1900 trips to the John Day Basin from Berkeley resulted in a plant collection submitted to Frank Knowlton of the Smithsonian Museum. Knowlton himself visited here in the summer of 1901 and his *Fossil Flora of the John Day Basin, Oregon,* 1902, provided a relatively complete list of Mascall plants. The Mascall Formation was reexamined in 1920 by Ralph Chaney, who took the old stage road from Dayville to the John Day region. Travel was primitive, and there were no motels, so Chaney and other visitors customarily stayed at local farms. The pioneer Mascall family often hosted paleontologists on their ranch near Picture Gorge. Systematically collecting the Mascall flora, as well as examining those from various museums, Chaney assessed the forest in papers from 1925 onward, culminating in his 1959 *Miocene Floras of the Columbia Plateau,* co-authored with Daniel Axelrod. Based on megafossils (leaves) as well as microfossils (pollen) they sketched the landscape here as an area of low relief and uniform climates, where abundant plant remains were deposited on floodplains and in lakes created when volcanic ash plugged local stream systems. The numerous browsing and grazing hoofed mammals entombed in the Mascall imply these freshwater lakes must have been surrounded by open grassy forests.

With the Cascades well in place, rainfall during Miocene time in east-central Oregon was reduced to 30 inches annually, producing vegetation comparable to that of a modern oak forest typical of the Ohio Valley today. The swamp cypress *Taxodium* is the most copious leaf along with lower slope plants such as *Carya* [hickory] and *Quercus* [oak]. Occupying higher regions were *Acer* [maple], *Betula* [birch], *Ginkgo, Pinus* [pine], and *Sequoia* [redwood].

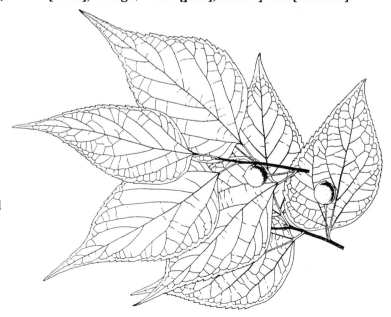

Innumerable hackberry [*Celtis*] seeds are layered in ash of the Mascall Formation [from Sudworth, 1908].

Although the flora is distinctive, the actual frequency of Mascall leaves is only modest. For example, Bridge Creek shales typically yield over 200 leaves per cubic foot of rock examined, whereas the Mascall generally has 10 or less. This disparity may reflect the size of the lake basins. Where the smaller waterways of the Bridge Creek concentrated leaves, the extensive lakes of the Mascall dispersed material.

Even though vertebrate remains from the Rattlesnake Formation were studied during the 1920s, leaf impressions weren't found until 1947 by a field party from Oregon State University led by Professor William Wilkinson. As chairman of the Geology Department between 1960 and 1968, Wilkinson spent years working with students throughout the state. His trips culminated in the immensely popular *Field Guidebook to Geologic Trips along Oregon Highways*, an early roadside geology, which went out-of-print shortly after it was issued in 1959. Briefly mentioned by Chaney in 1959, the Rattlesnake flora has rare leaf impressions of *Platanus* [sycamore], *Salix* [willow], and *Ulmus* [elm].

In the Deschutes River drainage, two basins, the older Miocene at The Dalles and the younger Pliocene Deschutes north of Madras in Jefferson County entrapped plants. Fragmentary vegetation of The Dalles flora is found in flood deposits and volcanic debris of the 11 to 8-million year old formation of the same name. This flora was initially brought to the attention of John Newberry, State Geologist at Columbus, Ohio, when he received nine plant specimens sent by Thomas Condon in 1869. Condon recorded his discovery of leaves from an old quarry on Chenoweth Creek, Wasco County, labelling the specimens "Group C". The specimens, still with his handwriting on them, are in the Museum at the New York Botanical Garden. The

flora was ignored for almost 50 years until the ubiquitous Ralph Chaney visited the locality in 1916. Ultimately described by Chaney in his unprecedented 1944 *Pliocene Floras of California and Oregon,* The Dalles plant community characterizes a cool, semiarid climate that supported *Acer negundoides* [a new species of box elder], *Amorpha* [indigo plant], *Cercis* [redbud], *Quercus* [oak], and *Ulmus* [elm]. The accumulation is represented by only 12 species, and the lack of many broad leaf deciduous plants and conifers along with the presence of small-leafed evergreens suggests reduced summer rainfall and a low elevation where the plants grew near a streambank.

A beautiful rendering of flowers and seeds of the redbud [*Cercis*] [from Sudworth, 1908].

In contrast to the nearby Eagle Creek flora, The Dalles is notably more modern, and an *Aelurodon* [a primitive wolf] and horse teeth [*Hipparion*] found at this local indicate a late Miocene age.

MIOCENE FORESTS OF WESTERN OREGON

Volcanism also played a major role in plant preservation in the Willamette Valley and Western Cascades. Here three similar floras were buried in ash layers of the Little Butte Volcanics. Delineated in the classic 1964 monograph on the Western Cascades by Dallas L. Peck and his co-authors, these are the Collawash, Molalla and Eagle Creek plant communities. In addition, the monograph reported small plant populations from six localities between Eugene and Portland scattered over the west flank of the range. Although Peck's doctorate from Harvard in 1960 focused on economic geology, a field study assignment early in his career with the U.S. Geological Survey in California and Oregon led to publications which helped unravel the structure and volcanic history of the Cascades. Peck remarked once that one of the most pleasant phases of his life was spent mapping this area. After serving as director of the Survey, he retired in 1993.

The examination of pollen and vegetative matter from these three Miocene floras formed the basis of Jack Wolfe's PhD dissertation from Ralph Chaney at Berkeley in 1960. A career paleobotanist with the U.S. Geologic Survey, Wolfe's interest in fossil plants began when he participated at the Oregon Museum of Science and Industry summer camp in the eastern part of the state. As a Portland high school student at Camp Hancock he worked with Lon and Berrie Hancock on Eocene Clarno plants. Putting together a Clarno plant display, Wolfe finished among the top 10 for the Westinghouse scholarship, a contest judged by Geological Survey paleobotanist Roland Brown. When he went to Harvard in 1953 to study with

A young Jack Wolfe and paleobotanist Roland Brown in the garden at Cape Arago State Park in Coos County [photo courtesy E. Baldwin].

famous paleobotanists, Richard Scott and Elso Barghoorn, Wolfe was amazed to discover that he was already known there because Barghoorn "had talked with Dr. Brown in Colorado this year" His letter to Hancock continued "I told him that I had some fruits from the Clarno, and guess what? The person that I passed walking into his office turns out to be [paleobotanist] Dr. Scott!!" Wolfe showed Scott photos of Clarno seeds and "upon being informed that [the owner Tom] Bones would part with it for a price, Scott seemed very interested."

While a sophomore at Harvard, Wolfe collected the Collawash locality. A 1956 letter from Wolfe noted that in a course from Professor Barghoorn, "I worked on the megafossils from the Collawash River locality, and this term I turned my attention to the microfossils ... As for future plans, this summer I will collect with Prof. Chaney in the John Day Basin ..."

In spite of their similarity in age, the Molalla [from Butte and Abiqua creeks in Marion County] is viewed by Wolfe as subtropical, whereas the Collawash and Eagle Creek are more temperate. Frosts during this interval at these localities were not severe, and the 50 to 60 inches of annual rainfall was much like western Oregon today. The presence of swamp cypress [*Taxodium*], *Quercus* [oak], and *Carya* [hickory] in the Collawash and Molalla suggested to Wolfe adjacent hills around what was probably an upland swamp and cypress grove requiring copious warm rains. Both contain plants of predominantly broad leaf deciduous trees such as members of the walnut family [Juglandaceae], oaks [Fagaceae] and witch hazel family [Hamamelidaceae].

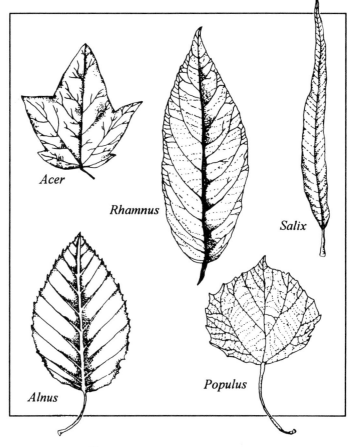

A variety of leaves from the Miocene forests of western Oregon [from Orr and Orr, 1996].

60

Of particular interest in Wolfe's study are his speculations on the origin or source of individual floras. He interprets major vegetation changes during the Tertiary cooling of the Pacific Northwest as the product of invasions by plants from higher elevations. Coastal subtropical Molalla plants received very few immigrants during this migration, but the more temperate Collawash and Eagle Creek fossil assemblages contain several introduced species. These movements have been traced through various floras across the Great Basin showing that, with time, many of the plants that had a low tolerance for cooler climates had been eliminated in the Pacific Northwest while others, such as the temperate Pinaceae, expanded.

Eagle Creek fossils in the Columbia River Gorge were noted as far back as 1873 by Joseph LeConte, who had been appointed to a faculty position teaching botany, zoology, and geology at the newly established University of California in 1869. Even though the plants were briefly listed by Frank Knowlton in 1900, it wasn't until 1918 that a more complete description of them was made by Ralph Chaney. Chaney based his study of the Eagle Creek on collections by U.S. Geological Survey geologists as well as on those from his own summers in the field. This was followed by his thesis from the University of Chicago in 1919 where he had been encouraged to examine the locality by renowned Chicago professor, J. Harlan Bretz, of Pleistocene Missoula floods fame.

Chaney initially assigned the Eagle Creek flora to the late Eocene, inadvertently leading to an interesting exchange of letters between Bretz and Warren D. Smith, Chairman of the University of Oregon Geology Department, over the use of plants in stratigraphic dating. The dates of the Columbia River basalts were the focus of the correspondence. Smith felt that it was "rather risky" to trust dates based on leaf fragments and that there were better dating methods. Bretz responded that "the puzzle here is how you can think that identification of the leaves ... can have any bearing on the age of the Columbia River lava... What is 'rather risky' in trusting to Chaney's work if I *should* wish to mention it in publication? His conclusions are orthodox enough." Smith's final reply reiterates his opinion "that plant remains, particularly fragments of leaves, are very undesirable for determining age".

Leaves of the Eagle Creek depict a curious mixture of environments. One of the ecologic niches is an exposed high ridge habitat represented by fewer species but more individual leaves, whereas a second habitat, that of a protected valley, is represented by many species. Chaney speculated that oak leaves from the dry ridges blew into the moist stream valleys where they mixed with maples, elm, and other vegetation. Some tropical leaves as those of *Sterculea* indicate a climate substantially warmer than today. Even though *Cephalotaxus* [yew] is present, there is a remarkable absence of taxodiaceous plants.

An unusual local in Lincoln County turned up a unique new species of *Pinus* [pine] from the middle Miocene Astoria Formation. Found by Marian and Ross Berglund, residents of Bainbridge Island, Washington, *Pinus* was described in 1992 by Charles Miller, professor in the Biology Department at the University of Monana. The small seed cones of *Pinus berglundii*, preserved in this coastal location, are similar to modern forms, but distinctive characteristics point to a separate evolutionary lineage. This fossil material is housed in the Condon Museum at Eugene.

Reconstruction of a pine cone similar to those from the Astoria Formation near Newport.

PLIOCENE FORESTS OF OREGON

By the late Miocene to early Pliocene the modern topography of the Pacific Northwest was well-established. The Cascades and Coast Range had been elevated, concurrent with the development of the linear depressions of the Willamette Valley and Puget lowlands. The Pliocene epoch, between 5 and 2 million years ago, saw the continuation of cooler less humid conditions initiated during the late Miocene. Rainfall at this time in the northern Great Basin and Columbia Plateau was around 15 to 17 inches per year, and the temperate vegetation was comparable to that of the present-day. In addition to the disappearance of warm tropical plants, waning volcanic activity greatly diminished the optimum conditions for rapid burial and preservation of fossils. Scattered sedimentary basins, so conducive to preservation during the Miocene, vanished along with the dense forests and thick foliage. Pliocene floras, as a consequence, are poorly known here, and the climate, topography, and environment are not as well understood as those of earlier epochs in the Oregon Tertiary.

Only the Troutdale flora west of the Cascades and the Deschutes flora to the east are assignable to the Pliocene. Separated by the edifice of the volcanic range, these two floras constrast sharply. One reflects heavy rainfall, where the vegetation and climate were dominated by the nearby ocean, and the other a more arid habitat. The omnipresent J. B. Winstanley, one of Thomas Condon's students who resided in Portland, brought the Pliocene plants east of Troutdale to the attention of Ralph Chaney in 1916. They then hiked through thick brush to the local on Buck Creek to collect the plant fragments. A second locality was discovered above Camp Collins in Multnomah County by Ray Treasher and Lloyd Ruff, both of the incipient state Department of Geology and Mineral Industries in Portland. Winstanley and Treasher also helped compile the first comprehensive bibliographies of Oregon geology in 1912 and 1936.

Buried in silty layers between coarse conglomerates of the Troutdale Formation, leaves composing the flora imply a heavy summer rainfall with annual precipitation around 35 inches at a mean temperature of 50 degrees Fahrenheit. The topography was diversified between dissected valleys and a broad well-developed flood plain.

In the Deschutes River valley, volcanic sediments, lava flows, and ash derived from High Cascade volcanoes make up the Deschutes Formation. During relatively quiet periods between 5 and 3 million years ago, mammals and plants flourished around small lakes here until renewed volcanism buried and preserved them.

Cottonwood, cherry and madrone in the Pliocene of western Oregon compare well to modern-day trees [from Sudworth, 1908].

The presence of abundant fossil leaves in the Deschutes basin was first reported by highway engineers during construction of the Vanora grade near Madras. Plants were examined by Luther Cressman, anthropologist at the University of Oregon, who made a representative collection. Ralph Chaney saw the specimens in Cressman's laboratory and inspected the site himself in 1936 with a party of geologists. His monumental *Miocene and Pliocene Floras of Western North America* in 1938 summarizes the Deschutes forest as dominated by *Acer* [maple], *Populus* [aspen], *Prunus* [cherry], and *Salix* [willow] reflecting a fairly dry, cool climate. Along with the plants, a camel [*Auchenia*] bone was found here earlier by Thomas Condon.

A more recent examination of the Deschutes flora was made by Mel Ashwill of Madras during a 1990 to 1991 highway widening project near his home in Jefferson County. Ashwill took advantage of the excavation to salvage over 40 huge boulders in which he records up to 10,000 fossil leaf remains. The massive stones were moved to a variety of locations, some to the grounds of the museum at the Warm Springs Indian Reservation, some near the fossil site in anticipation of a formal display, and two were placed near Ashwill's home. Ashwill was able to add *Equisetum* [horsetail], *Mahonia* [Oregon grape], *Quercus* [oak], *Ulmus* [elm], and new species of both *Populus* [cottonwood] and *Salix* [willow] to Chaney's floral list. After careful examination of the fossil leaves and by comparing them to plants trapped in mudflows associated with the eruption of Mount St. Helens, Ashwill concluded the Deschutes material was entombed in a similar dramatic volcanic event that altered Oregon's climate.

Milkman, truck driver, logger, river rafter, and music instructor are among the professions of collector Mel Ashwill [photo courtesy M. Ashwill].

Because of his many contributions on a variety of geologic subjects, especially to paleobotany, Mel Ashwill was honored in 1991 by the Paleontology Society with the prestigeous Strimple Award. Ashwill, who grew up in North Dakota, moved with his family to Newberg, Oregon, during the depression of the 1930s. A beginning chemistry student at Pacific University, he switched to music for a graduate degree, going on to teach music for 23 years at schools in the state. Now retired, Ashwill maintains an extensive private fossil collection at his home in Madras, which he displays to visitors. Generous with his knowledge and expertise, he also provides enthusiastic help and knowledge from his own resources to anyone who expresses an interest in his work.

Microscopic algae [diatoms] beds near Terrebonne in Deschutes County and in the Fort Rock basin of Lake County mark the location of old lakes, which have been placed variously in the Pliocene and Pleistocene. At Terrebonne, test pits were made in 1930 into what has come to be the most extensively developed diatomite in eastern Oregon. At that time Kenneth Lohman of the U.S. Geological Survey analyzed samples sent to him, listing 33 species of diatoms. His report gives an economic evaluation of the deposit but provided no paleo-environmental assessment. The age, origin, and identifications of Terrebonne diatoms has been debated since Lohman's initial study. Sam VanLandingham's 1990 article suggests these problems have arisen because researchers failed to take into account the complexities of the diatom layers here. Providing a thorough assessment of previous work, VanLandingham concluded there are two different diatom deposits, Terrebonne West, which is Pleistocene, and Terrebonne East, which is Pliocene.

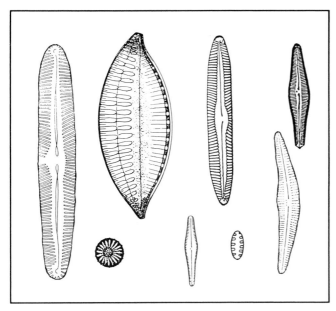

Late Cenozoic diatoms from near Terrebonne in Deschutes County.

Kenneth Lohman and Sam VanLandingham are among the very few researchers who specialize in diatoms. Born in southern California, Lohman completed his education there, but for most of his career he worked for the U.S. Geological Survey in Washington, D.C. Van Landingham, on the other hand, is a private consultant, who lived throughout the south and midwest, but is currently residing in Ohio. Because he feels that the Great Basin displays the most complete freshwater diatom record of any region of similar size in the world, Van Landingham has worked there for many years, analyzing samples and examining thousands of published documents to construct a more complete paleoenviromental picture.

Two University of Oregon geology students, Kent Colbath and Matthew Steele assessed the economic significance of diatom-rich layers near Christmas Lake in the Fort Rock basin for the Oil-Dri Company. In 1982 Oil-Dri was interested in exploiting their claim in order to market absorbent and filtering products from the crushed diatomite. Colbath and Steele microscopically examined 47 drill core and surface samples to reveal diatoms typical of freshwater Pliocene lakes. Suspended [planktonic] diatoms were more abundant than the bottom-dwelling benthic species suggesting the nutrient-deficient lake was relatively deep, but not stagnant. Volcanic ash and pumice, falling directly into the water, provided a ready source for silica, necessary for glassy diatom skeletons. The most commonly encountered genera were *Cyclotella, Melosira, Stephanodiscus,* and members of the Fragillariaceae family.

PLEISTOCENE FORESTS OF OREGON

Following the comparatively brief time span of the Pliocene, the Pleistocene epoch was an even shorter interval of dramatically increased rainfall and colder temperatures as continental ice sheets extended southward from British Columbia, while ice caps reached across the tops of the higher mountain peaks.

Most of the pollen work on the Pleistocene and post glacial periods in the state was by Henry P. Hansen, professor at Oregon State University, from 1939 onward. The bulk of Hansen's work was based on observations of pollen from peat bogs, an interest he developed

Professor and Dean of the Graduate School at Oregon State University, Henry Hansen pioneered studies in Pacific Northwest vegetational history by analyzing pollen in bogs of the northwest [photo courtesy Oregon State University, Archives].

through reading about the Pacific Northwest while working in Wisconsin during the 1930s. At that time pollen analysis of bog material and the recognition of its usefulness in interpreting post glacial vegetation was just beginning in this country. Hansen was born in LaCrosse, Wisconsin, in April, 1907, growing up in a region of extensive bogs between the LaCrosse and Mississippi rivers. After receiving his PhD from the University of Washington in botany with an emphasis on geology in 1937, he briefly taught at Eastern Oregon College then in Wisconsin and Wyoming before joining the Botany staff at Oregon State University in 1939. As Dean of the Graduate School from 1949 to retirement in 1972, he charted the direction of higher education during this period when the college enrollment went from 435 to 2,053. Hansen died in Corvallis in 1989.

In 1935 Hansen explored the northwest with George B. Rigg, Botany Professor at the University of Washington, who initiated the study of bog ecology in the Pacific Northwest. Rigg was intimately familiar with pollen from wetlands in Puget Sound and generously shared his knowledge with Hansen. In order to work, Hansen first had to build an extensive reference collection to familiarize himself with pollen from modern forests, a task that involved even more time and travel. To amass a collection from around seventy localities throughout the Northwest, he travelled over 16,000 miles by car and by foot. Even today, some of these bogs in remote mountainous terrain are accessed with difficulty. Among the results of this dilligence was his monumental 1947 paper on postglacial vegetation of the northern Great Basin. Hansen's pollen studies chronicle several distinct forest successions in the northwest during four phases of the late glacial and postglacial time frame between 20,000 and 5,000 years ago.

Since Hansen's synthesis, interim work on Pleistocene floras was sporadic until the 1990s. For example, U.S. Geological Survey paleobotanist Jack Wolfe points out an Ice Age plant local from Cape Blanco that is striking for its limited *Pseudotsuga* [Douglas fir] in comparison to frequent appearances of this tree elsewhere in the Pacific Northwest at this time. Wolfe surmised in a 1969 paper that the current dominance of Douglas fir did not take place here until quite late in the Pleistocene.

Further inland an unusual Ice Age fossil plant local has been identified in Lane County. On Lookout Creek in the Western Cascades the site was dated as 35,500 years old by A.S. and L.M. Gottesfeld of the University of California, Berkeley, and Fred Swanson of Oregon State University. Fragments of wood, needles, and pollen were apparently carried downstream from higher elevations where they were scattered across the valley floor. *Abies* [fir] and *Picea* [spruce] grew in somewhat warmer conditions than did *Pseudotsuga* [Douglas fir] and *Thuja* [arborvitae] may have populated lower cold valleys.

Beginning in the 1990s, research by Cathy Whitlock and Curt Peterson has been related to ice age vegetation and geologic processes. At the University of Oregon Geography Department, Whitlock, especially, is involved in deciphering the paleo-climate and vegetational history of the Pacific Northwest. Most of her work is confined to Washington and British Columbia because Pleistocene records for Oregon are incomplete. Putting together an overview for the Northwest is premature when pollen data are lacking, however, by relying on partial prior coring and by directing her own field projects in the state, Whitlock has developed records from certain areas such as in the central Coast Range and Cascades.

With this material she is now able to compile information on how plants responded to sudden environmental disturbances. Concentrating on vegetation changes during the last 20,000 years, she shows how plants responded to glacial advance and decline. Her summaries indicate that montane forests of spruce, white pine, and western hemlock during glacial conditions 20,000 to 16,000 years ago gave way to the establishment of Douglas fir, western hemlock, and western cedar 5,000 years before the present. In light of present day warming trends, her research is particularly timely and significant.

A rooted conifer stump, dating back thousands of years, is one of several exposed at Moolack Beach by the winter storms of 1998 [photo courtesy W. Orr]

The phenomena of "buried stumps" along the coast was noted as early as 1950 when Ewart Baldwin reported unidentified logs in the Pleistocene Coquille Formation at Newport. These were carbon 14 dated at 50,000 years old and were submerged as coastal river mouths were inundated when sea level rose. These stumps are now part of Curt Peterson's research on paleoseismic phenomena as it relates to tectonic plate subduction and earthquakes. A professor at Portland State University, Peterson and his students examined 275 rooted and buried stumps at 14 localities in the surf zone on the central coast. Their 1997 paper reports entire fields of buried stumps, roots, and cones of Sitka spruce [*Picea sitchensis*] and western hemlock [*Tsuga heterophylla*] near Newport as well as moss stems similar to *Scouleria aquatica* at China Creek north of Florence. The Newport field was exposed in January and May, 1995, then reburied by October of that year only to reappear briefly in 1996. Peterson and coauthor Roger Hart of the Hatfield Marine Science Center conclude that extensive Holocene conifer forests, growing on the wave-cut terraces, dunes, or in creek beds, were abruptly buried about 1.9 to 4.4 thousand years ago by rising sea level, coastal migration of sand, and catastrophic descent of tracts of the coastal region. The cycle of terracing, uplift, forestation, burial, flooding, and renewed platform cutting may have taken over 1,000 years.

Near Mt. Hood, forests were buried successively during the past 2,000 years as the result of volcanic activity. The children of Ken Cameron sit on these ancient cedar stumps, cut down by early pioneers, in the Lost Creek Picnic area [photo courtesy Oregon Department of Geology and Mineral Industries].

In more recent times, volcanic eruptions and accompanying mudflows on Mt. Hood buried the coniferous forests on the south and southwestern sides of the mountain as well as on the valley floor of the Sandy River. As late as 1400 and 1800 A.D. thick stands of trees were engulfed and covered in what is called the Stadter buried forest north of Paradise Park. First noticed in 1926 by Fred Stadter, a Portland judge, a line of logs projecting from the vertical face of the Sandy River canyon wall can only be reached after a seven mile hike. Here an extensive mudflow pushed the trees over and stripped off the bark. Most of the trees in this spectacular buried forest are large cedars and Douglas fir.

Cenozoic floral stratigraphy [after Orr and Orr, 1981].

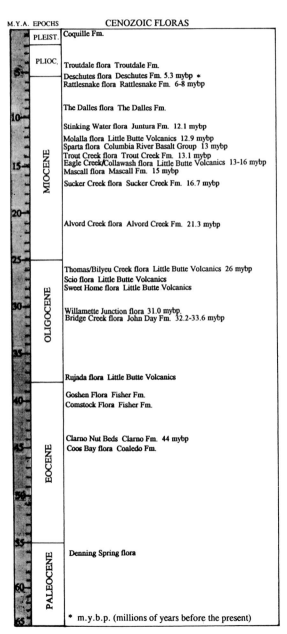

M.Y.A. EPOCHS   CENOZOIC FLORAS

PLEIST. — Coquille Fm.

PLIOC. — Troutdale flora Troutdale Fm.
Deschutes flora Deschutes Fm. 5.3 mybp *
Rattlesnake flora Rattlesnake Fm. 6-8 mybp

MIOCENE
The Dalles flora The Dalles Fm.

Stinking Water flora Juntura Fm. 12.1 mybp
Molalla flora Little Butte Volcanics 12.9 mybp
Sparta flora Columbia River Basalt Group 13 mybp
Trout Creek flora Trout Creek Fm. 13.1 mybp
Eagle Creek/Collawash flora Little Butte Volcanics 13-16 mybp
Mascall flora Mascall Fm. 15 mybp
Sucker Creek flora Sucker Creek Fm. 16.7 mybp

Alvord Creek flora Alvord Creek Fm. 21.3 mybp

OLIGOCENE
Thomas/Bilyeu Creek flora Little Butte Volcanics 26 mybp
Scio flora Little Butte Volcanics
Sweet Home flora Little Butte Volcanics

Willamette Junction flora 31.0 mybp.
Bridge Creek flora John Day Fm. 32.2-33.6 mybp

Rujada flora Little Butte Volcanics

EOCENE
Goshen Flora Fisher Fm.
Comstock Flora Fisher Fm.

Clarno Nut Beds Clarno Fm. 44 mybp
Coos Bay flora Coaledo Fm.

PALEOCENE
Denning Spring flora

* m.y.b.p. (millions of years before the present)

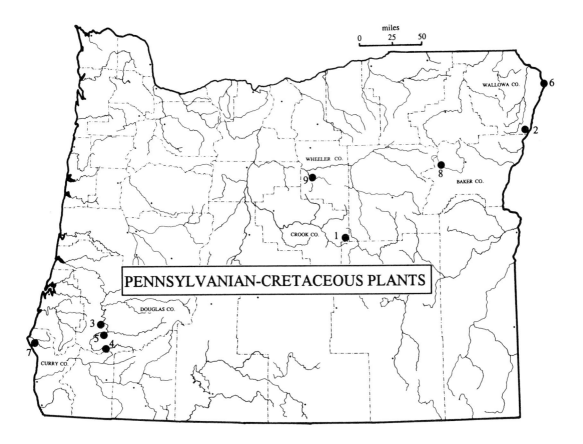

The following are selections of Oregon fossil plant localities and authors who list floras from them.

PENNSYLVANIAN
1. Spotted Ridge, SW of Suplee, Crook Co. Spotted Ridge Fm. Spotted Ridge flora. Arnold, 1953;
    Mamay and Read, 1956.

TRIASSIC
2. Red Gulch, Wallowa Mtns., Wallowa Co. Hurwal Fm. Flugel, Senowbari-Daryan, and Stanley, 1989.

JURASSIC
3. Buck Peak, NW of Riddle, Douglas Co. Riddle Fm. Diller, 1908; Knowlton, 1910.
4. Cow Creek, SW of Riddle, Douglas Co. Riddle Fm. Diller, 1908; Knowlton, 1910.
5. Riddle, Douglas Co. Riddle Fm. Diller, 1908; Knowlton, 1910.
6. Snake River Canyon, Wallowa Co. Coon Hollow Fm. Ash, 1991.

CRETACEOUS
7. Elk River, Curry Co. Humbug Mtn. Conglomerate. Lowther, 1967.
8. Lightning Creek, N of Sumpter, Baker Co. No Fm. Dake, 1969; Read and Brown, 1937.
9. Mitchell, Wheeler Co. No. Fm. Gregory, 1968; Thompson, Yett, and Green, 1984.

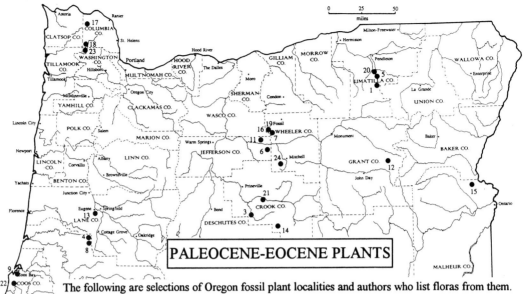

The following are selections of Oregon fossil plant localities and authors who list floras from them.

PALEOCENE
1. Denning Spring, Umatilla Co. No Fm. Gordon, 1985.
2. Floras Creek, Curry Co. No Fm. Baldwin, 1974

EOCENE
3. Bear Creek valley, Crook Co. Clarno Fm. Clarno Flora. Hergert, 1940; Lowry, 1940.
4. Bear Creek, SW of Cottage Grove, Douglas Co. Fisher Fm. Comstock Flora. Peck, 1964.
5. Birch Creek, Umatilla Co. Clarno Fm. Clarno Flora. Hergert, 1961.
6. Cherry Creek valley, Jefferson Co. Clarno Fm. Clarno Flora. Chaney, 1927; 1956.
7. Clarno, Wheeler Co. Clarno Fm. Clarno Flora. Bestland and Retallack, 1994;
     Chaney, 1927; Peterson, 1964; Retallack, Bestland, and Fremd, 1996.
8. Comstock, SW of Cottage Grove, Douglas Co. Fisher Fm. Comstock Flora. Sanborn, 1937.
9. Coos Bay, Coos Co. Coaledo Fm. Coos Bay Flora. Hopkins, 1967.
10. Crockett Knob, Grant Co. Clarno Fm. Clarno Flora. Mobley, 1956.
11. Currant Creek, Jefferson Co. Clarno Fm. Clarno Flora. Knowlton, 1902.
12. Dixie Mtn., Grant Co. Clarno Fm. Clarno Flora. Gregory, 1969.
13. Goshen, Lane Co. Fisher Fm. Goshen Flora. Chaney and Sanborn, 1933.
14. Hampton Butte, Crook Co. Clarno Fm. Clarno Flora. Hergert, 1961; Lowry, 1940.
15. Huntington, Malheur Co. Clarno Fm. Clarno Flora. Gregory, 1969.
16. Mammal Quarry, Wheeler Co. Clarno Fm. Clarno Flora. Bestland and Retallack, 1994;
     McKee, 1970.
17. Mist, Columbia Co. Keasey Fm. Moore, 1971.
18. Nehalem River valley, Columbia Co. Cowlitz Fm. Warren and Norbisrath, 1946.
19. Nut Beds, Wheeler Co. Clarno Fm. Clarno Flora. Bones, 1979; Manchester, 1994;
     Scott, 1954.
20. Pilot Rock, S of Pendleton, Umatilla Co. Clarno Fm. Clarno Flora. Gregory, 1969; Pigg, 1961.
21. Post, Crook Co. Clarno Fm. Clarno Flora. Hergert, 1961.
22. Riverton, Coos Co. Coaledo Fm. Coos Bay Flora. Hergert, 1961.
23. Timber, Washington Co. Cowlitz Fm. Warren and Norbisrath, 1961.
24. West Branch Creek, SW of Mitchell, Wheeler Co. Clarno Fm. Clarno Flora. Chaney, 1956.

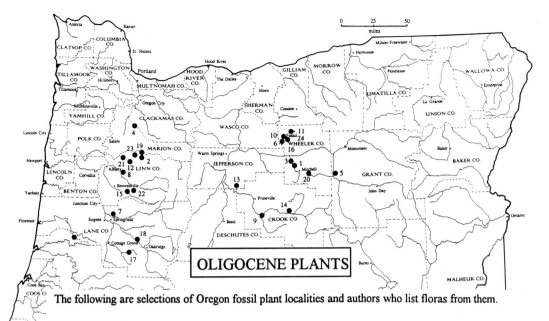

OLIGOCENE PLANTS

The following are selections of Oregon fossil plant localities and authors who list floras from them.

OLIGOCENE

1. Allen Ranch, NW of Mitchell, Wheeler Co. John Day Fm. Bridge Creek Flora. Chaney, 1927; Meyer and Manchester, 1997.
2. Bilyeu Creek, Linn Co. Little Butte Volcanics. Thomas Creek Flora. Klucking, 1964.
3. Bridge Creek valley, Wheeler Co. John Day Fm. Bridge Creek Flora. Chaney, 1925; Brown, 1937.
4. Butte Creek valley, Marion-Clackamas Co. Scotts Mills Fm. Steere, 1959.
5. Cant Ranch, W of Dayville, Grant Co. Bridge Creek Flora. Chaney, 1927; Knowlton, 1902.
6. Clarno, Wheeler Co. John Day Fm. Bridge Creek Flora. Chaney, 1927; Brown, 1959; Meyer and Manchester, 1997.
7. Coburg Hills, Lane Co. Little Butte Volcanics? Willamette Junction Flora. Lewis, 1950.
8. Crabtree Creek, Linn Co. Little Butte Volcanics. Scio Flora? Peck, 1964.
9. Crooked River valley, Crook Co. John Day Fm. Bridge Creek Flora. Chaney, 1925.
10. Dugout Gulch, NE of Clarno, Wheeler Co. John Day Fm. Bridge Creek Flora. Chaney, 1927; Peterson, 1964.
11. Fossil, Wheeler Co. John Day Fm. Bridge Creek Flora. Brown, 1959; Knowlton, 1902; Meyer and Manchester, 1997.
12. Franklin Butte, Linn Co. Little Butte Volcanics. Scio Flora. Sanborn, 1947.
13. Gray Butte, Jefferson Co. John Day Fm. McFadden, 1986.
14. Gray Ranch, Crook Co. John Day Fm. Meyer and Manchester, 1997.
15. Holley, Linn Co. Little Butte Volcanics. Sweet Home Flora. Richardson, 1950.
16. Knox Ranch, E of Clarno, Wheeler Co. John Day Fm. Bridge Creek Flora. Meyer and Manchester, 1997; Peterson, 1964.
17. Laying Creek, Lane Co. Little Butte Volcanics. Rujada Flora. Lakhanpal, 1958.
18. Lookout Point Res., Lane Co. Little Butte Volcanics. Rujada Flora. Lakhanpal, 1958.
19. Lyons, Linn Co. Little Butte Volcanics. Lyons Flora. Meyer, 1973.
20. Painted Hills, Wheeler Co. John Day Fm. Bridge Creek Flora. Bestland and Retallack, 1994.
21. Scio, Linn Co. Little Butte Volcanics. Scio Flora. Sanborn, 1947.
22. Sweet Home, Linn Co. Little Butte Volcanics. Sweet Home Flora. Richardson, 1950.
23. Thomas Creek, Linn Co. Little Butte Volcanics. Thomas Creek Flora. Klucking, 1964.
24. Twickenham, Wheeler Co. John Day Fm. Bridge Creek Flora. Chaney, 1956.

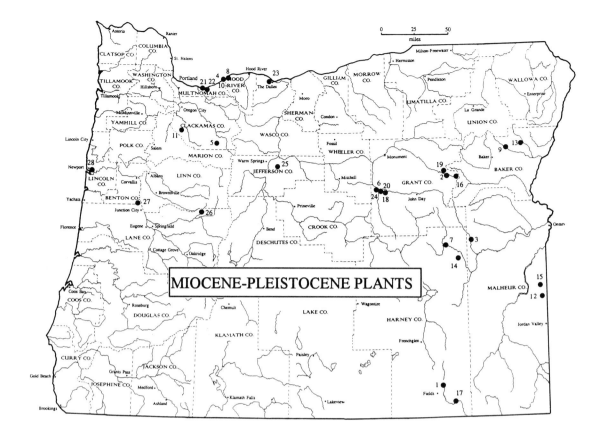

MIOCENE-PLEISTOCENE PLANTS

EARLY MIOCENE

1. Alvord Creek, Harney Co. Alvord Creek Fm. Alvord Creek Flora. Axelrod, 1944.

MIDDLE MIOCENE

2. Austin, Grant Co. Columbia River Basalt. Blue Mountain Flora. Chaney and Axelrod, 1959; Oliver, 1937.
3. Beulah, Malheur Co. Juntura Fm. Beulah-Stinking Water Flora. Chaney and Axelrod, 1959.
4. Bonneville, Multnomah Co. Eagle Creek Fm. Eagle Creek Flora. Chaney, 1920.
5. Collawash River valley, Clackamas Co. Little Butte Volcanics. Collawash Flora. Wolfe, 1954; 1960.
6. Dayville, Grant Co. Mascall Fm. Mascall Flora. Chaney and Axelrod, 1959.
7. Dry Creek, NE of Buchanan, Harney Co. Juntura Fm. Stinking Water Flora. Chaney and Axelrod, 1959
8. Eagle Creek Valley, Hood River Co. Eagle Creek Fm. Eagle Creek Flora. Chaney, 1920.
9. Keating, Baker Co. Juntura Fm. Sparta Flora. Hoxie, 1965.
10. Moffatt Creek valley, Multnomah Co. Eagle Creek Fm. Eagle Creek Flora. Chaney, 1920.
11. Molalla, Clackamas Co. Little Butte Volcanics. Molalla Flora. Wolfe, 1960.
12. Rockville, Malheur Co. Sucker Creek Fm. Sucker Creek Flora. Smith, 1932.

13. Sparta, Baker Co. Columbia River Basalt. Sparta Flora. Hoxie, 1965.
14. Stinking Water Creek valley, Harney Co. Juntura Fm. Stinking Water Flora.
    Chaney and Axelrod, 1959.
15. Succor Creek valley, Malheur Co. Sucker Creek Fm. Sucker Creek Flora. Graham, 1963;
MacGinitie, 1933.
16. Tipton, Grant Co. Columbia River Basalt. Blue Mountain Flora. Brown, 1937; Oliver, 1934.
17. Trout Creek, Harney Co. Trout Creek Fm. Trout Creek Flora. Graham, 1963; MacGinitie, 1933.
18. Van Horn Ranch, Grant Co. Mascall Fm. Mascall Flora. Chaney and Axelrod, 1959; Chaney, 1925.
19. Vinegar Creek valley, Grant Co. Columbia River Basalt. Blue Mountain Flora. Chaney and Axelrod,
    1959.
20. White Hills, E. of Dayville, Grant Co. Mascall Fm. Mascall Flora. Chaney, 1925.

LATE MIOCENE
21. Buck Creek valley, E of Troutdale, Multnomah Co. Troutdale Fm. Troutdale Flora. Chaney, 1944.
22. Camp Collins [on Sandy River], Multnomah Co. Troutdale Fm. Troutdale Flora. Chaney, 1944.
23. Chenoweth Creek valley, Wasco Co. The Dalles Fm. The Dalles Flora. Chaney, 1944.
24. Dayville, Grant Co. Rattlesnake Fm. Rattlesnake Flora. Chaney, 1927; 1948.

PLIOCENE
25. Madras, Jefferson Co. Deschutes Fm. Deschutes Flora. Ashwill, 1983; 1996.

PLEISTOCENE
26. Lookout Creek, Lane Co. No. Fm. Gottesfeld, Swanson, and Gottesfeld, 1981.
27. Monroe, Benton Co. No Fm. Roberts and Whitehead, 1984.
28. Newport, Lincoln Co. Coquille Fm. Baldwin, 1950.

William Gabb, seated in the center with the long beard, worked as a paleontologist with the California survey. Shown here with his field party in approximately 1888, Gabb was responsible for recognizing, describing, and illustrating great numbers of fossil invertebrate species from the Triassic, Cretaceous, and Tertiary. Much of the region he and his party explored was almost inaccessible, and, considering the incipient state of the science and random availability of geologic literature, this group should be given credit for significant results, notwithstanding inaccuracies perceived with present day resources. Gabb's Northwest explorations began in 1863 when he and his party travelled for three months through what he termed *terra incognita* north of Fort Klamath to Vancouver Island, obtaining Cretaceous and Tertiary fossils [photo courtesy Archives, Geological Survey, Denver].

OREGON FOSSIL INVERTEBRATES

Historically Oregon has long been known for its superb array of fossil invertebrates, a reflection of the state's watery past. The best preserved and most abundant are from the Tertiary period, between 65 and 2 million years ago, but diverse faunas occur in Paleozoic and Mesozoic rocks of displaced exotic terranes, which are up to 400 million years old. During these earlier eras volcanic island chains, many from tropical settings, were inhabited by a variety of organisms that became part of the Oregon landscape once the island fragments were annexed to the North American landmass.

Invertebrates comprise a wide range of creatures, defined as animals without backbones. This covers single celled organisms or protozoa such as radiolaria and foraminifera, multicelled animals as sponges, corals, arthropods, molluscs, brachiopods, bryozoa, echinoderms, and trace fossils. Marine vertebrates and plants make up an important part of the modern marine biota, but their occurrence when fossilized is very sparce when compared to the numbers of preserved invertebrates. Molluscs alone are estimated to be represented by over 100,000 living species. While the Oregon fossil record contains representatives of all of the above invertebrates, the molluscs are by far the most numerous and diverse.

In order for a reef to form, several environmental requirements of temperature, water energy, and nutrients must be met.

Frequently invertebrate shells are so abundant that they construct complex limestone rock masses which project from the sea floor as a monolith or reef. Simple accumulations of loose shells of the clam *Buchia* are often found in Jurassic and Cretaceous sediments of southwest and east-central Oregon. These biostromal mounds lack internal structure and do not qualify as reefs. A true reef, or bioherm, has a rigid interlocking internal architecture much like a skyscraper with frame-building corals thoroughly cemented together by calcareous encrusting algae.

The reef must have a solid foundation or substrate to build upon, and corals that construct this early phase in the life of a reef are quite distinct from those making up the bulk of the overlying structure. After the base has formed, the bioherm grows like a fortress to the zone of wave action and maintains itself in that high energy environment. Corals that stud the rough windward side of the reef are easily distinguished from those in less turbulent environments on the flanks or in the lagoon. Today living reefs are restricted to warm shallow waters at subtropical latitudes.

DATING USING INVERTEBRATES

Because they are so abundant in marine rocks, fossilized invertebrate shells are of particular importance for determining the age of strata. However, geologists working in Europe in the 19th century were slow to see the value of fossils as tools to measure geologic time. It wasn't until 1808 when the stratigraphy of the Paris basin was worked out that the usefulness of molluscs was recognized. The first molluscan chronologies were based on European species, and early efforts to apply these successions elsewhere in the world failed because, like most modern plants and animals, fossils tend to have only limited geographic distribution. Paleontologists soon realized that it would be necessary to establish local successions of fossils for use in the immediate vicinity. These were later followed by correlations between far-flung regions to produce a global chronology.

In Paleozoic and Mesozoic rocks, the coiled shells of ammonites are among the best time markers for earth history. Since they evolve rapidly and move about globally owing to their swimming ability, ammonites are natural tools for age dating. One drawback to the use of ammonites is that they tend to inhabit open ocean settings and are less frequent in reefs or near shore sediments.

Geologic time chronologies for the Cenozoic era, covering the interval from 66 million years ago to the present, were determined in 1833 by British born geologist Charles Lyell, whose text, *Principles of Geology,* set the direction that geologic thinking would take in the mid 19th century. Lyell began establishing a uniform faunal history of the marine Tertiary in Europe, basing his definition of the "Eocene," "Miocene", and "Pliocene" epochs on the percentage of fossil species that are found still living today in each of these intervals. After counting the number of fossil species in a formation, Lyell would calculate what percentage of these had living representatives. A high number of modern equivalents in a fauna would reflect younger strata. Thus the Eocene would have fewer modern species than the Pliocene. The Paleocene, Oligocene, and Pleistocene epochs were later added and subdivided from Lyell's original three epochs.

In spite of the shortcomings of Lyell's percentage method, this strategy was initially used on the West Coast to approximate the Tertiary epochs here. The first chronologies were developed in California and were based on the name of the geologic rock formation where the characteristic fossils were found, and not on spans of time or stages. This confusion of time and rock concepts led to an unfortunate situation where, for example, the Vaqueros Stage was distinguished by the fossils that are found in rocks of the Vaqueros Formation. Since rock units or formations frequently extend over more than one time interval or have different ages at various locals, the Vaqueros Formation includes the Miocene but extends into the late Oligocene as well. Because of the reliance on rock components and not a range of time, considerable irregularities were apparent on the chronologic charts between what were rock units or formations and what were time units or stages.

This problem wasn't resolved until 1944, when Charles Weaver of the University of Washington chaired a committee of 21 stratigraphers and paleontologists who prepared a master time-stratigraphic framework for all of the Pacific Coast Cenozoic. Standard European time designations were largely ignored by the committee. Among the results of this early effort of "science by committee", microfossils [mainly foraminifera] were recognized along with megafossils [mostly molluscs] for their important role in West Coast stratigraphy. The awakening of interest in foraminifera, as reflected in stratigraphic charts, accompanied the rapid growth of the petroleum industry at the end of World War II. It was realized that foraminifera are especially useful with marine layers, which tend to be rich in microfossils, yet often lacked stratigraphically definitive megafossils, and visa versa. Pulling together prior work of numerous paleontologists, the committee's graphic presentation of 21 separate stratigraphic sections from California and Mexico, through Oregon, Washington, and into southern British Columbia was a critical step in the comparision of stages and formations.

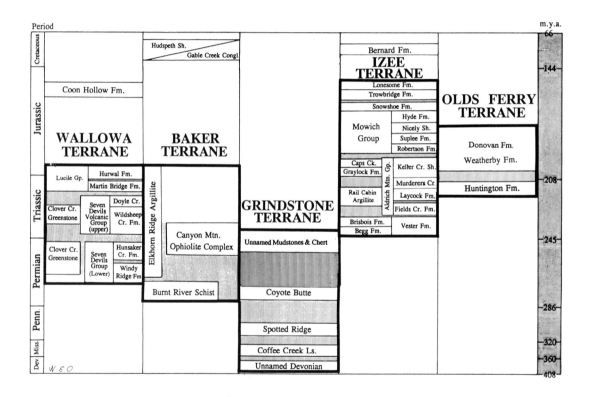

PreCenozoic stratigraphy of the Blue Mountains [from Orr and Orr, 1996]

The process of fine tuning and adjusting rock correlations is ongoing locally as well as internationally, particularly when new paleontological and radiometric data emerges. Warren Addicott of the U.S. Geological Survey and John Armentrout of Mobil Exploration revised, formalized, and refined the West Coast Tertiary and Quaternary time scale in 1981 with the publication *Pacific Northwest Cenozoic Biostratigraphy*. Compiled for an annual meeting of the Geologic Society of America, this important paper focused on carefully defined and updated time scales since Weaver's work, placing local chronologies and stratigraphy into a world-wide framework. The COSUNA chart - *Correlation of Stratigraphic Units of North America* - that included the regional *Correlation of Cenozoic Stratigraphic Units of Western Oregon and Washington* - accessed and incorporated further data in 1983. These charts furnish today's stratigraphic standards.

Crouching aligator-like creatures face each other across a gathering of shells in an imaginary Triassic seascape that could have been part of Oregon's past [from Fugier, 1891].

PALEOENVIRONMENTS AND INVERTEBRATES

In addition to their usefulness as geologic time markers, invertebrate fossils are employed to reconstruct prehistoric settings or paleoenvironments. Examination of any modern beach and continental shelf shows profound variation in the marine conditions from the beach down across the shelf toward deeper water. These changes include gradual reductions of wave turbulence, the light penetration of the water, oxygen concentration, turbidity, and water temperature along with differences in the ocean floor or substrate. All bottom dwelling invertebrates mark these influences by diminishing rapidly in diversity and frequency toward deeper water. Fossil shells can then be used to extrapolate paleodepth as well as proximity to the shore. Often these deductions can even be made without referring to particular species or genera. For example, unless a clam is a burrowing type, those in deep quiet water are ordinarily thin-shelled, whereas robust thick shells reflect shallow turbulent water. In the highly specialized environments of estuaries, lagoons, and bays, where salinity and temperature may be extreme or may vary rapidly over a short interval, the diversity or number of invertebrate species tends to be much smaller than in a normal open ocean. Although the number of specimens or biomass may be much higher because of richness in nutrients, diversity is also markedly lower in the turbulent surf zone, on the outer continental shelf, in deeper water below wave base, and below the light penetration [photic] zone.

PALEOZOIC AND MESOZOIC IN OREGON

Oregon's oldest rocks are found in the Blue Mountains and Klamath provinces where they are parts of exotic terranes. During the Paleozoic and Mesozoic wandering crustal fragments of what had been volcanic island chains were annexed to the West Coast of North America. Terrane fragments of volcanic archipelagos form the foundation of the Blue Mountains in north-east and central Oregon and the adjacent states as well as in the Klamath Mountains. Around 400 million years ago, Oregon was covered by a broad seaway with a shoreline to the east across what is now Idaho and Nevada. Ocean plateaus and small volcanic land masses, that rose from the floor of the ancient Pacific, were being carried slowly eastward as on a conveyer belt to merge with the North American landmass. The process of continental accretion continued into the Mesozoic era. At that time the Blue Mountains and Klamaths, which projected as low islands above the ocean, hosted dense populations of shallow water clams, snails, corals, ammonites, crabs, and squid. After the smaller landmasses were annexed, thousands of feet of ocean sediments and volcanic material blanketed them during the Cretaceous and Tertiary periods. Today bits and pieces of these ancient terranes can be glimpsed through erosional breaks or windows in the covering of younger rocks.

Most of these terrane rocks have been altered by the heat and pressure of metamorphism and often only microfossils, and, in particular radiolaria, remain. Recently developed techniques for extracting the glassy skeletons of radiolaria from altered sedimentary rocks have made them particularly useful for determining geologic age. Thought to be the remains of tiny extinct fish-like organisms, conodonts are another group routinely employed in deciphering ages of exotic terranes. These microfossils also reflect the temperature history of their entombing rock. Since they change color when subjected to elevated temperatures, conodont fossils can be used to measure the degree and extent of metamorphism. Increasing temperatures darken conodonts from pale yellow to amber to black, and continued heat alters them from black to gray to white. At extremely high temperatures conodont fossils may become almost crystal clear.

Several microcontinental terranes show evidence of having evolved in more tropical regions since the fossil remains of animals and plants found within the bits and pieces of these exotic rocks reflect warmer environments. Fossils are recognized as a critical tool for deciphering, among other things, the complex environments and time relationships between jumbled terrane rocks, and even the paleo-latitude at which terrances originally developed. One of the most exciting areas of paleontology today is using fossils to trace the pathways of terranes as they moved across the globe. Microfossils and fossil invertebrates reveal that most Oregon terranes were positioned in a more southerly warm Tethyan province of the eastern Pacific Ocean during the late Paleozoic, Triassic, and early Jurassic. By middle Jurassic time, 180 million years ago, the terranes had moved to a mid latitude position, and by late Jurassic fossils in the terranes reflect a more northerly cooler latitude.

A simple criteria, based on the presence of certain key radiolaria, was devised by micropaleontologists Emile Pessagno, Charles Blome, and co-authors to determine characteristic climatic realms of each terrane. For example, the presence of the radiolarian *Ristola* and an abundance of members of the Pantanelliidae family in terrane strata indicate the archipelago originated in the warm tropical Tethys Ocean, whereas the rocks of the cooler northern boreal province are distinguished by the abundance of *Parvicingula* and by a lack of members of the family Pantanelliidae.

Radiolaria [l.to r.]: *Ristola*, members of the Pantanellidae family, and *Parvicingula/Praeparviingula* are key indicators of Jurassic latitudes.

Environmental evidence presented by megafossils supports that of radiolaria. Ralph Imlay, invertebrate paleontologist with the U.S. Geological Survey, has, for example, demonstrated that the fossil ammonites *Arieticeras, Grammoceras, Protogrammoceras,* and *Fuciniceras*, along with the pelecypod *Weyla* from Oregon's past, reflect subtropical settings similar to those of Italy and the Mediterranean today.

BLUE MOUNTAINS PROVINCE

From southwest to northeast, the separate terrane blocks that make up the complex Blue Mountain archipelago are the Grindstone, Izee, Baker, Wallowa, and Olds Ferry. Since the reinstatement of continental drift as plate tectonics in the middle 1960s, there has been a flood of papers dealing with the fossils and biostratigraphy of these terranes. As a result the

Blue Mountains province has been extensively treated by many authors, but, among these, Tracy Vallier, of the U.S. Geological Survey, and Howard Brooks, of the Oregon Department of Geology and Mineral Industries, stand out for their 30-year long record of careful research and numerous publications. Probably no one has been more thorough in deciphering the complex Blue Mountains geology than these two.

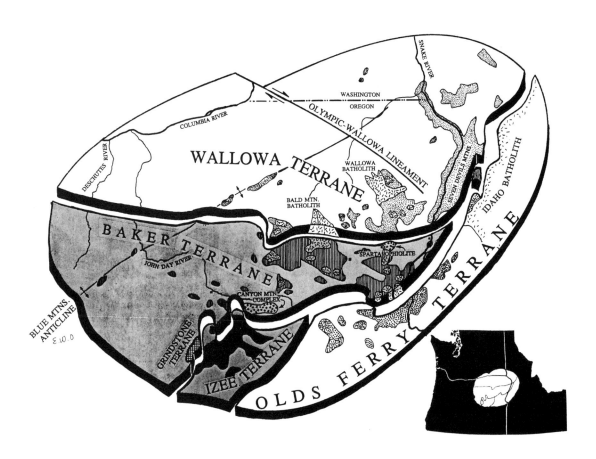

The Blue Mountains of eastern Oregon are divided into five distinct terranes [from Orr an Orr, 1996].

Their publications during the late 1960s treat the Snake River area, and by the 1970s they were unravelling the tectonic evolution of eastern Oregon and adjacent Idaho. Five Professional Papers, which they edited from 1986 to 1995, are especially helpful in surveying the paleontology, biostratigraphy, volcanism, and tectonics of this region. These works summarize current thinking on island arc accretion, batholith intrusions, and Cenozoic events.

Howard Brooks, graduate of the Mckay School of Mines, and Tracy Vallier, Oregon State University, are two of the foremost authorities on the geology of the Blue Mountains. Since retirement Brooks continues to work on Oregon geology projects as well as on his golf score. Vallier has moved to Idaho where he recently completed a guide book on the geology of the Snake River [photo courtesy H. Brooks and T. Vallier].

GRINDSTONE TERRANE

The Grindstone is the smallest of these eastern Oregon accreted fragments, and in Crook, Harney, and Grant counties exposures of Devonian through Permian Grindstone rocks range from 400 to 250 million years before the present. This terrane, once thought to represent subducted and partially ground up pieces of a continental margin, was reinterpreted in 1991 and 1992 by Charles Blome of the U.S. Geological Survey and Merlynd Nestell in the Geology Department at the University of Texas, Arlington. Their study of radiolaria from the Grindstone showed that the rocks are a mixture or melange composed of massive slump blocks or olistoliths, which were detached from shallow water limestone banks adjacent to volcanic knolls. The huge slabs then slid downslope to mix in with younger rocks of the nearby Izee terrane. Today the Grindstone terrane is plastered to the western edge of the Izee. Their 1992 field guide to pre-Tertiary geology of eastcentral Oregon provides a nice up-to-date condensation of the paleontology here.

The Grindstone terrane has been subdivided into the oldest unnamed Devonian limestones, followed by the Mississippian Coffee Creek Formation, the Pennsylvanian Spotted Ridge, the Permian Coyote Butte, capped by a late Permian to early Triassic chert-mudstone layer.

At the base of the Grindstone terrane a 200-foot thickness of Devonian limestones, sandstones, and mudstones occurs just south of the abandoned village of Suplee in eastern Crook County and in a second small exposure to the south in Harney County. These represent the oldest sedimentary rocks in the state. Although it is difficult to pinpoint many early fossil locations, the presence of these ancient rocks first came to the attention of Chester Washburne in 1899, while he and a companion, John Platts, were on a bicycle trip through this part of the state. A student of Thomas Condon, Washburne found the coral *Zaphrentis* and the clams *Aviculopecten* and *Pseudomonotis* on upper Beaver Creek in Crook County. The fossils were sent to George H. Girty, a paleontologist in the U.S. Geological Survey, who concluded that only two were Paleozoic and that one, *Zaphrentis*, indicated "the Carboniferous, though it may, in fact, be Devonian."

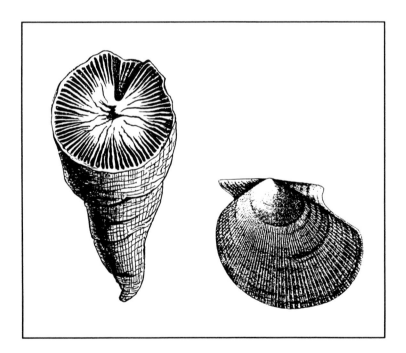

The solitary horn coral *Zaphrentis* and the clam *Aviculopecten* both inhabited long intervals during the Paleozoic [from Nicholson, 1897].

The northern limestones from the Weberg Ranch near Suplee are rich in fossil corals and brachiopods. These were briefly described in an abstract by Russell Jeffords and Walter Kleweno, who discovered the outcrop in 1961. Both Kleweno, whose Masters degree from Washington State University was in Permian stratigraphy, and Jeffords, a Paleozoic coral and crinoid specialist, worked for Humble Oil Company. The first in-depth study of these fossils was in 1978 by Jess Johnson, professor at Oregon State University, and Gilbert Klapper at the University of Iowa. Processing rock samples provided by Roger Tiller, a resident of Burns, these authors found conodonts, but no identifiable brachiopods, and it wasn't until Jeffords sent his original brachiopods to Johnson that verifications were made and the specimens illustrated. Additional brachiopod material was collected in 1975 on a field trip by David Perry, a Canadian paleontologist. Unfortunately Perry's research here was cut short by his death in a helicopter crash.

In 1979 Clay Amundson, a student at Portland State University, and Norman Savage, professor at the University of Oregon, used conodonts from south of Suplee to assign a mid-Devonian age, while noting that the carmel brown-colored microfossils had been altered by temperatures reaching 200 to 400 degrees Fahrenheit as the result of metamorphic processes.

The southern outcrop, reported as Devonian by Kleweno and Jeffords, yielded only *Sinucosta* and *Zugmayerella* when analyzed by David Bostwick, professor at Oregon State University. On the basis of these fossils, Bostwick assigned this strata a Triassic date.

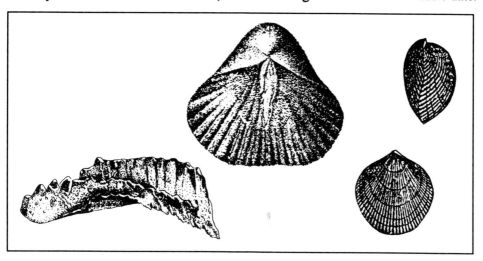

The Devonian age of limestones in the Grindstone terrane has been corroborated by conodonts and brachiopods [left to right, the conodont *Polygnathus;* brachiopods *Grypidula,* and *Atrypa*].

Above the Devonian, thick Mississippian limestones, mudstones, sandstones, and cherts of the Coffee Creek Formation in eastern Oregon are also part of the Grindstone. Notations in the catalog at the University of Oregon Museum indicate Thomas Condon collected the first Paleozoic molluscs in Oregon from the Crooked River drainage, but by the 1920s these specimens could not be located in the museum.

Earl Packard and his summer field students were the next to compile extensive fossils from here. These early university camps were important in that they often undertook a geologic examination of unsurveyed regions of the state. Packard routinely held field camp on the Orin Mills ranch, about 15 miles southeast of Paulina, and during the 1927 season he focused on the old town of Suplee. Putting together a considerable number of fossils, Packard remarked that they would take several years to process. Eventually this collection provided the basis for the subdivision of Paleozoic stratigraphy in central Oregon. Then as now field camp was required for geology students, and in the 1930s the registration fee for the two months was about $20.00 and an additional $20.00 for board. Students were expected to pay transportation and gasoline costs to the field as well as maintain the camp, provide their own outdoor equipment, and get a shot against Rocky Mountain fever. The camp relocated to the Mascall Ranch near Dayville when science classes transferred to Oregon State University.

Well-liked, Earl Packard was given a gift of *North American Index Fossils of* **by students, who bought the expensive volume after taking up a collection. The appreciative Packard remarked to them that he slept with it under his pillow [photo courtesy Archives, Oregon State University].**

Earl L. Packard's promotion of research in Oregon for over 40 years and his diverse record of publications made him one of the state's most dedicated geologists. Packard was born in Massachusetts in 1885, but his family moved to Washington state, and he received a Masters degree from the University of Washington in 1912. At the University of California, Berkeley, where he took classes from the renowned paleontologist John Merriam, his PhD dealt with Cretaceous geology and invertebrate paleontology in southern California. However, his work and training with Merriam gave Packard a lifelong interest and appreciation for vertebrate fossils. Except for the years 1916 and 1917, when he taught in Washington and Mississippi, Packard remained in the Oregon system of higher education. Employed as a geology professor at the University in Eugene, he became Dean of the new school of science after science departments were transferred to Oregon State College at Corvallis in 1932. As a beginning assistant professor, he was paid $1400 annually to teach Historical Geology and Paleontology. Renting a small furnished house near the University cost $20.00 a month. Resigning as dean in 1938, he conducted research and taught until until 1950 when he retired to California. Very frail and deaf, but still pleasant and engaging, Packard died in Palo Alto in 1983 at nearly 98 years of age.

Some years after his initial work, Packard asked Charles Merriam, professor at Cornell University, and Sheridan Berthiaume, a student there, to work out a more detailed stratigraphy for central Oregon. Son of the celebrated paleontologist, John Merriam, Charles completed his academic work at Berkeley in 1932 on West Coast Tertiary invertebrates, but his interests soon shifted to the largely untouched Paleozoic faunas of western North America. While teaching at Cornell from 1935 to 1942, he spent summers in Nevada and Oregon. Returning to the west in 1942, he remained at the U.S. Geological Survey for the rest of his career. Merriam and Berthiaume worked from 1937 to 1939 in the field, mainly relying on a

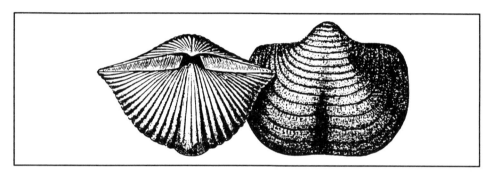

In 1928 Packard sent his Suplee fossils to the famous Yale paleontologist Charles Schuchert, who identified *Productus giganteus,* a brachiopod of remarkable size measuring ten inches across and the wide-hinged or winged brachiopod *Spirifer striatus* [*Spirifer* left, *Productus* right. From Dana, 1875].

map of the Dayville quadrangle by Bill Wilkinson and geology students from Oregon State University. Naming three Paleozoic formations, the Coffee Creek, Coyote Butte, and Spotted Ridge, Merriam and Berthiaume constructed their stratigraphy around the presence of invertebrate and plant fossils. Many of Packard's specimens still reside in the Condon Museum at the University of Oregon, while those collected by Merriam and Berthiaume were sent to Cornell or the Smithsonian.

Molluscs, corals, and fusulinids in the 350-million year old Mississippian Coffee Creek Formation have yet to be described in detail, but the corals *Campophyllum, Dibunophyllum,* and *Lithostrotion,* the brachiopods *Gigantella* and *Striatifera,* the foraminifera, *Tetrataxis,* small gastropods, and sponge spicules were reported by Merriam and Berthiaume in 1943. To that list , J. Thomas Dutro, with the U.S. Geological Survey, was able to add the brachiopod, *Titanaria,* in 1985. Dutro compared this fauna to one in northcentral Washington reaching the conclusion that the Coffee Creek was an olistolith or a chaotic mass that had broken broke loose to move as a block down a submarine slope.

Above the Coffee Creek Formation in central Oregon, the only known Pennsylvanian invertebrates in the state consist of a few poorly preserved clams, snails, and a scaphopod in the shallow water marine layer of the Spotted Ridge Formation. Ferns and fern-like plants are found in non-marine intervals, indicating a shoreline environment.

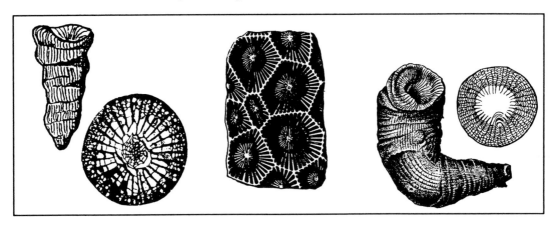

The Grindstone terrane corals *Dibunophyllum, Lithostrotion,* and *Campophyllum* [from Grabau and Shimer, 1910].

Early Permian rocks of the Grindstone terrane consist of sandstones, limestones, and cherts of the Coyote Butte Formation. The upper portion is dominated by brachiopods but has few fusulinids, in contrast to the older lower portion, which yields abundant corals, fusulinids, and crinoids from a shallow shelf paleoenvironment. This mutually exclusive distribution of brachiopods and fusulinids has been documented many times elsewhere as representing varying water depths.

Two decades after Merriam and Berthiaume's field work, G. Arthur Cooper described Oregon brachiopods from the Coyote Butte Formation in 1957. For this work, Cooper was invited by Charles Merriam to inspect collections he and Berthiaume had made along with those of paleobotanist Charles Read and Earl Packard. At that time Cooper found it difficult to correlate these faunas with others in North America because so few studies had been done. Naming *Pseudomartina berthiaumei* and *Rostranteris merriami,* Cooper noted the Oregon faunas were peculiar because many of the genera were not recorded elsewhere in the North American Permian. He went on to compare the Coyote Butte fauna to fossil assemblages in Russia, but the significance of this astonishing observation would not be recognized for almost 30 years when the role of plate tectonics was applied to Northwest geology.

G. Arthur Cooper is doubtless the preeminent brachiopod specialist in the world. Throughout a career that spanned over 40 years, he generously shared his knowledge and ideas with other paleontologists in specially conducted seminars, while he refined stratigraphic and taxonomic methods, and built an un-matched brachiopod reference collection at the Smithsonian. Born in February, 1902, in New York, Cooper, or "Coop", as he is known, became attuned to fossils while an undergraduate student at Colgate University when he spent

G. Arthur and Josephine Cooper working in their laboratory at the Smithsonian [photo courtesy Archives, Smithsonian Institution].

much of his time examining rocks and fossils near the campus. Finishing a PhD from Yale, he specialized in Devonian faunas even though his expertise extended throughout the entire Paleozoic and to associated invertebrates such as pelecypods, echinoderms, and trilobites. Aside from paleontology, Civil War history and flowering plants are interests that have engrossed him since retirement to Raleigh, North Carolina.

Corals and fusulinids are a large part part of the shallow marine shelf fauna characterizing the lower Coyote Butte strata. The corals *Waagenophyllum* and *Lithostrotion* from this formation were reported from near Suplee by Charles Merriam as early as 1942, and almost exactly 40 years later Cal Stevens and Barbra Rycerski of San Jose State University added

Heritschiodes, Thysanophyllum, and *Petalaxis*. Stevens mapped the distribution of Permian coral reefs that developed along the northern and western margins of the Pangea supercontinent as well as around offshore volcanic islands that lay to the west of the landmass. The tropical Tethyan seaway formed an open embayment eastward between arms of this large landmass. Today the *Thysanophyllum* coral belt on the western margin of North and South America and into the Ural Mountains of Siberia is a scattered remnant of these ancient coastal reefs and offshore atolls. By carefully comparing the shallow water reef faunas, Stevens and Rycerski have been able to distinguish between nearshore mainland Pangea corals and those which are more remote, fringing offshore volcanic archipelagos. Although Permian corals are known from the California Klamaths, none have been found to date in Oregon.

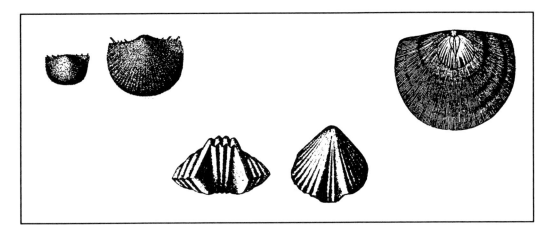

Permian brachiopods *Chonetes, Stenoscisma,* and *Derbya* [from Grabau and Shimer, 1910].

Microfossils are especially useful when working with juxtaposed terrane material where relationships between strata are unclear. Merriam and Berthiaume's 1943 work initially recognized the presence of wheat grain-size fusulinids *Schwagerina* and *Parafusulina* in the Coyote Butte Formation, but the first micropaleontologist to work extensively with Permian fusulinids of eastern Oregon was David Bostwick, a professor at Oregon State University. In 1965, Bostwick and an interested math student, Merlynd Nestell, examined a float boulder from possible Coyote Butte rocks near the Walter Colpitts homestead cabin in Grant County. The 30 pound boulder, first noticed by retired Shell Oil geologist Harold J. Buddenhagen, had abundant specimens of a new fusulinid species *Polydiexodina oregonensis*. Even though he had examined local outcrops for fusulinids, Bostwick had never found similar species. However, he assigned the boulder to the Coyote Butte two years later when he listed Permian faunas from the northwestern United States.

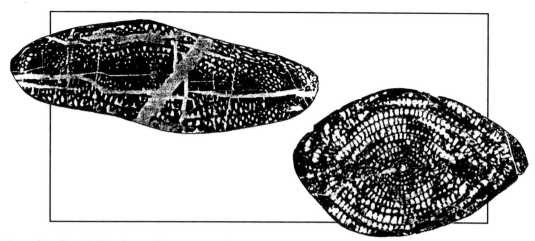

Permian fusulinids from limestones of the Grindstone terrane [after Blome and Nestell, 1992].

David Bostwick's interest in Oregon Paleozoic microfossils preceeded that of others by almost 20 years. Bostwick came to Oregon State University as an instructor in 1953, finishing a PhD from the University of Wisconsin five years later. Born in Helena, Montana, he gravitated to the west for his field work in Idaho and central Oregon and a career at Corvallis that lasted until his illness and retirement in 1978. Summers were spent with students looking at Paleozoic rocks, in particular the Burnt River Schist. As long as a student was interested in geology, whether a major or not, Bostwick provided encouragement, even allowing full access to his labs and collections and generously hiring those who needed money to assist him on summer projects. **[1969 photo courtesy M. Nestell].**

At the top of the Grindstone terrane, almost 900 feet of black, green, and red chert and mudstone have been separated from the Coyote Butte layer because the cherts have distinctive Triassic radiolaria and conodonts, but lack molluscs. The division was made by Charles Blome of the U.S. Geological Survey, a specialist in preCenozoic radiolarians. As a micropaleontology student of Emile Pessagno at the University of Texas at Dallas, Blome completed a PhD in 1981 on Triassic radiolaria from eastern Oregon and British Coumbia. Since then he produced important papers in 1991 and 1992 on late Permian and early Triassic radiolaria from melange sediments of the Grindstone terrane in which he notes that faunas from the unnamed Oregon Triassic chert are nearly identical to those of the same age found in Japan.

Born in North Carolina in 1937, Merlynd Nestell received graduate degrees at the University of Wisconsin and Oregon State University in math, but his expertise extends to microfossils. At present he teaches at the University of Texas, Arlington.

In a 1985 photograph Coyote Butte limestones of the Grindstone terrane provide comfort for Chuck Blome [left] and Merlynd Nestell [photo courtesy M. Nestell].

WALLOWA TERRANE

Lying in a wide belt to the northeast of the Grindstone exposures in the Blue Mountains, remnants of the Wallowa terrane take in the Snake River canyon, most of the Wallowas, and parts of the Elkhorn and Greenhorn mountains. These rocks span the Permian, Triassic, and Jurassic. The Wallowa terrane is generally considered to be a fragment of the larger Wrangellia volcanic archipelago that travelled eastward to accrete to North America during the Cretaceous. The terrane was then sliced by faults and the pieces were displaced northward to be scattered from Oregon to Alaska. With outstanding insight, U.S. Geological Survey paleontologist, David Jones and co-workers were the first to compile a picture of the scattered slivers of Wrangellia when they noticed the striking similarity of rocks and fossils in Hells

Canyon, Vancouver Island, Queen Charlotte Island, and the Wrangell Mountains of Alaska. Their conclusions were published in a landmark paper in 1977.

However, not everyone agrees that northeast Oregon is part of the larger Wrangellia terrane. George Stanley of the University of Montana notes that middle Triassic corals from the Wallowa terrane at Pittsburg Landing on the Snake River are quite distinct from those of other accreted Wrangellia fragments. He has proposed that the Wallowa terrane was geographically isolated and not connected to Wrangellia or even in the warm Tethyan ocean. Stanley synthesizes that about 180 million years ago the Wallowa terrane was located well to the north of Wrangellia, perhaps adjacent to the interior seaway across North America. The position of the Wallowa terrane, closer to North America than others of the Blue Mountains archipelago, makes its tectonic history of particular importance. A faunal exchange between corals and clams of this terrane and North America may have taken place, and the plentiful fossils in its rocks are critical for tracing its past.

The most comprehensive early publication on the Wallowas was in 1941 by Warren Smith and Lloyd Staples of the University of Oregon and John Allen and Wayne Lowell from the State Department of Geology and Mineral Industries. Much of the preliminary work was carried out by students at University of Oregon geology field camp. Under Smith's supervision, students had already sketched out a map, and in 1927 Smith wrote to his uncle James P. Smith at Stanford about Triassic corals, clams, and pelecypods from a black marble locality. His field notes tell of riding on horseback up Joseph Peak to faulted cliffs where the fossils were eroding out of crumbling talus slopes. Even though the focus of this work was examining the region for its ores and minerals, Smith and his coauthors carefully described the stratigraphy and characteristic fossils for each formation.

Working with Warren Smith in the Wallowas, Jim Stovall was hired to teach at the University of Oregon, pursuing a career there until his unexpected death in 1968. An extremely popular lecturer with classes numbering hundreds of students, even today Stovall is familiar to Oregonians throughout the state. Ewart Baldwin relates that when his car broke down in a remote section of eastern Oregon, Stovall was the only staff member at Eugene known or of interest to the local garage repair man [photo courtesy University of Oregon, Archives].

The oldest rocks of the Wallowa terrane encompass the Clover Creek Greenstone, which spans the Permian to Triassic intervals, and the late Permian Hunsaker Creek Formation. Four thousand-foot thick sediments of the Clover Creek Greenstone in northern Baker County contain middle Permian fossils in the lower portion and late Triassic in the upper. The Permian invertebrates here are dominantly spiny productid brachiopods. In 1992 Cindy Shroba and her field assistants Tom and "Goober" employed invertebrate fossils to interpret the tectonic setting of the Clover Creek Greenstone as part of her PhD thesis from the University of Oregon. The presence of the productid brachiopods *Kuvelosia* and *Waagenoconcha* and similar brachiopods of boreal [cool] environments prompted Shroba to speculate that the Wallowa terrane was at a northern latitude during the Permian, moving southward to a more tropical region in the Triassic before accreting to North America during the late Mesozoic. The presence of *Kuvelosia* further suggests the Wallowa may not share the same tropical origin as the larger Wrangellia terrane.

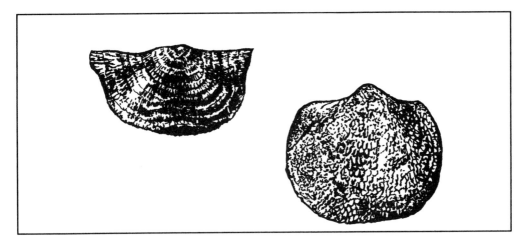

Kuvelosia and *Waagenoconcha,* **from the Permian Clover Creek Greenstone, are key brachiopods to interpreting environments of the Wallowa terrane.**

In contrast to the Clover Creek, fossils of the Hunsaker Creek Formation in the Snake River canyon near Homestead have not been studied in depth. This two-mile thick sequence of volcanic debris, shales, and limestones seems to be the eastern equivalent of the Permian Clover Creek Greenstone, and the brachiopods, echinoderms (crinoids), bryozoa, and pelecypods from this formation are exceptionally abundant and well-preserved in the limestone intervals. One of the few sources of information on these fossils is Tracy Vallier's PhD thesis from Oregon State University in which he lists the small brachiopod *Megousia* that has a distinctively ornamented shell.

Mass global extinctions at the end of the Permian period, about 245 million years ago, mark the end of the Paleozoic era of ancient life and the beginning of the Mesozoic or middle life, which proceeded until 66 million years ago. The opening of the Mesozoic, following the catastrophic loss of up to 95% of Permian plants and animals, saw an almost entirely new bi-ota. Although the cause of the extinctions isn't known, one possibility may have been profound volcanic activity in Siberia when voluminous flood basalts were exuded across vast regions of northern Asia. Another theory attributes these extinctions to the impact of a major meteorite in the southern hemisphere. After the debacle, plants and animals slowly reestablished themselves in new environments during the Triassic. In the ocean that covered the Pacific Northwest, the development of stromatolite-algae mounds and ultimately of coral reefs signalled the return of a rich diversity of marine life by late Triassic and early Jurassic time.

Triassic formations that make up the Wallowa terrane are the Clover Creek Green-stone, the Seven Devils volcanics of Idaho, the Wild Sheep Creek Formation, the Doyle Creek Formation, the Martin Bridge Limestone, the Hurwal Formation, and the Lucile Group in Idaho. Undersea volcanic eruptions of ash and lava, forming the Seven Devils, Wild Sheep Creek, and Doyle Creek formations were covered by limestones, sandstones, and shales of the Martin Bridge and Hurwal as the volcanic island archipelago ceased activity and subsided.

Ammonites, crinoids, and an armored fish populate an ancient ocean setting [Fugier, 1891].

Fossils are scarce in the middle and late Triassic Wild Sheep Creek and Doyle Creek formations and unknown from the Seven Devils volcanics. Along the Snake River, limestones of the Wild Sheep Creek - which developed as shallow platforms around volcanic islands - supported a variety of organisms such as the clam *Daonella.* By contrast, within the marine sandstones, mudstones, and limestones of the Doyle Creek a meagre fauna of the flat clam *Halobia*, ammonite molds, and plant fragments may imply one or more basins of an upper shelf or slope environment.

The most productive fossil layer of the Wallowa terrane is the Martin Bridge lime-stone where environments range from warm shallow water of an outer shelf adjacent to deeper slope settings. Over 1,500 feet of limestone, shales, and conglomerates of this formation were deposited in a narrow basin bordered by carbonate sandy shoals. The rich well-preserved corals, molluscs, and algae of the Martin Bridge are particularly useful in evaluating the paleoecology of this interval.

In 1908 James Perrin Smith, a popular and energetic paleontology professor from Stanford, discovered corals in a thin bed of the Martin Bridge at the junction of the two forks of Eagle Creek as well as at a second location nearby on Paddy Creek. The presence of the abundant pelecypod *Halobia* in the beds above and below the limestone established it as late Triassic. Unfortunately Smith's Eagle Creek locality was later destroyed by highway construction. Through J.P.'s influence, as he was known, his nephew, Warren D. Smith, went into the study of paleontology and ultimately became chairman of the Geology and Geography Department at the University of Oregon following Thomas Condon's death.

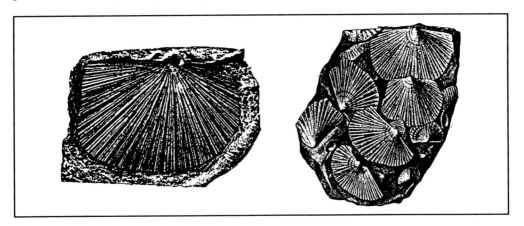

The Triassic clams *Daonella* and *Halobia* belong to a loosely knit group of intermediate to deep water molluscs known as "flat clams" [from Zittel, 1913].

During the 1980s and 1990s Martin Bridge invertebrates were studied by Cathryn Newton in the Department of Geology at Syracuse University as well as by George Stanley at the University of Montana. Newton's PhD thesis from the University of California, Santa Cruz, 1983, treated the paleoecology of late Triassic molluscs from three accreted exotic terranes, two in the Blue Mountains and one in Alaska, and her research has been issued in a number of papers on the Pacific Northwest. She compared the Martin Bridge fauna to that in fragments of the scattered Wrangellia terrane in Canada and Alaska, and in 1987 she recorded 35 species of late Triassic clams in sponge and coral reef-like masses at the Spring Creek locality in Baker County. First discovered by Survey geologist, Tracy Vallier, these rich shell beds were deposited under stormy conditions on a shallow limestone platform surrounding a volcano. This important site, which represents an almost complete stratigraphic section, includes many new pelecypods, named by Newton, that are not known from elsewhere in western North America.

Newton and her co-workers accumulated over 5,000 fossil molluscs during the summers of 1982 and 1983. At the same time they examined, among others, collections by Vallier and by Michael Whalen at the University of Montana. She noted the similarities of Martin Bridge molluscs to those in the adjacent North American landmass and because of these comparisons was able to demonstrate the shells had only been transported short distances between North America and the offshore Wallowa terrane.

A paleontologist who has spent several field seasons mapping and collecting in the Blue Mountains is George Stanley, of the Geology Department University of Montana. Born in Chattanooga, Tennessee, in 1948, he attended the University of Tennessee for a Bachelors Degree, then completed his PhD from the University of Kansas in 1977. His graduate research focused on Triassic corals in western North America, and since that time his emphasis has been on taxonomy and paleoecology of modern and ancient coral reefs. Awarded a Fulbright Scholarship, Stanley spent time in the Smithsonian as well as overseas in Germany and Japan, which prepared him admirably for his work on global paleobiogeography.

George Stanley is a dedicated and patient scholar who has shown remarkable versatility in his study of Blue Mountains terrane rocks and fossils. To trace and compare fossils from this region, Stanley has familiarized himself with Russian literature on similar Triassic invertebrates [photo courtesy G. Stanley].

An important new exposure of a tropical coral reef in the Martin Bridge at Summit Point in Baker County was discovered during the summer of 1985 by Michael Follo. A student at Harvard University, Follo introduced the site to Stanley and visiting German paleontologist Baba Senobari-Daryan, a specialist on Mesozoic coral reefs of Germany and Austria. Senobari-Daryan was amazed to see fossil sponges, algae, molluscs, sea urchins, and corals that were nearly identical to those in the central European Alps. What Stanley and Senobari-Daryan were examining was the first coral-dominated reef of Triassic age to be recognized in North America and in the eastern Pacific region. Although late Triassic reefs are common in tropical sediments of the Alps, they are virtually unknown from comparable shallow water deposits of North America. In 1986 Stanley proposed that the similarity between coral faunas of the Alps and those of Oregon and Idaho may have come about because the numerous volcanic islands that characterized the ancient Pacific were the "stepping stones" by which coral species were dispersed across the ocean.

As with other reef-like structures in western North America, this coral framework originated along the edge of a tropical shallow water volcanic island. One solitary coral, *Distichophyllia*, by rapidly budding upward, formed the main network of a reef, which was additionally supported by the branching coral, *Retiophyllia*. Other corals, algae, sponges, foraminifera, crinoids, and echinoids made up the remainder of the reef habitat.

Focusing on corals and spongimorphs at another locality of the Martin Bridge near Spring Creek, Stanley and his student Michael Whalen recorded 21 species of Triassic corals and 3 species of spongimorphs including two new species of coral, *Maeandrostylis grandiseptus* and *Reticostastraea wallowaensis*, one new genus *Recticostastraea*, and a new sponge *Colospongia whaleni*, named in honor of the discoverer. Currently at Syracuse University working on a PhD from Cathryn Newton, Whalen has since taken the position that true late Triassic reefs, similar to those in the European Alps, have yet to be recognized in North America. However, some carbonate build-up and organic debris are found in several locations, such as in the Martin Bridge Formation. He also came to the conclusion that extensive reef development here could have been hindered by a rapidly rising sea level even though the rising water was not overwhelming enough to inhibit limestone production entirely.

Two distinct corals, *Reticostastraea* [left] and *Distichophyllia* [right], and the sponge *Colospongia* [center] built massive reefs in the Blue Mountains during the Triassic [after Stanley, 1989].

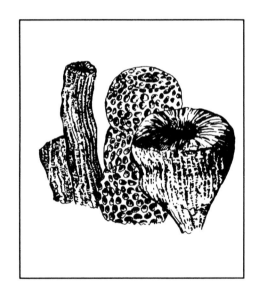

Up to 1,500 feet of late Triassic to early Jurassic carbonate mudstones of the Hurwal Formation were derived from local volcanic activity and carried downslope by turbidity currents before settling into the shallow subsiding basin over strata of the Martin Bridge. The Hurwal yields fewer fossils, and near Excelsior Gulch along Eagle Creek in Baker County the well-preserved clam *Halobia*, the belemnite *Aulacoceras*, and the trace fossil *Chondrites* were noted by Michael Follo for his PhD in 1986. The study, published as a Professional Paper in 1994, addresses the sedimentology and stratigraphy of the Martin Bridge and Hurwal formations. According to Follo, an analysis of the sedimentary sequences does not show that the Wallowa terrane originated in the southern hemisphere but indicates it was close to the North American continent.

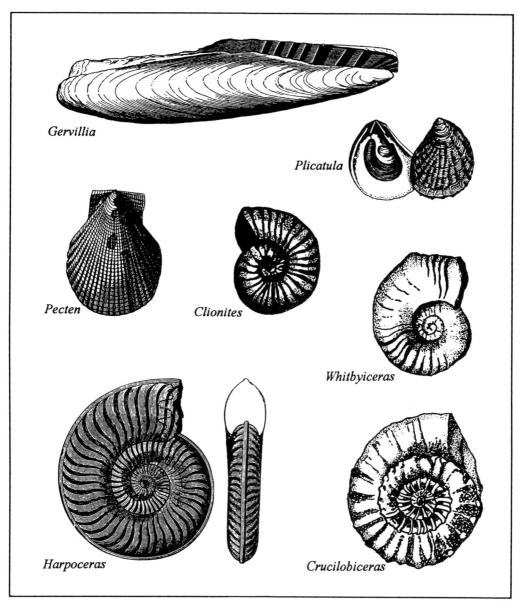

Triassic invertebrates [from Zittel, 1913].

Above the Wallowa terrane, sandstones and mudstones of the Jurassic Coon Hollow Formation, while rich in plant remains, also have few invertebrates and radiolaria. During the fall of 1988 George Stanley investigated a thin limestone bed just north of Pittsburg Landing on the Snake River in which there were numerous corals and molluscs. First discovered by Tracy Vallier and summarized in his 1994 paper, the fossils included two new colonial corals, *Coenastraea hyatti* and *Thecomeandra vallieri*, of middle Jurassic age. These corals together with the ammonites *Harpoceras* and *Lupherella*, the pelecypods *Inoceramus*, *Lima*, *Mysidiella*, and *Plicatula*, and the radiolaria *Canoptum*, *Capnodoce*, *Latium*, *Triassocampe*, and *Xipha* were part of a basin that subsided during uplift and erosion of the surrounding rocks.

BAKER TERRANE

Spread across Crook, Wheeler, Grant, and Baker counties to the Snake River and into Idaho, the Baker terrane is an important component of the Blue Mountain volcanic island chain. Rocks of this terrane were trapped in the subduction zone between massive converging plates, and, owing to the heat and pressure of metamorphism during collision, few fossils remain. The chaotic nature of these rocks along with rare fossils makes the history of this terrane difficult to decipher. The three formations that comprise the Baker terrane are the sparcely fossiliferous Permian Burnt River Schist, the Permian to Jurassic Elkhorn Ridge Argillite, and the Permian to Triassic Canyon Mountain Complex.

Only microfossils have been reported from these highly altered rocks. In a 1986 Professional Paper, Ellen Bishop of LaGrande and Bruce Wardlaw of the U.S. Geological Survey report the middle to late Triassic conodonts *Neogondolella* and *Xaniognathus* in limestone pods of the Burnt River schist along Burnt River, near Durkee, and on the Snake River in Baker County. Similarly, the radiolaria *Canoptum*, *Follicucullus*, and *Pseudoalbaillella*, conodonts, and fusulinids *Boultonia*, *Cancellina*, and *Schwagerina* were noted in the Elkhorn Ridge Argillite by micropaleontologists David Bostwick, Charles Blome, and Merlynd Nestell.

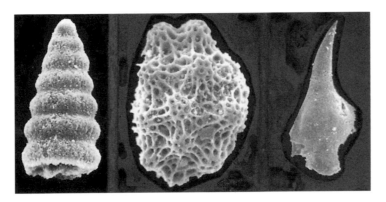

The Permian radiolaria *Canoptum*, *Hegleria*, and *Pseudoalbaillella* [after Blome and Nestell, 1992].

IZEE TERRANE

At the adjoining corners of Grant, Harney and Crook counties, the Izee terrane spans the time period from early Triassic through middle Jurassic, 245 to 140 million years ago. This small fragment was formerly part of a forearc basin environment lying between the volcanic islands represented by the Wallowa and Olds Ferry terranes. Erosion of the Olds Ferry provided much of the fossil-rich marine Jurassic sediment that filled the Izee depression. Today an erosional hole through the younger Cenozoic volcanic deposits allows a view into these Mesozoic sediments near Suplee in Crook County and Izee in Harney County. This key area of approximately 250 square miles takes in the South forks of Beaver Creek and the John Day River as well as the upper reaches of Silver Creek and Silvies River.

The Izee is significant because a long interval of continual deposition resulted in an one and one-half mile thick stratigraphic sequence, which has been divided into almost a dozen formations. The oldest is the Vester Formation, followed by the Graylock and Caps Creek formations, the Aldrich Group, the Mowich Group, and the youngest Snowshoe, Trowbridge, and Lonesome formations.

A systematic study of Paleozoic and Mesozoic rocks near Izee and Suplee was begun by Earl Packard, who was instrumental in encouraging many students to work here. Of those motivated to study paleontology by Packard, one of the most remarkable was Ralph Lupher. Receiving his Masters from Packard at the University of Oregon, Lupher went on to a PhD in 1930 from California Institute of Technology, that dealt with the Jurassic stratigraphy of central Oregon. A careful and methodical worker, Lupher spent many summers working out a detailed stratigraphy for his 1941 paper in which he named most of the formations in the east-central part of the state. His first wife, Anna Woodward from Roseburg was a geology student who assisted Packard in the Condon Museum as well as Lupher in the field.

When he had a new species of foraminifera *Pyrgo lupheri* named after him, Ralph Lupher remarked, "Well it looks like me, short and fat" [photo courtesy D. Lupher].

Woodward died as a young woman, and Lupher married Lucretia Battles, a Home Economics Professor at Washington State University where he worked. Because of a nepotism rule, the Luphers were forced to leave Pullman. He went to Shell Oil Company where he stayed until retirement to Olympia, Washington, in 1964. The eclectic Len, or "Doc", as he was known, cultivated flowers, worked on wood and mechanical inventions, played the violin, and was an enthusiastic fisherman. Over three decades later, in 1973, utilizing Lupher's collections for his own study of the Izee, Ralph Imlay paid lavish tribute to Lupher for the quality of his stratigraphy and accuracy of his fossil identifications.

One of Packard and Lupher's most consequential discoveries was of the Jurassic oyster-like pelecypod *Plicatostylus* [now called *Lithiotis*]. Growing upright from a stalk-like base, innumerable cohesive masses of this clam together with the large gastropod *Nerinea* occur along Beaver Creek in Grant County imbedded in reef-like limestones of the Robertson Formation. Of this particular find, Lupher was fond of saying he was "one step ahead of Packard" to the location. This occurrence was published by the University of Oregon in 1930, but Packard and Lupher submitted a second article naming a new species, *Plicatostylus gregarius*. However, due to the vagaries of publishing, it was never issued. As Lupher later remarked, "I can't be sure what the trouble was with the *Journal of Paleontology* ... I suspect that the main trouble ... lay in one of the editors - not in the merits of the paper itself."

Siemon Muller was another of Packard's students, who went on to become an extremely popular Stanford professor. A White Russian who fled the Bolshevik revolution, Muller finished a PhD at Stanford University, where he later taught paleontology. Much of the eastern Oregon mollusk work during the 1940s to 1960s was his. During World War II Muller specialized in Russian permafrost for the United States government using his skills both in geology and the Russian language **[photo courtesy Geology Dept. University of Oregon]**.

Studies of ammonites from the Suplee-Izee area in the 1960s and 1970s by Ralph Imlay show the Izee terrane originated in the tropics during the late Triassic but by middle Jurassic it was sited at a more northerly cooler latitude. He pointed out that early Jurassic ammonites are distinctly Tethyan or tropical as shown by dominant warm water members of the Hildoceratidae and Dactylioceratidae families, which have closer affinities to those found in the Mediterranean than in northern Europe.

Since the early 1960s Imlay of the U.S. Geological Survey has been working on ammonites in Triassic to Cretaceous sediments of the West Coast, and his landmark 1980 publication, *Jurassic Paleogeography of the Conterminous United States in its Continental Setting*, represents the sum of four decades of work. In this volume he uses a detailed ammonite stratigraphy to unravel a complex series of paleogeographic changes. His conclusions corroborate the early Mesozoic tectonic movement of landmasses that brought together differing terrane fragments of contrasting paleo-environments.

Without question one of the most distinguished authorities on Jurassic and Cretaceous invertebrate faunas, Ralph Imlay's career took him all over the world [left to right: G.N. Pipiringos, J.C. Wright, and R. Imlay] [photo courtesy Archives, U.S. Geological Survey, Denver].

Born in 1908 in Hampton, Iowa, Ralph Imlay moved with his family to Montana where he ultimately attended the University for a Bachelors degree in geology in 1930. As a graduate student at the University of Michigan he became interested in the Jurassic and early Cretaceous of Mexico, which became the focus of his 1933 doctoral dissertation. Mesozoic faunas continued to dominate his research during most of his professional life with the U.S. Geological Survey. His ammonite stratigraphy, correlations, and paleoenvironmental deductions set an unmatched standard for others in his field. Upon retiring from the Survey, Imlay proposes to devote all of his time to paleontology.

By far the most definitive work on the Suplee and Izee was an Oregon Department of Geology and Mineral Industries Bulletin by William Dickinson and Laurence Vigrass in 1965. This publication combined the careful field work and research that went into the PhD theses of both authors studying under Si Muller at Stanford University. Focusing on the structure, petrology, and stratigraphy of this area, they produced maps and a comprehensive list of characteristic fossils and paleo-environments for each of the multiple rock formations. Completed just prior to the new understanding of the implications of moving continents and plates, Dickinson and Vigrass' classic study was easily translated into the revised framework of geologic thinking. Data from this bulletin has been heavily utilized since it was issued.

After receiving his PhD, Lawrence Vigrass [left] became professor at the University of Regina but has since gone into private practice, whereas William Dickinson taught at Stanford for a period before moving to Arizona to direct studies of a new generation of sedimentologists [photos courtesy L. Vigrass and W. Dickinson].

The Poison Creek Fault, trending southwest from the Aldrich Mountains to Izee, divides rocks of this terrane into two separate tracts. Rocks west of the fault are part of the late Triassic to early Jurassic Vester Formation, while those to the east include the late Triassic to early Jurassic Aldrich Mountains Group.

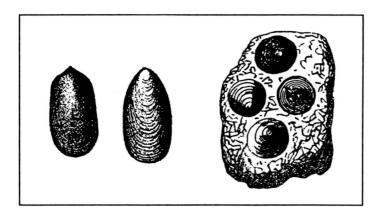

Thick-shelled oysters, the tidal brachiopod *Lingula* [left], algae, and frame-building corals in the Rail Cabin Mudstones attest to calmer waters of a shallow carbonate shelf, whereas the presence of the brachiopod *Discina* [right] in the Graylock reflects a quiet brackish embayment [from Grabau and Shimer, 1910].

The Vester Formation, in turn, was subdivided into the Begg and Brisbois members. This formation, as well as the somewhat younger Graylock and Caps Creek formations, represents a diversity of ancient marine settings. Sediments of the Begg were eroded from rocks of the surrounding Paleozoic highlands into a marine basin, whereas deposits of the Brisbois and younger Rail Cabin Mudstone were part of a warm nearshore environment. The Begg Formation contains occasional invertebrates, but above it the Brisbois is rich in fossil ammonites, pelecypods, and brachiopods.

A diverse radiolarian fauna, predominantly members of the Pantanellidae family that characterize the Rail Cabin interval, was described in the 1980s by Emile Pessagno and Charles Blome from samples previously collected by Dickinson and Vigrass. Pantanellidae radiolaria are characteristic of tropical latitudes, and their presence indicates this terrane block was initially at a more southerly position in the late Triassic. The decline of diversity and abundance of this family in the middle and late Jurassic and subsequent replacement by bizarre long-spined members of the Capnodocinae family such as *Capnodoce, Loffa*, and *Renzium*, signalled the repositioning of the terrane to a cooler boreal climate.

Members of the radiolarian family Capnodocinae have distinctive triple horns projecting from a central body and are excellent guide fossils to Triassic strata [from Blome, 1984].

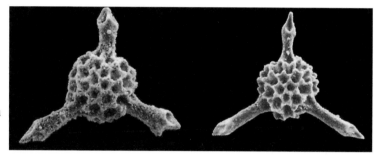

Nearly 30,000 feet in thickness, the late Triassic to early Jurassic Aldrich Mountains Group includes the oldest Fields Creek Formation, the Laycock and Murderers Creek Graywacke, and youngest Keller Creek Shales. Numerous slide blocks of limestone in the massive beds of dark mudstone and sandstone of the Fields Creek contain the brachiopod *Halorella*, ammonites *Arnioceras, Crucilobiceras, and Eoderoceras,* and well-preserved radiolaria. Although the animals lived on a shallow water platform, the limestone blocks were broken up and displaced to deeper water by submarine sliding. No fossils are recorded in the Laycock, but the ammonites *Placerites, Psiloceras, Sanglingites, Vredenburgites,* and *Waehneroceras* are reported from sandstones of the Murderers Creek above.

Over the Aldrich Mountain strata, the middle Jurassic Mowich Group and the Snowshoe, Trowbridge, and Lonesome formations are the youngest sequence in the Suplee forearc basin. Originally defined by Ralph Lupher in 1941, the Mowich is a 1,500-foot thickness of conglomerates, sandstones, volcanic detritus, and massive fossil-rich biostromal limestones subdivided into the Robertson, Suplee, Nicely, and Hyde formations. Sediments of this group were deposited in a transgressing [advancing], deepening ocean that flooded a relatively smooth landscape, and fossils here reflect a shallow coastline with some wave turbulence. The tropical shells point to a much more southerly latitude for the origin of the terrane.

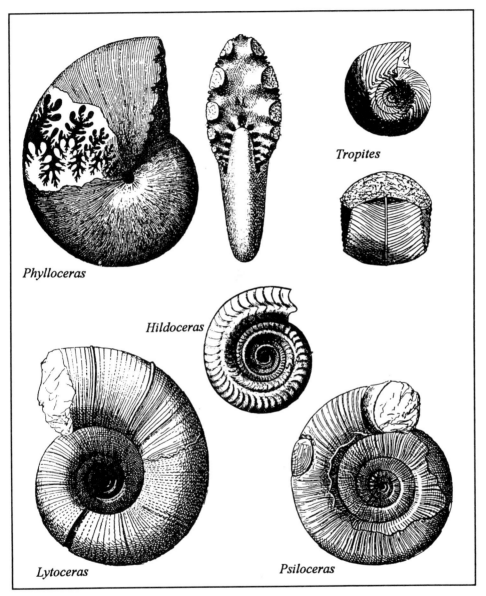

Phylloceras

Tropites

Hildoceras

Lytoceras

Psiloceras

Jurassic fossil ammonites [from Zittel, 1913].

As the oldest of the Mowich Group, the Robertson has massive reef-like limestone lenses composed almost entirely of the closely packed, oyster-like clam *Lithiotis* [*Plicatostylus*], often preserved upright in the growth position. Tightly bound shells of

Lithiotis dominate the reef community. Accompanying these are the snail *Nerinea* and other pelecypods including the bivalve *Weyla*, which points to very shallow open shelf conditions.

Lithiotis is characteristic of the tropical east Pacific and Tethyan oceans in Jurassic times. This pelecypod constructed extensive reef bioherms across the Suplee shelf during the early Jurassic, but by the late early Jurassic it had become extinct. A 1988 study by Anne Nauss and Paul Smith of the University of British Columbia found that the massive bioherms were best developed in the Robertson Formation where the reefs consisted of three separate environments or biofacies: a life accumulation of *Lithotis in situ* at the core of the reefs, a scattered death assemblage of worn *Lithotis* shells aligned with the current, and on the flank of the reefs diverse shelly debris of gastropods, brachiopods, and broken pieces of *Lithiotis*. The internal reef structure and succession of changes as the reef grew and developed elevates these shell accumulations to the status of true reefs or bioherms and not as unstructured masses of shells of biostromes.

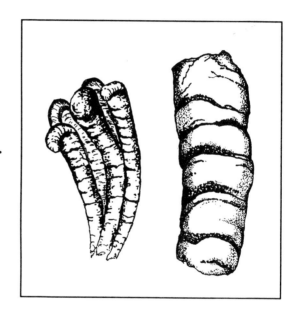

**Tightly packed *Lithiotis* shells
are part of reefs built up in
eastern Oregon during the Jurassic.**

The limey, sandy Suplee Formation above the Robertson had a similar shallow water shelf setting with minimal wave and current activity. Numerous specimens of the oyster-like clam, *Gryphaea,* as well as a large scallop *Weyla*, brachiopods, few corals, and the snail *Nerinea* make up the Suplee fauna. Ammonites are scarce in the Suplee, but Imlay was able to collect a few from this strata as well as from the overlying Nicely where they are extremely numerous. In the black shales and mudstones of the deeper water Nicely, large carbonate concretions, as much as two feet in diameter, are frequently endowed with fossil shells at their core. Even more rare are open ocean reptile [ichthyosaur] and fish remains, which turn up in these shales. In contrast, the Hyde Formation, the youngest of the Mowich group, has relatively few fossils except for fragmental rhynchonellid brachiopods and the ammonite *Hildoceras*.

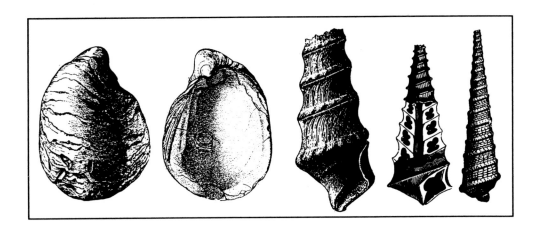

The thick-shelled Jurassic clam *Gryphaea* occurs in gregarious accumulations on muddy bottoms, whereas *Nerinea* is typical of reef margins [from Zittel, 1913].

Above the Mowich, the Snowshoe, Trowbridge, and Lonesome formations are a variety of middle to late Jurassic siltstones, mudstones, sandstones, shales, and volcanics. The Snowshoe, which was broken into three members by Dickinson and Vigrass, has a complicated depositional history recorded in a varied rock record. Debris from local volcanoes was deposited on the shallow platform in the Suplee district and into a deeper basin near Izee. A thick wedge of volcanic sediments was transported downslope into the basin from a volcanic source further east. The brachiopod *Lingula* and thick-shelled clams *Ostrea,* and *Posidonia* substantiate the shallow water setting. *Posidonia,* which could have attached itself to seaweeds, is especially common as are a large number of ammonites. Snowshoe strata is rich with tropical Tethyan radiolaria identified by Emile Pessagno and Charles Blome. Particularly distinctive are the bizarre Nassellariina radiolaria *Perispyridium* and *Turanta* that have a remarkably short duration from their first appearance in the middle Jurassic to their disappeance during later Jurassic time. In conjunction with the warm water ammonites, *Haugia* and *Catulloceras,* they confirm a geographically remote origin for the terrane.

The radiolaria *Turanta* and *Perispyridium* [Pessagno and Blome, 1982].

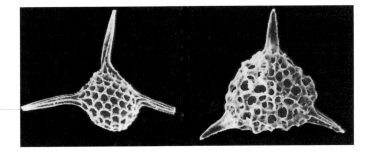

Since publication of Bulletin 58 by Dickinson and Vigrass, Snowshoe invertebrates have been examined in some detail by David Taylor of Portland State University and Paul Smith of the University of British Columbia. Taylor, who received a 1981 PhD from the University of California, Berkeley, on the biostratigraphy of this formation, suggests that key ammonites of the Snowshoe can be used to provide a basis for shallow water biostratigraphic zones. Because the paleo-communities represent a complete range of shallow water tropical conditions, zones of the Snowshoe are applicable elsewhere over wide geographic areas. In 1980 Paul Smith, whose PhD from McMaster University was on the Jurassic of eastern Oregon and western Nevada, also compared the ammonite stratigraphy of the Izee basin to that elsewhere in North America and Europe when he revised and renamed members of the Snowshoe Formation.

About 12,500 feet of late Jurassic strata comprises the Trowbridge and Lonesome formations of the Izee terrane. Unlike the older Mowich Group and Snowshoe Formation, rocks of these two formations yield only scattered fossil pelecypods and ammonites. Dickinson and Vigrass interpret these formations as deposited in a deep water marine basin that was periodically inundated by catastrophic muddy clouds of sand in submarine landslides or turbidites.

OLDS FERRY TERRANE

Curving through eastern Malheur and Baker counties, the Olds Ferry terrane extends across the Snake River in Oregon to Cuddy Mountain, Idaho. Distinctly volcanic in nature, the Olds Ferry represents a collision zone between merging crustal plates. Sedimentary rocks of the Huntington, Weatherby, and Donovan formations make up this terrane. Occasional limestone pods imbedded in the volcanic debris of the Huntington have late Triassic ammonites as well as the pelecypod *Halobia* while, above it, Imlay found Jurassic ammonites at widely separated locals in black shales of the Weatherby.

The Donovan Formation is less than a half of a square mile exposure of fossiliferous red oxidized sandstones, shales, and conglomerates about 2,500-feet thick in Harney County. A very small collection of Donovan fossils in the Condon Museum at the University of Oregon are recorded as "John Day's collection from Beaver Creek of Silver River (not Crooked River)". Condon's shells were identified as early Jurassic in age.

This age designation was confirmed by Lupher in his summary 1941 paper on the Jurassic stratigraphy of central Oregon. Ralph Lupher, of Washington State University, inspected this same location in northern Harney County with the assistance of his wife Anna Woodward and local ranchers Walt Freeman, Melvin Weberg, and Willard Colpitts, amassing a significant number of Donovan fossils. Since Lupher's efforts, this formation has curiously been ignored despite the richness of its fossils.

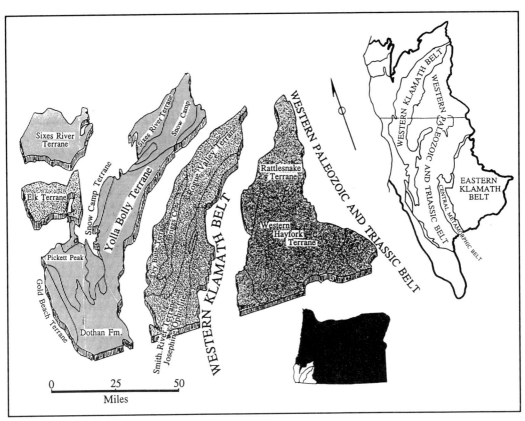

Interpretations of Klamath Mountains structures took a profound turn as plate tectonics was adopted during the mid 1960s [from Orr and Orr, 1996].

KLAMATH MOUNTAINS PROVINCE

Like the Blue Mountains, southwest Oregon is a structurally complex region containing some of the oldest rocks in the state, and an understanding of geologic problems here has only recently come after the application of the modern principles of plate tectonics. The history of geologic research, from the mapping of formations and unravelling of stratigraphy to the gradual realization of the critical role of accreted terranes, is a reflection on a small scale of how geologic thought evolved from the 1880s to the 1960s. Even today the geologic picture of the Klamaths is still emerging.

Thomas Condon was one of the first geologists to explore southern Oregon, a trip that he undertook once the Oregon and California railroad had made its way through the Siskiyou Mountains in 1884. Cretaceous shells *Anomia* and *Trigonia*, ammonite fragments, and a fossil cycad helped him reach the conclusion that these mountains began as an island in the midst of a seaway covering the state.

Just about the same time Joseph Diller, who contributed enormously to the knowledge of Oregon's geology, also had begun to look at this region. Much of Diller's professional career was spent in southwest Oregon and adjacent California, and in the course of his work he doubtless walked across most rock exposures in the Klamath Mountains. In the field, Diller was frequently assisted by George Kay, a Canadian mineralogist, a private collector James Storrs, and Will Q. Brown, a geologist residing in Riddle. In those days field work involved travelling on foot over mountain trails, hiring pack trains, hauling enough supplies for a week or more, and camping out. The most overwhelming aspect would have been that vast areas had not been explored or mapped. Diller and his field assistants contended with all of these difficulties in 40 years of working in Oregon and California. Authoring over 165 papers on paleontology, petrology, volcanology, economic geology, and stratigraphy, Diller's contributions provided the basis for most of the later studies of the Klamath province. Even though much of his stratigraphy has been revised, his work has been unequalled, and Diller remains something of a legend.

Joseph Diller provided the first and only U.S. Geologic Survey map folios of southwest Oregon, which have been of incalculable assistance for the past 100 years. [photo courtesy Archives, U.S. Geological Survey, Denver]

Joseph Silas Diller was born in Plainfield, Pennsylvania, in 1850 of straight-laced German farmers. He began his education in Massachusetts where one of his instructors introduced him to geology. Graduating from Harvard in 1879, Diller spent the following four years in additional studies between Harvard and Heidelberg, Germany, before joining the U.S. Geological Survey in 1883. Marrying the same year, the Dillers built a house in Washington, D.C. It was probably the last his long-suffering wife ever saw of him as Diller then began to work on the West Coast. His field notes of Tuesday, June 5, 1900, note "Wedding Anniversary" as he was leaving Gardiner by boat for Marshfield on the coast. Diller early recognized the Klamaths as a separate geologic province and thereafter concentrated much of his efforts in that region. His map folios of the Coos Bay, Port Orford, Riddle, and Roseburg quadrangles, in which he delineated and named many formations, covered approximately one thousand square miles, but his detailed field notes indicate he examined a far greater area. Having joined the Survey in its fourth year of existence, Diller knew most of the early geologists in America when he retired in 1923. He died in 1928 and was buried in his hometown.

When faced with deciphering Klamath stratigraphy, Diller, of necessity, made some sweeping conclusions. On the basis of the pelecypods *Buchia* [*Aucella*], *Pecten operculiformia*, and *Trigonia aequicostata* Diller assigned the 6,000-foot thick sandstones, shales, conglomerates, and limestones covering broad areas of southwest Oregon to the Cretaceous period, lumping them together as the Myrtle Formation. Similar strata near Coos Bay and Port Orford quadrangles were also mapped as Myrtle. Even as they were being made, Diller's conclusions on age, extent, and stratigraphy of the beds incited a controversy which was defended in a letter by Will Brown. "I will state that Diller could not include Cretaceous with Jurassic or visa-versa ... I have done a great deal of geologic work ... with Diller, Kay, and Becker, and I assure you that Diller makes very few mistakes - his man Storrs can smell fossils." These sediments have since been reexamined and the boundaries for the formations redrawn.

Refinement of the Klamath stratigraphy in 1959 by the U.S. Geological Survey's Francis Wells, Ralph Imlay, and Dallas Peck, accompanied by Hollis Dole of the Oregon Department of Geology and Mineral Industries was based on the Jurassic clam *Buchia piochii* and the Cretaceous *Buchia crassicollis*. The discovery of a 2,000-foot continuous exposure near Days Creek in Douglas County allowed the team to measure a complete stratigraphic sequence and plot the occurrence of fossils in detail. Imlay not only examined all the Myrtle Creek fossils collected in 1906 and 1907 by Diller and Storrs, which had been placed at the Survey, but he spent the summer of 1954 in the field. The result was to remove the name Myrtle for strata inland and replace it with the Jurassic Riddle and Cretaceous Days Creek formations. Similarly, rocks of the old Myrtle Formation on the coast were reevaluated in 1966 by John Koch, a student at the University of Wisconsin. Koch dropped Diller's old Myrtle designation and replaced it with the Otter Point Formation, the Humbug Mountain Conglomerate, and the Rocky Point Formation, thus eliminating entirely the term "Myrtle."

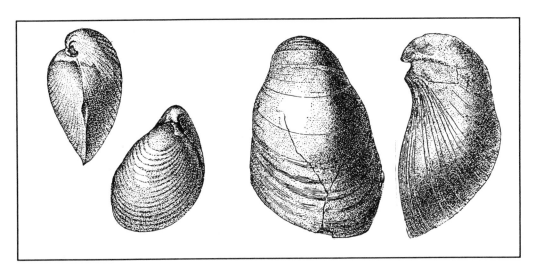

The slender Jurassic clam *Buchia piochii* [left] is readily distinguished from the thicker Cretaceous *Buchia crassicollis* [Grabau and Shimer, 1910].

Under the direction of Robert Dott, members of the Department of Geology from the University of Wisconsin initiated a detailed study of the southwest Oregon coast in 1959. Dott, who devoted a significant part of his career to stratigraphy and marine sediments of the Pacific Northwest, regarded the area from Port Orford to the California border as critical to understanding the late Mesozoic geologic history here. With a PhD from Columbia University in 1955, Dott went to Wisconsin three years later, where he has remained throughout his career. Of the theses he directed, John Koch's PhD treated the western Klamath province. Koch spent the summers of 1960 and 1961 studying the area from Humbug Mountain south to the Rogue River. His comprehensive work summarized the stratigraphy, structure, paleontology, and paleoenvironments of the region, listing invertebrates and microfossils as well as mentioning plants and vertebrates for the local formations.

Bob Dott's research took him from Wisconsin to the southern Oregon coast and Butte Creek in the Western Cascades [photo courtesy M. Chan].

In the middle 1960s the advent of plate tectonics presented new solutions to long-standing problems associated with the complex rocks of the Klamath Mountains province. The current view is that the structure of the Klamaths is a series of sheet-like slabs of displaced terranes stacked like dominos in an arcuate pattern across southwest Oregon and northern California. Originating as multiple volcanic chains and tracts of ocean floor out in the ancient Pacific Ocean, these slabs of rock were carried eastward toward the margin of North America where they were affixed or accreted to that continent in late Mesozoic time. Some of the smaller fragments or slivers in the coastal areas of the province have been moved northward by faulting from Mexico and California. Many of the fossil-rich limestones of the Klamaths developed in the shallows around volcanic island chains. As the crustal slabs moved, huge blocks of limestone broke loose and were transported to deeper marine water by submarine sliding. These disconnected slabs or olistoliths are common in Klamath terranes.

The boundaries and geologic history of terranes are continuously being refined and revised. At present the Klamaths are broken into three main belts, composed of multiple smaller terranes. From east to west these crustal slabs are the Eastern Klamath Belt in California, along with the Western Paleozoic and Triassic Belt and the Western Jurassic Belt that extend into Oregon.

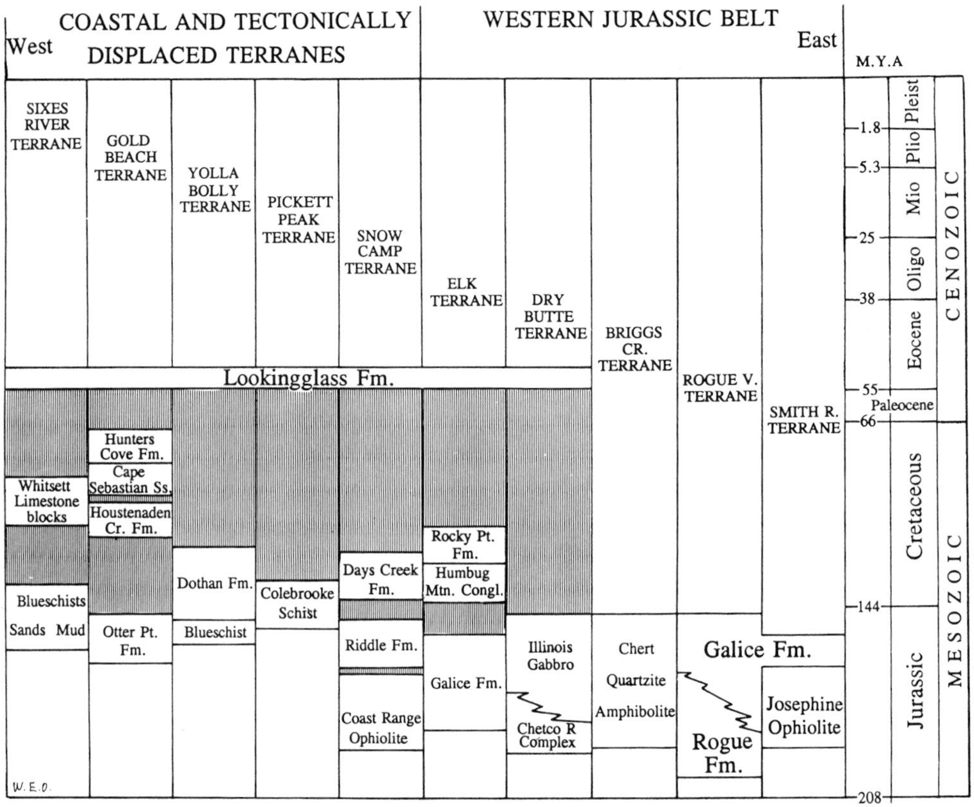

COASTAL AND TECTONICALLY DISPLACED TERRANES (West)								WESTERN JURASSIC BELT (East)				M.Y.A		

Chart labels (east to west / by age):

SIXES RIVER TERRANE · GOLD BEACH TERRANE · YOLLA BOLLY TERRANE · PICKETT PEAK TERRANE · SNOW CAMP TERRANE · ELK TERRANE · DRY BUTTE TERRANE · BRIGGS CR. TERRANE · ROGUE V. TERRANE · SMITH R. TERRANE

Lookingglass Fm.

Hunters Cove Fm. · Cape Sebastian Ss. · Houstenaden Cr. Fm. · Whitsett Limestone blocks · Rocky Pt. Fm. · Days Creek Fm. · Humbug Mtn. Congl. · Blueschists · Dothan Fm. · Colebrooke Schist · Sands Mud · Otter Pt. Fm. · Blueschist · Riddle Fm. · Illinois Gabbro · Chert · Galice Fm. · Galice Fm. · Quartzite · Josephine Ophiolite · Amphibolite · Coast Range Ophiolite · Chetco R Complex · Rogue Fm. · Josephine Ophiolite

Time scale (M.Y.A): 1.8 — 5.3 — 25 — 38 — 55 — 66 — 144 — 208

CENOZOIC: Pleist · Plio · Mio · Oligo · Eocene · Paleocene
MESOZOIC: Cretaceous · Jurassic

W. E. O.

Stratigraphy of the Klamath Mountains [Orr and Orr, 1996].

WESTERN PALEOZOIC AND TRIASSIC BELT

    The Western Paleozoic and Triassic Belt projects from Canyonville, Oregon, to the South Fork of the Trinity River, California. The name is somewhat out-of-date as radiolarian fossils of Jurassic age are now known from the strata. Cherts and tuffs associated with scattered limestone blocks throughout the belt yield radiolaria and conodonts, but most of these fossils are confined to California. The few fossiliferous Oregon locals are near Waldo in Josephine County in rocks formerly known as the Applegate Group. A longtime worker in Klamaths, William Irwin reported the radiolaria *Archaeodictyomitra* and *Praeconocaryomma* from Jurassic cherts here, noting their abundance in 1978. He also pointed out that the age of the radiolaria supports the idea that the tectonic slabs making up the Klamaths become successively younger toward the west. Although much of his career with the U.S. Geological Survey was spent in California, Irwin's interest in the Klamaths encompassed southern Oregon.

Several years later Irwin and coauthors recovered conodonts from these same rocks in Oregon and California. They processed material from previously assembled collections along with their own samples taken between the 1960s through 1980s. Successfully extracting Paleozoic and Mesozoic conodonts from 37 of the samples, they found just three were from the Triassic of southern Oregon in Josephine and Jackson counties. By analyzing the color changes of conodonts from yellow to dark amber, Irwin was able to ascertain temperatures between 500 and 1000 degrees Fahrenheit in the history of these rocks.

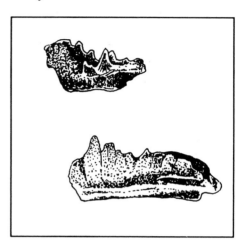

The serrate-toothed conodont *Epigondonella* was the only Triassic Oregon genus recorded, although both this and *Neogondolella* were common in California. *Neogondolella* also occurs in rocks of the Baker terrane.

WESTERN JURASSIC BELT

Adjacent to the Western Paleozoic and Triassic Belt, the Western Jurassic Belt, stretching for over 200 miles from southwest Oregon into California, is divided into five distinct terranes, the Smith River, Rogue Valley, Briggs Creek, Dry Butte, and Elk. Of these, only the Smith River, Rogue Valley, and Elk terranes have yielded fossils.

The Smith River and Rogue Valley are composed of volcanic flows and ash of the middle Jurassic Rogue Formation and mineral-impregnated layers of the Josephine ophiolite, covered by sand, shales, and conglomerates of the late Jurassic Galice Formation. While the Smith River was deposited offshore in a deep back arc marine basin between the volcanic archipelago and the mainland, lavas and volcanic ash of the Rogue Valley terrane accumulated around the periphery of a volcanic island chain. Over the Galice, coarse gravels of the Cretaceous Humbug Mountain Conglomerate and Rocky Point Formation, making up the Elk terrane, have fragmentary plant debris and scattered ammonites.

Few radiolarian microfossils have been extracted from Rogue Formation rocks, but the pelecypod *Buchia concentrica* and ammonites *Amoeboceras* and *Perisphinctes* [*Dichotomosphinctes*] were noted by Joseph Diller throughout the Galice in 1907 and confirmed by Imlay in 1980. Microfossils have come into their own more recently for unravelling terrane stratigraphy, and during the 1980s and 1990s Emile Pessagno, at the University of Texas, Dallas, and his student Charles Blome, now at the U.S. Geological Survey, reported

27 new species, eight new genera, and one new family [Bernoulliidae] of radiolaria from Galice rocks as well as from volcanic sedimentary intervals within and above the Josephine ophiolite. The tropical nature of these fossils indicates the Smith River terrane moved from an equatorial latitude to a cooler boreal position during the middle to late Jurassic.

Diller is credited with noting what few Cretaceous fossils are to be found in Rocky Point and Humbug Mountain strata over the Galice, both now considered as part of the Elk terrane. In 1907 Diller sent James Storrs to the Forks of Elk River in Curry County, where he found a layer of poorly preserved shells and plant remains in the Rocky Point Formation. More than a half century after Diller's brief note, John Koch observed that the fossils scattered throughout the strata are dominated by the clam *Buchia crassicollis,* which he used to assign both formations to the Cretaceous interval. Beach abrasion on the pelecypods, ammonites *Hannaites,, Olcostephanus, Phylloceras,* and *Sarasinella,* and the fossil squid [belemnite] *Aulacotheuthis* are evidence of very shallow water for the Rocky Point.

SMALLER TERRANES

Adjacent to the Elk terrane, five smaller accreted fragments make up the southwest Oregon coast. These are the Snow Camp, Pickett Peak, Yolla Bolly, Gold Beach, and Sixes River. Most have been shifted northward by fault movement from California. Sands and silts of the late Jurassic Riddle and Cretaceous Days Creek formations make up the Snow Camp terrane. From locations here Diller reported fossil tree ferns, ginkgoes, and other exotic-looking tropical plants along with the ubiquitous clams *Buchia piochii* from the Riddle as well as *Buchia crassicollis* from the Days Creek. The plump *Buchia crassicollis* is easily distinguished from the slender *Buchia piochii.* While reviewing the stratigraphy here in 1959, Imlay noted pelecypods, ammonites, and numerous echinoids [sea urchins], fossil evidence of a shallow coastline along an oceanic island.

Between the Snow Camp and Yolla Bolly terranes, Pickett Peak rocks have been altered by heat and pressure of metamorphism and are devoid of fossils. In southern Curry County, the Yolla Bolly terrane includes sands, muds, and cherts of the Dothan Formation, interpreted as deep water deposits on a marine continental slope adjacent to a volcanic island chain. One of the very few notices of Dothan fossils was by Len Ramp, who worked for 37 years as an economic geologist for the the Oregon Department of Geology and Mineral Industries in southern Oregon. Ramp noted the Jurassic clam *Buchia piochii* imbedded in loose rocks at the mouth of Boulder Creek, but even today it is not certain that the boulders originated from the Dothan. Robert Dott reported in 1971 that he searched the Dothan diligently for both megafossils and microfossils and found only worm tubes and carbonized plant remains in what may be Dothan at Chetco Point near Brookings.

Over 10,000 feet of sands, silts, cherts, and volcanic debris of the late Jurassic Otter Point, covered by sands and silts of the Cretaceous Houstenaden Creek, Cape Sebastian, and Hunters Cove formations, comprise the Gold Beach terrane, a small elongate slice on the Oregon coast south of Port Orford in Curry County. Otter Point strata yield only a meagre package of broken plant fragments, poorly preserved radiolaria *Dictyomitra, Ethmosphaera,* and *Hagiastrum,* pelecypods, and ammonites. John Koch reported that the oyster-like *Buchia piochii* almost invariably occurs in mudstones suggesting the clams may have died as they were swept into deep water by submarine slides or turbidity currents. The remains of a large aquatic marine reptile, an *Ichthyosaur,* from this formation at Sisters Rock may have suffered the same fate.

Fragmental molluscan shells, indicators of beach conditions during the Jurassic, gave way to fine sandstones and mudstones as the ocean deepened during the Cretaceous. The picture of this time painted by Robert Dott and his students was of embayments where sands and muds, carried by rivers, accumulated in deltas or on shallow shelves. The large well-preserved ammonite *Pachydiscus multisulcatus* was found in the channel-like sands of the Hunters Cove, whereas *Inoceramus turgidus* and other clams were from a strongly agitated marine setting of the Cape Sebastian.

A coiled shell up to three feet in diameter, *Pachydiscus* would have been a riveting sight in Cretaceous seas [Zittel, 1913].

On the southwestern margin of the state, the Sixes River terrane, taking in the watershed of the Sixes River eastward from Cape Blanco, is a melange or mixture of Jurassic and Cretaceous muds and sands studded with huge loose grey to white and even pink limestone blocks. The carbonate blocks, named the Whitsett limestone by Joseph Diller, are chaotic, and details of their stratigraphy, age, and origin are still poorly understood. Foraminifera are numerous in a few of the blocks, but megafossils are absent. In the early 1900s Joseph Diller and James Storrs reported many broken *Buchia* shells in and around the limestones, but Ralph Imlay and Hollis Dole, who searched the locality during the 1950s, were unable to find even a single specimen.

CRETACEOUS OF OREGON

By the end of the Cretaceous period, 66 million years ago, the major accretionary events had already transpired in the Klamath Mountains and in eastern Oregon. A broad growing shallow seaway covered most of the Northwest, and shorelines ran through eastern Washington and Idaho. Although most of the foundations of the state were in place, minor terrane movements and fault displacement of rock slabs northward out of California continued into the Tertiary. Dispersed marine microfossils, invertebrates, and plants are found throughout Crook, Grant, Wheeler, and Baker counties, but the most abundant well-preserved Cretaceous fossils are from the Klamath Mountains province. Here, for the most part shelled animals lived on a shallow shelf along the continental margin of North America.

The notion that the Cretaceous sea over eastern Oregon was connected to the open ocean near the Klamath Mountains was presented on a 1960 map by David Jones of the U.S. Geological Survey. Jones shows that the ammonites *Cleoniceras, Lyelliceras,* and *Oxytrophidoceras* as well as clams *Inoceramus* and *Megatrigonia* from near Mitchell are similar to those from Grave Creek permitting the paleogeographic reconstruction of a diagonally curving shoreline from Wheeler to Jackson County.

Thomas Condon was the first to recognize and collect Oregon's Cretaceous fossils. In July, 1864, soldiers of Captain John Drake's volunteer cavalry company, camping on Beaver Creek in Crook County, came across a rocky ledge imbedded with innumerable shells. Some of the soldiers thought the fossils might be marine, but Drake, in a letter to Condon, was doubtful. Sent by wagon train to Condon at The Dalles, the fossils proved to be the Cretaceous molluscs *Dentalium, Fusus, Pholadomya,* and *Trigonia,* and ammonites such as *Turrulites.* The shells, along with some leaves, were turned over to William Blake, state mineralogist and professor at the University of California, who visited "Mr. Congdon" while on a tour through Oregon. Blake was putting together a display of fossils for the International Exposition at Paris and once he had reached New York, he retained the beautiful Bridge Creek leaves but turned the shells over to Fielding Meek for identifications. While not officially connected to the Survey, Meek prepared and identified many of the shells from western explorations. He took up a small room in the Smithsonian building, a quiet worker, who is little remembered because of his unobtrusive manner.

During the summers of of 1899 and 1900 numerous invertebrate fossil specimens from Mitchell and Spanish Gulch in Wheeler and Grant counties were collected by vertebrate paleontologist John C. Merriam. Placed in the hands of U.S. Geological Survey paleontologist, Timothy Stanton, the molluscs included the unmistakable Cretaceous clam *Trigonia,* along with *Anomia, Meekia, Mytilus,* and *Tellina,* among others. Stanton also examined "a hasty collection of fossils" from Beaver Creek made by John Platts and Chester Washburne, a student of Condon, on their bicycle trip along the old Prineville-Izee road during the summer of 1899. Many of these were undescribed species and included such late Mesozoic genera as *Anthonya, Fusus, Gyroides, Meretrix, Ostrea,* and *Trigonia.*

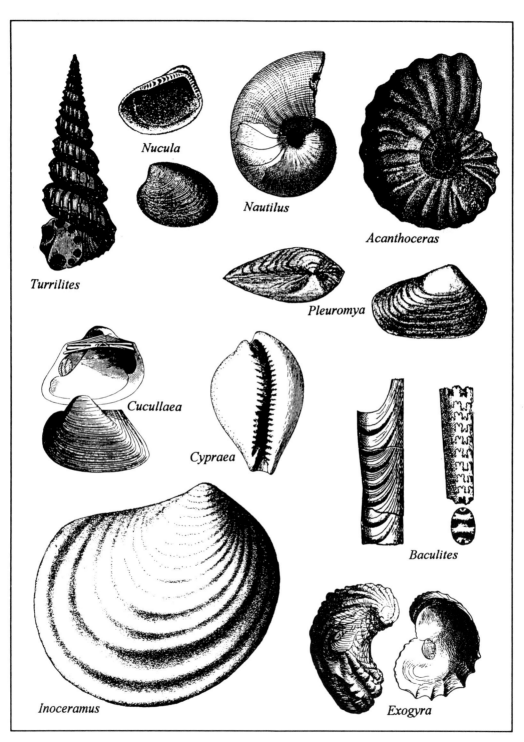

Cretaceous invertebrates [from Zittel, 1913].

Knowledge of Cretaceous rocks of the Pacific Coast was advanced significantly when Frank M. Anderson began to compare West Coast invertebrate faunas and formations. Most of his publications concentrated on California molluscs, but several fossil localities and formations from Oregon were listed. Anderson grew up with Cretaceous fossils in southern Oregon where his family operated placer mines near Phoenix. An enthusiastic collector, he served as a field assistant to Joseph Diller in California and Oregon during the 1880s, all the while maintaining a correspondence with Thomas Condon. In 1892 Anderson wrote that he had spent some time in the Rogue Valley and "in my uncle's mines west of Phoenix" in Jackson County collecting shells, some of which he had not seen in Condon's museum in Eugene. Following a Masters degree from Stanford University in 1897, Anderson worked as a geologist with the Southern Pacific Railroad and, at the same time, volunteered as the paleontology curator for the California Academy of Sciences in San Francisco. Along with numerous other papers, his work was published as three outstanding monographs on the Cretaceous of the West Coast in 1905, 1938, and 1958. His *Upper Cretaceous of the Pacific Coast,* unfinished at his death in 1947, wasn't compiled and published until ten years later. Shortly after this, in 1960, William Popenoe of the University of California, Los Angeles, and his coauthors' *Correlation of the Cretaceous Formations of the Pacific Coast* synthesized the Cretaceous stratigraphy for all three Pacific states.

Looking very much the part of a westerner, the young Frank Anderson grew up in a mining family near Medford, where he first came into contact with Cretaceous invertebrates [photo courtesy Southern Oregon Historical Society].

CRETACEOUS ENVIRONMENTS OF EASTERN OREGON

Eastern Oregon Cretaceous rocks the Hudspeth, Gable Creek, and Bernard formations are scattered over broad areas of Wheeler and Crook counties. The Hudspeth and Gable Creek comprise more than 70 square miles of exposures with a combined stratigraphic thickness of 8,000 feet. Tor Nilsen's 1984 monograph on this region features paleoenvironmental reconstructions based on the microfossils radiolaria and foraminifera. He depicted a shallow continental shelf near present day Antone, submarine fans near Mitchell, and a deeper offshore marine basin in the vicinity of the Muddy Creek Ranch [Rajneeshpuram].

Trigonia, Inoceramus, Ostrya, and *Exogyra from* Bernard strata suggested wave washed shallows to William Dickinson and Laurence Vigrass, who named the formation in 1965. A veneer of sediments over the Izee terrane, the Bernard has not been re-examined since these two workers first looked at it over three decades ago.

The eastern-most marine Cretaceous in Oregon was mentioned briefly in a 1956 Masters thesis from the University of Oregon by Bruce Mobley, when he described beach worn fossils in the Prairie Creek area of eastern Grant County. This meagre fauna includes the snails *Anomia, Aphrodina* [*Meretrix*], and *Meekia.*

CRETACEOUS ENVIRONMENTS OF SOUTHWEST OREGON

In the southwestern part of the state, the Hornbrook Formation yields numerous Cretaceous invertebrates. Deposited in a forearc basin west of the volcanic activity taking place in central Idaho, Hornbrook sediments filled a depression across northern California and southern Oregon approximately 100 million years ago. The immense seaway was bounded on the north by the Blue Mountains, to the east by the Idaho batholith, and to the southwest by the Klamath Mountains. The varied Hornbrook settings of freshwater streams, calm lagoons, and wave washed beaches were progressively covered by deeper deposits as the ocean transgressed landward, a trend that was taking place worldwide.

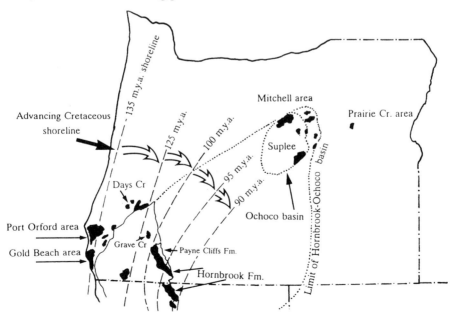

Map of the Cretaceous seaway across Oregon [Orr, Orr, and Baldwin, 1992].

In 1956 the late Cretaceous Hornbrook was named by Dallas Peck and examined by Ralph Imlay, both of the U.S. Geological Survey. Imlay also studied Hornbrook invertebrates housed in the Smithsonian Museum and California Academy of Sciences before joining Peck in the field for 11 days of work in Siskiyou County, California, and Jackson County, Oregon. They were able to divide the formation into three units from lower shallow water coarse conglomerates and sandstones upward to deep water fine siltstones and mudstones. Hornbrook strata were additionally broken into five members by Tor Nilsen, who edited the definitive *Geology of the Upper Cretaceous Hornbrook Formation, Oregon and California*. This was the outcome of the 1984 annual meeting of the Society of Economic Paleontologists and Mineralogists in Ashland. Multiple papers in the guidebook provide detailed coverage of Hornbrook geology as well as general stratigraphy and structure of the Klamaths. Microfossils and megafossils were used for dating and to depict paleoenvironments.

Often more than three feet in length, the sheer size of the partially uncoiled ammonite *Anisoceras* from Hornbrook sediments frequently defies collection in an unbroken piece. [after Packard and Jones, 1965].

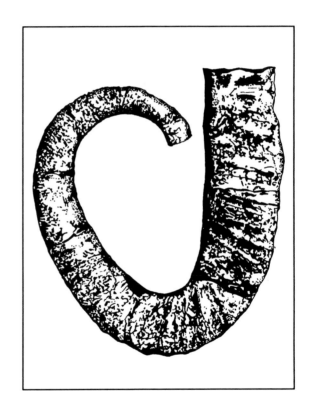

One of the outstanding West Coast stratigraphers, Ralph Arnold [on the right] was
the first to construct paleogeographic maps of the Pacific coast and draw environmental conclusions based on molluscan faunas. Arnold's companion is unknown
[photo courtesy Archives, U.S. Geological Survey, Denver].

CENOZOIC MARINE ENVIRONMENTS

Throughout the Tertiary period, the ancient Pacific Ocean was confined to a
steadily decreasing shelf west of the Cascades. At the beginning of this time interval, 65
million years ago, shorelines stretched from the Klamath Mountains northward across
eastern Oregon and into Washington. This was the last broad seaway in the state before
volcanic activity and crustal plate movements combined to generate regional uplift and
subsequent withdrawal of the water. By middle Miocene time, about 15 million years ago,
the ocean was restricted to the western margins of the present Coast Range.

Short cycles of cooling and warming mark the early Tertiary of Oregon. Eocene climates were tropical, but after this overall temperatures cooled as environments became more temperate. Following a brief warming trend during the middle Miocene, tropical conditions were steadily narrowed to the equator. These changes were reflected by vegetation and marine life, plentiful in the shallow waters of the many basins that were characteristic of this time.

INVERTEBRATES OF THE PALEOCENE EPOCH

Spanning a little over 8 million years, the Paleocene is one of the shortest of the Tertiary epochs. Yet this interval in geologic history is critical as it represents the period of recovery after the destruction of Mesozoic floras and faunas. Only a single Paleocene fossil invertebrate occurrence is known from western Oregon, and even this scant record has not been published. While working on his dissertation during the summers of 1964 and 1965, Ken Bird collected samples from near Bandon which turned out to contain Paleocene foraminiferal microfossils. Corroborated by three micropaleontologists, William Orr, Greg Miles, and Dan McKeel, the microfauna included the definitive species *Chiloguembelina wilcoxensis, Globanomalina planoconica, Pseudohastigerina wilcoxensis, Subbotina linaperta,* and *Truncorotaloides wilcoxensis.*

The precise locality proved to be elusive. McKeel, who, at the time, was living at Otis, Oregon, and consulting privately for oil companies, urged Miles not to reveal where the sample originated. In a series of letters to University of Oregon student Miles in February, 1980, McKeel stated that Bird "tried 3 times to duplicate Bandon 10 sample" and he [McKeel] planned "to go hunting for the Paleocene fauna in early March." Miles sent $10.00 for gas, but almost one year later McKeel again wrote "Unfortunately I have not been south to collect the Paleocene locality..." but he had received a map of the area from Bird. There was discussion of publishing what Miles called "Oregon's first confirmed Paleocene!" in a letter of July, 1978, but the sample could not be located before McKeel and Miles temporarily left the state.

GEOLOGY OF THE EOCENE OCEAN

The Eocene epoch, spanning the period between 55 to 38 million years ago, was marked by great undersea tears or crustal rifts which became the site of massive lava flows. The combined flows built a submarine basalt platform now beneath the Coast Range. Deep marine silts, shelf sands, and deltas accumulated atop the rapidly subsiding submarine slab as the weight of the lavas created an elongate ocean basin. Fossil shells, plants, and microfossils mark the boundaries of the Eocene basin near Cape Arago and Coos Bay on the south coast, in the Willamette Valley and Coast Range from Roseburg and Eugene northward to Polk and Lincoln counties, and in the northwest corner of the state in Washington and Columbia counties.

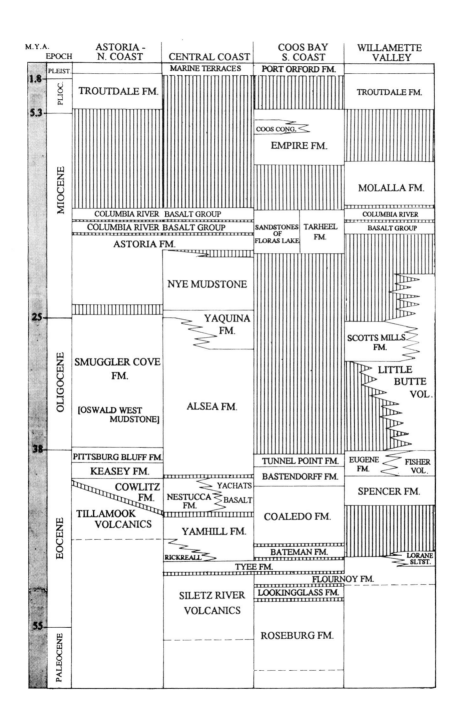

Oregon Cenozoic stratigraphy [after Orr and Orr, 1996].

The presence of Eocene rocks in Oregon wasn't firmly established until Thomas Condon, geology professor at the University of Oregon, recognized the distinctive Eocene clam *Cardita planicosta* [now *Venericardia hornii*] in the Willamette Valley and on the southern coast. The mollusc was among a group of shells sent to him by Judge J. Quinn Thornton. Something of a character, Thornton wrote about the hardships of his overland journey in *Oregon and California in 1848*, a volume that has a chapter on the geology and mineralogy of Oregon. In these paragraphs Thornton described finding shells near Albany in dark-colored shales a few feet below the surface during a cistern excavation.

Similar shells were collected by Condon and his wife, Cornelia, in 1885 while on a trip to the south coast. Then such a trip was an arduous and complicated affair. The Condons travelled south from Eugene by train to the village of Drain, where they spent the night, thence by stagecoach to Scottsburg. Leaving Scottsburg in the evening by boat down the Umpqua River, they reached Gardiner about 10:00 pm. The final leg of the journey was by steamer to the mouth of Winchester Bay followed by a 20-mile wagon ride to Coos Bay. Spending some days there with a friend, Condon picked up a large but broken *Cardita* [*Venericardia*], while walking along a winding road north of Marshfield, as well as a number of similar specimens at Cape Arago.

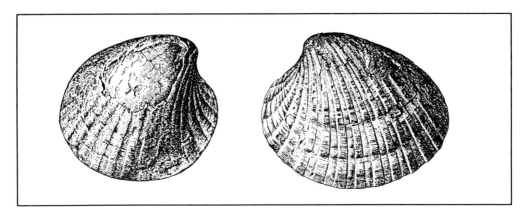

The thick-shelled clam *Venericardia hornii* first signified the presence of Eocene strata in Oregon [from White, 1885].

Condon's recognition of the Eocene was substantiated by his friendship, correspondence, and exchange of fossil material with Charles A. White, a paleontologist at the U.S. Geological Survey. White had been in the field in northern California for the three summer months of 1884 and, along with George Becker, in charge of the Pacific Section of the Survey, had visited Condon in Eugene. Condon wrote to a family member that "they came looking for definate information and found it in my boxes". For the next several years Condon sent duplicate fossils from his collection to White, including the *Cardita*, on which White published papers in 1885 and 1889.

EOCENE INVERTEBRATES OF SOUTHWEST OREGON

From the time when Condon first recognized *Cardita,* deciphering the complex stratigraphy of southwest Oregon by means of invertebrates and microfossils has been an ongoing process. At the turn of the century Joseph Diller, who spend most of his career mapping in the west for the U.S. Geological Survey, described Eocene rocks in southern Oregon in his 1896 *Annual Report.* He lumped all of the Eocene here into the Arago Beds, but several years later in his classic maps covering the Roseburg and Coos Bay quadrangles he subdivided this strata into the Umpqua, Tyee, Coaledo, and Pulaski formations. *Cardita planicosta* [*Venericardia hornii*] and the high-spired tropical snail *Turritella uvasana* were listed as as characteristic Eocene fossils.

Diller's work was followed by that of Francis Turner, who completed a Masters degree at the University of Oregon and a PhD in paleontology from the University of California in 1934. His career as a professor of Geology at the Agriculture and Mechanical College of Texas and with Union Oil Company after 1950 focused on broad areas of Mesozoic and Cenozoic paleontology and stratigraphy of the Pacific and Gulf coasts and Rocky Mountains. In a definitive 1938 monograph, *Stratigraphy and Mollusca of the Eocene of Western Oregon*, Turner divided the Umpqua into upper and lower units, comparing them to similar strata in California. Work, which formed the foundation of Turner's paper, was begun by Bryan Hendon whose Masters from the University of Oregon in 1926 treated fossiliferous Eocene rocks near Glide in Douglas County. Hendon's plans for additional study of the molluscs were never completed as he died unexpectedly of a tropical disease while carrying out geologic exploration in Venezuela.

Working on his advanced degree from 1929 to 1934, Turner not only examined a variety of locations from Cape Arago to Eugene, but he inventoried collections of other West Coast paleontologists as well. In his 1938 work Turner listed specific collecting sites in Lane, Douglas, and Coos counties. Of these, the exposures in the streambed at the mouth of Little River near Glide are probably one of the best for Eocene invertebrates in Oregon. Here well-preserved diverse tropical shells, among them the large, thick-shelled clam *Venericardia,* indicate very shallow marine water above a sandy upper continental shelf. Of the new species described by Turner, *Turritella uvasana hendoni* was named in recognition of Hendon's efforts.

Charles Weaver took up where Turner left off. Born in New York but choosing to complete graduate studies at the University of California, Weaver worked on Paleocene and Miocene faunas near Mt. Diablo, California, under direction of Berkeley paleontologist John Merriam. Moving to Seattle in 1907 Weaver began what was to be a 43-year teaching career at the University of Washington. His early studies of the Tertiary in western Washington led to the first geologic map there along with descriptions of rock formations and invertebrate faunas. After years of research, Weaver compiled a complete revision of Tertiary stratigraphy and paleontology of Washington and Oregon based on new data and interpretations. For three years he had collected faunas from 35 selected areas to produce the unmatched *Tertiary Stratigraphy of Western Washington and Northwestern Oregon*, which appeared as a three volume, 790 page set, in 1942. Included in this monograph are fossils from the Eocene Umpqua, Tyee, and Coaledo formations of Oregon along with those of Washington. Detailed field investigations during the summers of 1940 and 1942 produced an historic summary, a refined stratigraphy, and list of fossils for the Coos Bay Tertiary.

A native New Yorker, Charles Weaver was attracted to Berkeley, California, by the reputation of vertebrate paleontologist John Merriam. Once his PhD was completed, Weaver took a position at the University of Washington [photo courtesy of Oregon Dept. of Geology and Mineral Industries].

A quiet, reserved person, Weaver was physically very strong. Even after retirement in 1951, he could easily walk longer distances and with more stamina than most of his students. As a professor in Washington, he would frequently reach his field area by train, bus, or on foot, then collect and map all day, before sleeping on the ground to continue the following morning. Moving to Stanford University in 1951, Weaver was still working on details of West Coast Tertiary stratigraphy when he died in 1958.

Overlapping with Weaver, Ewart M. Baldwin spent more than three decades mapping in southwest Oregon and elsewhere in the state, resulting in innumerable publications. Born in Pomeroy, Washington, in 1915, Baldwin's undergraduate and Masters work in 1938 and 1939 was directed by Ralph Lupher at Pullman before he went on to take a PhD in 1943 at Cornell from invertebrate paleontologist Charles Merriam. Baldwin's field work began that same year when he was employed by the Oregon Department of Geology and Mineral Industries to map coal resources in the vicinity of Coos Bay. After he joined the staff of the Geology Department at the University of Oregon in 1947 he expanded his focus and, with the assistance of his many graduate students, ultimately mapped over 4,000 square miles of the south and central coast.

Baldwin's early interest in the southwestern part of the state was expressed in a 1945 letter to Warren Smith, Chairman of the Geology Department at Eugene. When a large "rather perfect" ammonite was found near Agness, Baldwin remarked "am glad to hear about the excellent ammonite ... That region down there is very interesting and I would like to do some work down there sometime." One of Baldwin's crowning contributions was his classic 1974 Bulletin on the *Eocene Stratigraphy of Southwestern Oregon*, in which he divided the Umpqua into three separate formations, the Roseburg, Lookingglass, and Flournoy. For his stratigraphy, Baldwin collected and identified his own fossils, also relying on Turner's work as well as that of northwest micropaleontologists. His book *Geology of Oregon,* issued in 1959, the first overview since Condon's *Two Islands,* made him well-known throughout the northwest. The amount of territory covered in a vehicle on his field trips brought him equal fame among university geology students many of whom have maintained contact with him throughout the years. Baldwin retired from the University in 1980, but continues to give talks, lead field trips, and travel extensively, currently residing in Eugene with his wife Margaret.

Ewart Baldwin is the stratigrapher and paleontologist whose work provides a thread through Oregon's geologic research from the 1940s to 1980s [photo courtesy G. Miles].

Siletz River, Roseburg, Lookingglass, Flournoy, and Tyee sediments are all part of the early Eocene seaway, which covered what is now the Willamette Valley, Coast Range, and upper continental shelf. Volcanic layers, siltstones, and sandstones were deposited in a fluctuating ocean that advanced and retreated with some regularity. Submarine fans, coastal deltas, and shallows were all part of this setting as reflected by both megafossils and microfossils along with some plant remains. The invertebrates have not been examined extensively since Turner's 1938 monograph, but Baldwin gives a comprehensive summary and overview in his 1973 and 1974 publications.

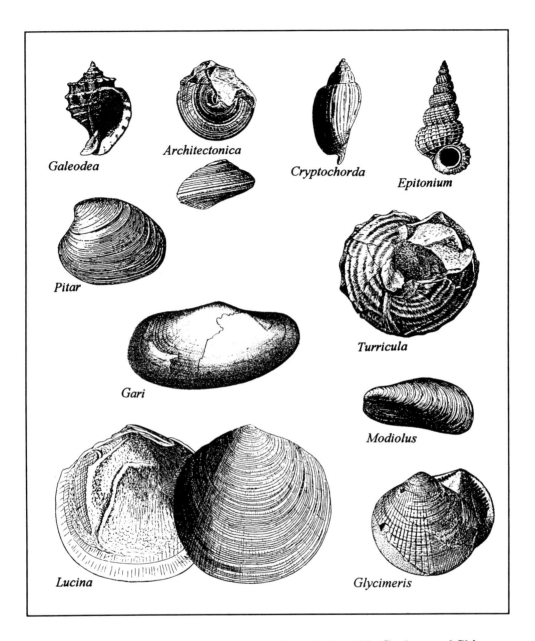

Eocene invertebrates - southwest Oregon [from Dall, 1909; Grabau and Shimer, 1910; Zittel, 1913].

The oldest rocks of this seaway are submarine lavas and sands of the Roseburg Formation in the south and the Siletz River Formation in the north. Between the basalts, sedimentary layers yield microscopic foraminifera as well as invertebrate shells. One of the first studies of these microfossils was Orville Bandy's 1944 paper on gray shales of the Roseburg Formation at Cape Blanco that recorded 33 species of Eocene foraminifera, of which 11 were new. Microfossils are also diverse in the Siletz River volcanics at the Ellendale Limestone Quarry and on Rickreall Creek in Polk County. Examined by Roscoe Stewart, the coin-shaped large warm water foraminifera *Amphistegina* and *Discocyclina* were identified for Baldwin's 1964 publication on the geology of the Dallas and Valsetz quadrangles.

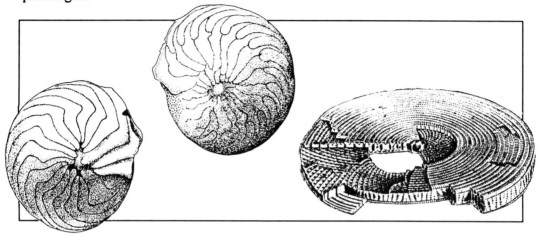

Coin-shaped, warm water foraminifera *Amphistegina* and *Discocyclina*

Much of the early micropaleontology in the Pacific Northwest was carried out by Roscoe Stewart of the Oregon Department of Geology and Mineral Resources, and his wife, Katherine Stewart, an independent consulting geologist. Roscoe "Doc" and Katherine Stewart graduated with bachelors degrees from the University of Chicago and Masters from the University of Southern California in 1935. They went on to study with Jesse Galloway at Columbia and Joseph Cushman of the Cushman Labs in Sharon, Massachusettes, both eminent early micropaleontologists. Doc Stewart was born in Coldwater, Michigan, in 1894 and worked as an oil company geologist until 1944 when he was hired by the state Department of Geology. Something of an individualist, Stewart worked irregular hours, frequently at night, and sometimes at home, distancing himself from other members of the State office. Since micropaleontology on the West Coast was in its infancy, it may have been that the value of Stewart's "bug" work was not fully appreciated. In conjunction with Joseph Cushman, the Stewarts published Bulletin 36 in the late 1940s that provided a preliminary listing of Tertiary foraminifera from western Oregon's sediments. The friendship with Cushman lasted until his death, and the Stewarts looked to him for confirmation and consultation about their local identifications. After Stewart's retirement from the Department in 1959, most of the micropaleontological work was shifted to Weldon Rau in Washington. Tragically, Stewart's two children and wife predeceased his 1975 death.

Two graduate theses which focused on Eocene microfossils of southwest Oregon were Richard Thoms' PhD from the University of California, Berkeley, in 1965, and that of Greg Miles from the University of Oregon, Eugene, in 1977. Thoms, recently retired as a professor at Portland State University, was born in Olympia but grew up in Seattle where his transportation to school was often by kayak. Completing his field work during the summers of 1961 through 1964, his subsequent processing of the samples disclosed 225 species of smaller foraminifera and 25 species of the larger disc-shaped foraminifera from the Siletz River, Umpqua, Tyee, and Elkton formations. In the Siletz River and Umpqua, members of the family Lagenidae are easily the most numerous and diverse. *Pseudophragmina* and *Operculina* from these two formations occur today only in tropical waters.

Both growing up in Silverton, Greg and Gail Miles now live in Eugene, where camping and botany are among their additional interests. Miles is currently teaching at Lane Community College [photo courtesy G. Miles].

Thoms used the older Umpqua Formation designation for his PhD thesis, while Greg Miles followed Baldwin's more recent revision and employed planktonic foraminifera to study the environments and stratigraphy of the Roseburg, Lookingglass, and Flournoy formations. In addition to his own collections, Miles borrowed microfossil samples from Mobil Oil Company, the State Department of Geology and Mineral Industries, and from Thoms. He found that planktonic foraminifera here were marked by relatively low diversity, and dominated by the genera *Morozovella, Pseudohastigerina, Subbotina,* and *Truncorotaloides,* indicating tropical rather than temperate ocean waters during the early and middle Eocene. Other microfossils noted by Miles are radiolaria, calcareous nannofossils [a planktonic blue-green algae], holothurian spicules [sea cucumbers], and pollen.

EOCENE INVERTEBRATES OF THE SOUTH COAST

During the middle to late Eocene, approximately 50 to 38 million years ago, ocean waters receded near Coos Bay. A roughly circular and increasingly smaller basin here was filled by muds, silts, and sands of the Elkton, Bateman, and Coaledo formations. Swamp, marshes, and delta environments of the Bateman and Coaledo yield clams, snails, microfossils, and plant debris. Above the Coaledo, invertebrates and microfossils of the Bastendorff Formation represent deepening water of a very small embayment, while the

Tunnel Point, as a narrow shallow upper shelf setting, marks the end of the Eocene in this region.

Francis Turner's 1938 monograph and Ewart Baldwin's 1961 map record molluscs and foraminifera as locally abundant in the Elkton Formation, which, at that time, was considered part of the Tyee. Both Berkeley paleontologist, Wyatt Durham, who studied the corals and echinoids for Baldwin, and Weldon Rau, who examined the foraminifera, concluded the Elkton faunas represent middle shelf depths of about 300 feet and that overall climatic conditions were semitropical.

A significant graduate thesis, which focused on Tyee and Elkton strata, was that of Kenneth Bird from the University of Wisconsin in 1967. Bird, who graduated from high school in Grants Pass, received a bachelors degree at Oregon State University in 1961. While working as a student in Alaska for Shell Oil Company, he was involved in an accident in which he was permanently injured by a falling boulder. Shell generously assisted Bird who completed a PhD at Wisconsin under the direction of Robert Dott before going on to a career with the U.S. Geological Survey.

Basing his observations on numerical analyses of megafossils, foraminifera, and ostracods, as well as the less familiar fish teeth, diatoms, radiolaria, sea urchins [echinoids], and crabs [crustacea], Bird distinguished the Elkton from the Tyee as a separate formation. Of 120 samples collected during field work in the summers of 1963 and 1964, seventy had well-preserved fossils. Although plentiful, the molluscs were poorly preserved and marked by low diversity of species. Bird noted more than 110 species and 62 genera of foraminifera, the most numerous belonging to the families Lituolidae, Trochamminidae, Buliminidae, and Alabaminidae. In comparing foraminifera, radiolaria, and ostracod percentages he concluded there was an overall shallowing trend during this time span. Oysters and other megafossils, present in coal beds, sandstones, and mudstones, suggest a shallow marine to brackish and non-marine environment for the southern Tyee embayment near Coos Bay, while foraminifera reflect substantial ocean depths of 600 to 2,000 feet in the northern basin. The planktonic foraminifera *Globorotalia* and key radiolaria are good indicators of an open ocean with surface temperatures of 62 degrees Fahrenheit or above.

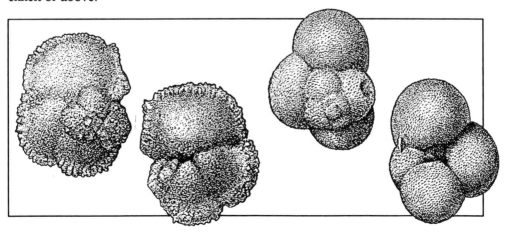

The open ocean [planktonic] foraminifera *Globorotalia* and *Globigerina*.
135

As the sea was withdrawing or regressing, thick sands of the early Coaledo delta built up near Coos Bay, whereas the later Coaledo and Bastendorff were deposited by advancing deepening waters of a transgressive ocean. Francis Turner was the first to list megafossils from the Coaledo in 1938 followed by Charles Weaver's record of the Tertiary faunas at Coos Bay in 1945. Turner used the extensive Coaledo molluscs along with a distinctive stratigraphic succession as the basis for his division of the formation into three members.

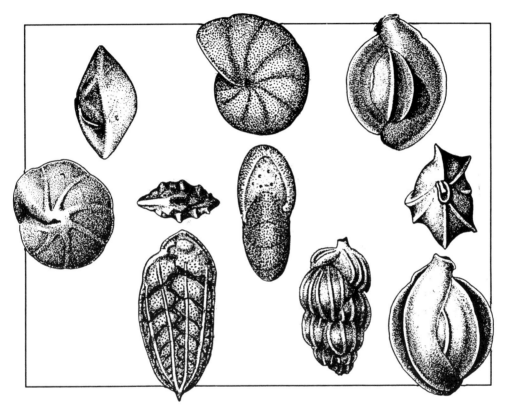

Bottom-dwelling [benthonic] foraminifera *Cibicides, Bolivina, Nonion, Uvigerina,* and *Quinqueloculina*

Paper-thin broken scallops are scattered and poorly preserved in the Bastendorff Formation, while shallow water molluscs and a few foraminifera are more numerous in the Tunnel Point. Foraminifera from Bastendorff shales were recorded as early as 1909 by the Smithsonian's William Dall. This list was lengthened significantly in 1928 by Hubert Schenck of Stanford, who found the outer shelf and slope - *Bulimina* and *Uvigerina* - to be very common and *Cibicides, Dentalina, Eponides,* and *Robulus,* among others, less numerous. However, the most comprehensive early report on these microfossils from the Coaledo and Bastendorff was in 1946 by Mildred Reichers Detling, supported by a Thomas Condon Fellowship at the University of Oregon. In 49 samples from Cape Arago to

136

Tunnel Point, Detling counted 47 species and subspecies of foraminifera. *Discorbis, Globigerina, Robulus*, and *Uvigerina* occurred most frequently. Detling was the first to observe contrasting species of foraminifera above and below the coal seams that divide the Coaledo at Yoakam Point. Since the coal developed under fresh water conditions, she concluded new species emerged between the alternating fresh water and marine episodes.

It has been suggested by author Michele Aldrich that many women entered geology and paleontology as professional scientific illustrators. Such was the case with Mildred Detling. Born in Montana in October, 1915, Detling moved with her family to Tillamook where she grew up. She turned to scientific illustration, expoiting a natural artistic talent and eye for detail. Marrying botanist LeRoy Detling, she was hired as an illustrator in the Museum of Natural History in Eugene, and most of the Museum bulletins contain examples of her beautiful work. Detling currently lives in Newport [photo courtesy E. Flory].

Guy Rooth's 1974 PhD thesis, directed by David Bostwick at Oregon State University, greatly enlarged on the paleoecology of the Coaledo and Bastendorff. During the summers of 1964 and 1965 Rooth examined a total of 231 samples from these two formations and extracted the foraminifera including *Clavigerinella, Globigerina, Pseudohastigerina*, and *Subbotina*. Because the microfauna reflects variable marine depths, Rooth concluded that, while the middle Coaledo was deposited in moderately deep water, the Bastendorff represents a significantly deeper open ocean setting. Advancing and retreating shorelines brought about profoundly varying water depths, and Rooth found evidence of strong vertical subsidence during and immediately after construction of the Coaledo delta.

Both Dall and Schenck include molluscs of the Tunnel Point sandstones in their assessments of the south coast. Named for a sea cave through the cliff, Tunnel Point has closely packed borings of the clam *Pholas* in the upper level. Dall noted *Acila, Marcia*, and *Saxidomus*, and Schenck added *Bruclarkia, Fusinus, Macrocallista, Pitar, Solen,* and *Spisula*. One of the most complete lists, produced by Charles Weaver in 1945, includes 33 species of molluscs dispersed throughout the formation.

A natural and gifted educator, Guy Rooth taught at at Western Oregon University for over thirty years, completing his PhD from Oregon State University. At Monmouth, Rooth has put together and cataloged a superb biostratigraphic teaching collection from about 70 fossil localities throughout the Pacific Northwest [photo courtesy G. Rooth].

EOCENE INVERTEBRATES OF THE CENTRAL OREGON COAST

While marine waters gradually withdrew from near Coos Bay during the middle to late Eocene, a wide shallow ocean across what is now western Oregon left behind sediments of the Yamhill and Nestucca formations along the central Coast Range, the Cowlitz and Keasey in the Nehalem Valley, and the Spencer and Eugene formations in the Willamette Valley. Within this ancient forearc basin just west of the youthful Cascade volcanoes, ash and lavas mixed with sands and muds to blanket the older Eocene deposits.

About 6,500 feet at its thickest, sandstones, siltstones, and conglomerates make up the Yamhill Formation in Polk County. Interspersed with offshore limestone banks and knolls rich with fossils, the Rickreall Limestone Member at the base of the Yamhill hosted diverse populations of molluscs, crustacea [barnacles and crabs], bryozoa, corals, and algae. Molluscs were the most abundant, and layers of broken shells confirm a shallow turbulent wave-washed setting, while fossil land plants suggest the shoreline proximity.

Megafossils were noted from the Rickreall limestones in 1936 by Hubert Schenck in his exhaustive monograph on the distinctively ornamented pelecypod, *Acila*. For this study, Schenck plotted the occurrence of this small clam on the west coast and in Puerto Rico to determine its usefulness as a biostratigraphic [age dating] tool. He also compared the shell morphology to living specimens in the Pacific and Indian oceans concluding that, while *Acila* could inhabit a variety of water conditions, it was generally found in cool to cold shallow waters. Today species of this primitive clam live in middle and outer shelf environments suggesting it has moved into deeper waters over time. This tendency for successions of invertebrates to adjust their habitats gradually downslope is not uncommon. Landmark papers in the 1980s on Paleozoic and Mesozoic assemblages suggest that the high energy surf zone is something of a crucible of evolution. After first being recorded in

138

very shallow water, invertebrate species appear in increasingly deeper shelf paleoenvironments before they eventually disappear forever from continental slope settings.

Also found in the lower Yamhill Formation, a large exotic and rare gastropod *Pleurotomaria* was the subject of a 1935 abstract by California paleontologists Schenck and Francis Turner. Concerned that he wouldn't be able to finish the proposed paper on the gastropod because of government responsibilities during the war, Schenck wrote to Warren Smith at the University of Oregon for maps and *Pleurotomaria* specimens from the Dallas quarry in Polk County "to put all my affairs in order ... Turner withdrew from the project but Miss [Myra] Keen has joined forces with me." Years later Schenck was planning to compile a catalog of Tertiary Pleurotomaridae of the world when he died. For this study he had borrowed a *Pleurotomaria* from the Oregon Department of Geology and Mineral Industries and a second one found in the Oregon Portland Cement Company quarry. The well-preserved state department specimen, donated by Leon Lambert, operator of the Ellendale Quarry in Polk County, is still housed in their Portland office. These carnivorous molluscs are fascinating in that they seem to occur exclusively in sedimentary layers between submarine basalt flows.

Ancient gastropods, Pleurotomarids briefly appeared in the northeastern Pacific during the Eocene 50 million years ago when water temperatures rose and offshore seamounts provided rocky habitats [from Zittel, 1913].

Schenck's correspondence also confirmed the presence of plants [Polypodiaceae, *Cinnamomum*, and *Mesophyllum*], several bryozoa, a nautiloid, fish bones, shark teeth, echinoids [sea urchins], and foraminifera [*Robulus*] from Yamhill limestones at the Ellendale Quarry. A decade after Schenck's work, Baldwin's mapping of the central Coast Range, a project that was ongoing, culminated in his Bulletin 35, revised and re-issued by the State Department in 1964. In this publication he discussed the Yamhill Formation and summarized earlier findings on the stratigraphy and paleontology. Microfossils for the Bulletin were identified by Roscoe Stewart, Oregon Department of Geology, and Weldon Rau, Washington Division of Geology and Earth Resources. Foraminifera in these sediments indicated to Rau that water depths for the Yamhill here were continental slope [1,000 to 6,000 feet], a conclusion supported in 1972 by Jere Lipps and Dan McKeel of the University of California, Davis. Curiously no open ocean [planktonic] foraminifera were found, and Lipps and McKeel surmised that heavy fluvial runoff from the nearby land created a deleterious environment for the open ocean microfossils.

Continuing marine deposition across the central Coast Range during the late Eocene produced as much as 7,500 feet of tuffaceous siltstones of the Nestucca Formation interlayered with sandstones, breccias, and submarine lava flows of the Yachats Basalt. In the southern Willamette Valley sandstones of the Spencer and Eugene formations represent coastline and continental shelf deposits of the same seaway. Characterized in part as deposited in brackish water, rare molluscs of the Nestucca indicate a shelf habitat just below the intertidal zone. Weldon Rau summarized the foraminifera for a Geological Society of America *Guidebook* in 1969. He notes that there were no planktonic foraminifera present, suggesting the Nestucca was an isolated embayment of variable depth. The embayment may have been separated from the open ocean by a barrier of islands such as the volcanic highland formed by the Yachats Basalt. Debris from sediments layered between the basalt preserves a splendid shallow water fauna inhabiting a fan on the slopes of a volcanic island. Foraminifera, bryozoa, brachiopods, crabs and barnacles, molluscs, and sea urchins from this setting are recorded in Cindy Shroba's 1992 dissertation from the University of Oregon.

Weldon Rau joined the Washington Division of Geology and Earth Resources in 1960, and since retirement continues to work there at his office in Olympia [photo courtesy W. Rau].

Weldon Rau, who performed much of the biostratigraphic micropaleontology work in the Pacific Northwest from the middle 1960s onward, enjoyed a reputation as a rapid but careful worker. Born in Tacoma in 1921, Rau completed his graduate education at the University of Iowa where he earned a PhD in paleontology in 1950. Taking a job as a micropaleontologist and stratigrapher with the Fuels Branch of the U.S. Geological Survey that same year, he specialized in benthic [bottom-dwelling] Tertiary foraminifera of the Pacific Northwest. Several extensive monographs on the Olympic Peninsula in addition to descriptions of many isolated faunas and local geology were the result. Two of his most interesting bulletins are on the scenic geology and history of the Washington coast.

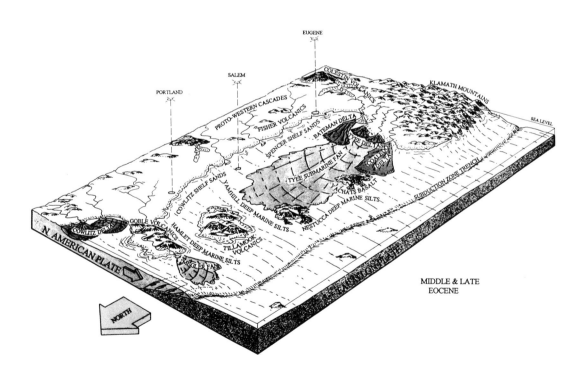

Middle and late Eocene marine environments of western Oregon [after Orr and Orr, 1996].

EOCENE INVERTEBRATES OF THE NORTHWEST COAST

During the middle 1980s Alan and Wendy Niem of Oregon State University and their graduate students began the ambitious process of revising the stratigraphy of the northwest coastal basins with an emphasis on sedimentology. In over six graduate theses, many of the traditional formations have been broken down into members or renamed. The new nomenclature remains informal, however, until changes are submitted and approved by the Geologic Names Committee of the U.S. Geological Survey.

In the northwest corner of the state, a wide range of environments from brackish and swampy to deep marine waters are represented by the Cowlitz and Keasey formations. These sediments were deposited in a northern extension of the seaway that covered the Willamette Valley from Eugene northward. Much of the 1,000-foot thickness of mudstones, siltstones, sandstones, and conglomerates of the Cowlitz was built up as deltas by streams draining adjacent volcanic highlands. Because of the various habitats, this formation displays a rich fauna of foraminifera, plants, trace fossils [*Rosselia, Skolithos*], and invertebrates. Shallow water molluscs as *Acmaea, Glycimeris, Mytilus,* and *Ostrea* in the lower conglomerate layer are succeeded by deep water *Acila, Nucula, Nuculana, Siphonalia,* and *Yoldia* in the upper portion. As noted in Daniel Mumford's 1988 Masters degree from Oregon State University, changing environments here can be characterized by different faunas. His thesis lists the fossils as identified by paleontologists Weldon Rau, Ellen Moore, and Kristen McDougall.

In contrast to the upper shelf environments of the Cowlitz, roughly 2,000 feet of volcanic ash and shales, siltstones, and clays of the Keasey Formation represent slope waters and, indeed, provide fossils from the deepest water deposits of the Oregon Tertiary. Keasey sediments have attracted considerable attention owing to their diverse faunas and excellent fossil preservation, but no comprehensive publications on the paleoenvironment and fauna have been produced. Crinoids [sea lily], echinoids [sea urchins], ophioroids [brittle stars], pogonophorans [worms], corals, glass sponges, decapods [crabs], sharks, and bony fish remains along with terrestrial plants, algae and a variety of microfossils are part of this remarkable late Eocene marine environment. One of the most widely known Keasey localities is near Mist, Columbia County, where crinoids and other echinoderms, as starfish, are beautifully preserved in an undisturbed "life" position.

Named by Hubert Schenck in his 1927 publication on the marine Oligocene of Oregon, the blue to gray Keasey shale in Rock Creek valley, Columbia County, was described more fully by the same author in 1928 as characterized by the shells *Turricula columbiana* and *Acila nehalemensis*. Schenck's paper provides checklists of Keasey crustacea, molluscs, and foraminifera.

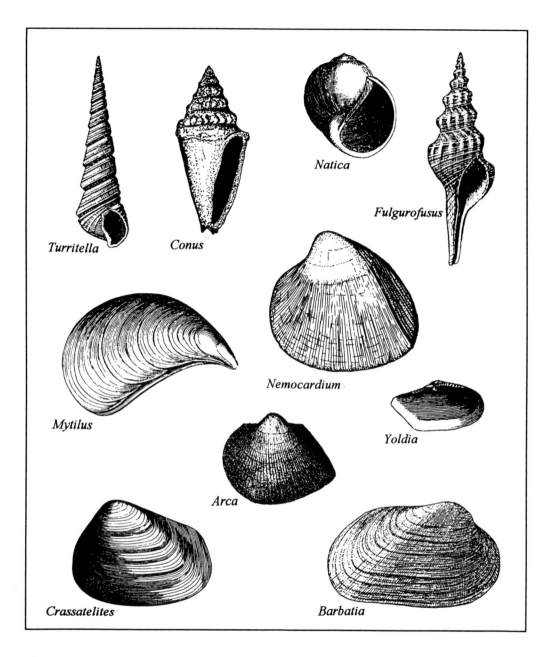

Eocene invertebrates - northwest Oregon [from Zittel, 1913; Gabb, 1869].

At present, Carole Hickman, professor at the University of California, Berkeley, has contributed the most contemporary data on the Keasey. Based on her PhD research from Stanford, Hickman's 1976 Bulletin reviews deep water gastropods of the diverse Turridae snail family, so abundant in Tertiary rocks of Oregon, Washington, and California. Inspecting public and private collections of these snails, she noted that they dominate the Keasey fauna, but in the past many have been misidentified and inadequately studied. Her detailed analysis proposed three new generic names and concluded that *Parasyrinx*, *Ptychosyrinx*, *Turricula*, and *Turrinosyrinx* are the most useful in determining biostratigraphic divisions. The invertebrate fauna inhabiting the deep water Keasey basin is strikingly similar to that of present day Sagami Bay on the Pacific coast of Honshu, Japan. Both areas have gastropod specimens restricted to bathyal depths up to 2,500 feet where cool, but not cold, temperatures of 40 to 45 degrees Fahrenheit are normal.

In a 1980 paper on gastropods, Hickman and others interpret the Keasey as deposited in a deep basin adjacent to offshore volcanic islands, but estimates as to the paleoodepths vary. In a U.S. Geological Survey Professional Paper Raymond Moore and Harold Vokes interpret Keasey sedimentation to have taken place close to the shore but in water well below wave action and as deep as 3,000 feet. However, in 1964 Victor Zullo, Professor of Geology at the University of North Carolina, was able to show that environmental conditions of the Keasey could be met in water less than half that depth. In this same paper on a new species of sea urchin, *Salenia schencki,* Zullo cited Keasey land plants, fish scales, and arthropods.

Foraminiferal studies support Hickman's temperature and depth conclusions for Keasey strata. In 1975 Kristin McDougall, paleontologist with the U.S. Geological Survey, publishing on the microfauna of the Keasey along Rock Creek, calculated that most of the conditions were outer shelf to upper slope. However, she also perceived that if there were a local upwelling of cold water foraminifera normally inhabiting deep water could have existed in much shallower depths. Her assessment of foraminifera for Daniel Mumford's thesis favors a somewhat deeper basin of 600 to 1,500 feet.

In a 1995 speech about women in paleontology, Carole Hickman relates that her own science is motivated by curiosity, the asthetics of nature, "the tension of uncertain outcome, and the joy of playing with ideas" [photo courtesy C. Hickman].

Born in LaSalle, Illinois, in 1942, Carole Stentz Hickman finished a Masters at the University of Oregon from William Orr before going on to a PhD at Stanford directed by Myra Keen. An amusing point in her very successful career came when she was given a Golden Fleece Award for her National Science Foundation funded study of Australian snail radula [tongues] by science demagogue Senator William Proxmire. Formerly married to equally meticulous botanist James Hickman, now deceased, at present Carole is a professor at Berkeley where her research focuses on Cenozoic marine molluscs.

An exceptional element of the Keasey are the crinoid [sea lily] remains. Stalked Tertiary crinoids are rare elsewhere in the world, and only five species have been recovered from North America. Two of these from Oregon, *Isocrinus oregonensis* and *Isocrinus nehalemensis,* were described in 1953 by Raymond Moore and Harold Vokes. The delicate fossils were collected in Keasey sediments on the west bank of the Nehalem River by Walter Warren, Rex Grivetti, and Vokes, members of a field mapping party from the U.S. Geological Survey. Vokes gathered up about 50 pounds of the material, which he shipped to Moore in Kansas. A celebrated crinoid specialist at the University of Kansas, Moore skillfully prepared specimens from this material as well as examining those stored at the University of California Museum. In addition to the new species of crinoids, they listed molluscs. All are now housed at the Smithsonian Museum.

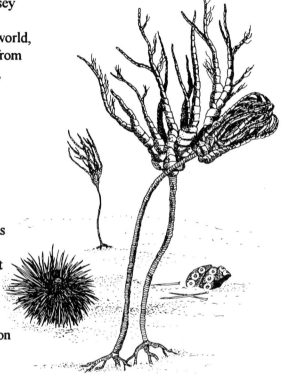

The stalked deep water Keasey crinoid

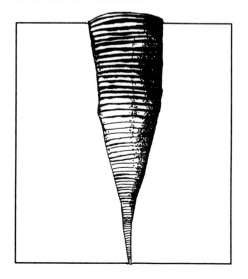

Even though extremely rare, several hundred thin conical shells of the swimming snail *Praehyalocylis cretacea* - an inch long - from the West Coast were reported in 1989 by Richard Squires at California State University, Northridge. Previously unknown in the northwestern United States, these hollow tube-like snails or pteropods were collected over many years from the Keasey as well as other regional formations [after Squires, 1989].

North of Mist, fossiliferous sandstones and conglomerates of the Gries Ranch Formation are from the same time interval and ocean basin as the Keasey but represent a vastly different ecologic setting. Because the Gries Ranch gastropods *Alvania* and *Puncturella* and pelecypods *Arca, Barbatia, Glycimeris,* and *Loxocardium* live today in shallow waters, these coarse sands are interpreted as an old shoreline of the Keasey basin.

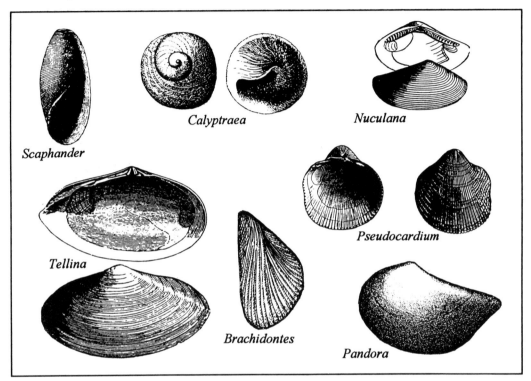

Eocene invertebrates - Willamettte Valley [from Gabb, 1869; Zittel, 1913].

EOCENE INVERTEBRATES OF THE WILLAMETTE VALLEY

Probably no one has done more to popularize Cenozoic fossils of the Willamette Valley and throughout Oregon than Margaret Steere. Living and working in the state for 50 years, she completed a number of articles on fossil collecting in Oregon, among them her *"Fossil Localities of the Eugene Area, Oregon"*. Her well-written accounts give the geologic history of each formation, describe precise locals with accompanying maps, and list faunas. All were written with an eye to the collector and are still considered standard references. Steere's career at the Oregon Department of Geology and Mineral Industries as a geologist, editor, and librarian began in 1947 after she completed a Masters degree from the University of Michigan, the state in which she was born. While her geology degree didn't focus on paleontology, Steere became the resident paleontologist out of necessity after Doc Stewart retired. In that capacity she identified fossils, led field trips, gave talks,

146

and contributed articles, culminating in the volume *Fossils in Oregon* in 1977. She retired in 1977 but continued to volunteer at the Department of Geology until her unexpected death from pneumonia in 1995.

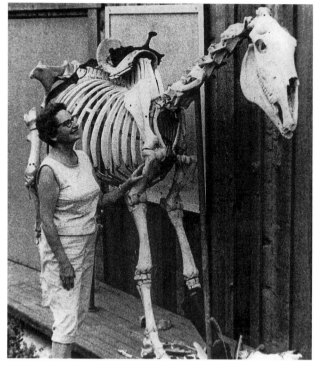

Margaret Steere and friend [photo courtesy Oregon Department of Geology and Mineral Industries].

Across the ancient forearc basin of the Willamette Valley late Eocene Spencer and Eugene strata were deposited throughout the southern region. Sandstones of the Spencer Formation can be traced west to Eugene and northward to Dallas in Yamhill County. Spencer molluscs, similar to those of the Nestucca and Coaledo formations, have been inventoried in Turner's Special Paper 10, and Doc and Katherine Stewart provided the first examination of foraminiferal microfossils.

In the southern Willamette Valley, some 5,000 feet of tuffaceous marine sandstones and siltstones of the Eugene Formation have been the center of continual controversy since the turn of the century. Occurring in a broad area from Eugene northward to Salem, these highly fossiliferous beds were variously considered Miocene or Oligocene until 1983 when they were placed into the late Eocene. In 1981 a significant reassessment of the Eugene Formation came during the annual meeting of the Geologic Society of America as the time frame covered by the Eocene epoch was greatly expanded and that of the Oligocene narrowed. The symposium based changes on new data and correlations of local strata dating back to the efforts of Charles Weaver and others in 1944. John Armentrout, a biostratigrapher from Mobil Oil Company, convened the symposium and edited the resultant 1983 COSUNA stratigraphic charts [*Correlation of Stratigraphic Units of North America*] as well as regional charts [*Correlation of Cenozoic Stratigraphic Units of Western Oregon and Washington*], which reflected these changes.

Eugene Formation fossils were repeatedly examined by Thomas Condon after he joined the staff at the University of Oregon in 1876. By monitoring excavations for wells, foundations, and quarries, Condon was able to accumulate an impressive number of invertebrates. Judging from Condon's notes and localities, deep hand-dug water wells were optimum to produce fossils, and the Condon Museum catalog lists *Crepidula, Cythera, Dentalium, Fusus, Modiola, Natica,* and *Solen* among others from local strata. Smithsonian malacologist, William Dall, who was a strong proponent of the Miocene epoch, listed the species *Epitonium, Tellina,* and *Thracia* from Eugene in 1909 but provided no discussion. Dall's brief note was followed by Chester Washburne's all-encompassing Bulletin in 1914 that lists fossil localities and genera throughout western Oregon, including those collected along an interrupted outcrop between College Hill in Eugene and Springfield.

Born into a family of geologists, Warren Smith directed earth sciences at Eugene for over 30 years [photo courtesy Condon Museum].

Warren D. Smith, longtime chairman at the University of Oregon, Geology Department, was an avid paleontologist, who had investigated shells in and around Eugene for many years. Arriving at the University of Oregon in 1914, just 7 years after Condon's death, Smith directed the course of geology and geography there for 33 years. During his tenure in Eugene, he experienced the emotional transfer of all science classes to Oregon State University at Corvallis in 1932. Electing to remain in Eugene, he steadily and vigor-

148

ously lobbied for the return of science to that campus, deploring the decision of the Board of Higher Education in letters and talks. When the science curriculum was finally reestablished there in 1942, Smith became Chair of the Geology Department during the short time until his retirement in 1947.

At age 10 years Smith was introduced to the study of fossils by his paleontologist Uncle James P. Smith, who taught at Stanford, and with whom Warren worked as a graduate student. Perhaps, to Warren Smith, one of his most memorable experiences was during 1906 to 1914 when he served with the Bureau of Mines in Manila. Ever afterward, at the mention of the Philippines, he would launch into stories and pleasant memories of his time there. Because much of Oregon's geology was still unknown when he arrived in the state, Smith was called on to participate in many solutions to flood control, land-use planning, mineral exploration, paleontology, even assisting to form the early State Department of Geology. His broad knowledge and experience led to some of the first popular books and articles on the geology of scenic spots in the state.

Smith at Oregon along with other geologists from California joined the controversy about the age of the Eugene Formation, and in 1915 Bruce Clark at the University of California told Smith he was "very anxious to see some of that [Eugene Formation] material ... There is one species which I would especially like to see ... Thracia condoni ... one of the forms which I find in the Oligocene of this region ..." Clark noted that the eminent stratigraphers Ralph Arnold and Harold Hannibal regarded the Eugene Formation as Oligocene, but William Dall considered the beds to be Miocene. By October of the next year Clark, after examining Hannibal's fauna from Eugene - *Diplodonta, Natica, Panope, Spisula, Tellina,* and *Thracia* - concluded that the molluscs were positive proof of the Oligocene age assignment.

In 1923 one of Smith's students, Hubert Schenck, wrote his Masters thesis on the Eugene Quadrangle in which he devoted much of his research to the Eugene Formation. For this and several later publications, Schenck acquired his material in excavations for the new University library building as well as for the heating tunnels beneath the campus. In addition, Schenck was exhorted by Professor, Earl Packard, to "pound rock one day at Sheridan, one at McCoy, and one at Holmes Gap..." He found clams and snails, the remains of cephalopods, fish, crabs, sand dollars, and starfish that inhabited what he regarded as a sheltered arm of the Oligocene ocean. In Schenck's scenario, the protected bay, surrounded by deciduous trees, was periodically covered by ash and debris from erupting Cascade volcanoes.

Among the most influential early West Coast paleontologists, Schenck's interest in fossils began in 1917 when he took classes from Earl Packard at the University in Eugene. Schenck [pronounced Skenk] received A.B. and Masters degrees from the University of Oregon and a PhD from Berkeley in 1926, followed by an appointment to the staff at Stanford University. Aware of the usefulness of microfossils as a stratigraphic tool, he taught the first West Coast course on micropaleontology. From Stanford he wrote to Warren Smith in December, 1942, that "I am trying to induce a number of young women to take up work in micropaleontology now, and in the near future the demand by oil companies for trained micropaleontologists will increase."

Commissioned as a Major in the Army during World War II, Hubert Schenck served in the Pacific. Afterward he remained in the Far East where he tackled problems of natural resources and economic development for the U.S. government [Schenck standing on the left with members of the Stanford Geologic Survey in camp, 1926. Photo taken by Philip Reinhart; courtesy R. Coleman].

Beginning with a trip to the Philippines accompanying Warren Smith in 1920, much of Schenck's career was spent as a government science advisor in the Far East, assessing natural resources, for which he received numerous awards. "Dear Jefe" he wrote to Smith in January of 1938, "at present I am not far from British Baluchistan ... travelled 10,000 miles in Persia, Afghanistan now lies ahead ... I expect to spend about four months there." Contracting a debilitating viral infection of the liver in 1953, he returned to Stanford but never fully recovered his health. Schenk's organizational abilities and strict Teutonic work habits allowed him to publish over 70 significant papers on micropaleontology and stratigraphy before his death in 1960.

Another Master's thesis at the University of Oregon, that of Carole Hickman in 1969, focused on marine invertebrates of the Eugene Formation, which she regarded as Oligocene. In addition to examining existing collections housed in several western Universities, her tireless collecting habits amassed several thousand fossils from throughout the formation. These were placed in the Condon Museum. Describing this rich fauna, Hickman reported 67 species of molluscs - including nine new species - with the remains of brittle stars [ophiuroids], sand dollars [echinoids], barnacles, foraminifera, crabs, and sharks. She suggests the environmental setting was a shallow marine upper shelf away from the open ocean and notes that at this latitude a profound transition was taking place from a tropical to more temperate climate during the middle Tertiary. Shallow embayments, such as that of the Eugene Formation, may have formed a protected area that retained, for a time, the resident tropical forms while receiving migrant refugees from cooler waters to yield an abnormally high diversity of fauna from mixed environments.

Recent examinations of foraminiferal microfossils and invertebrates of Eugene sediments compared them to specimens from three similar localities at Salem, Scotts Mills, and Brownsville. In 1992 Cindy Shroba's dissertation resulted in newly described depositional environments for the southern Willamette basin, noting paleo-communities inhabiting shallow estuaries to deep waters. That same year Carol McKillip's masters degree noted a deep water interval in the same formation from exposures along Interstate 5 south of Salem. Foraminifera and molluscs from siltstones pointed to bathyal depths.

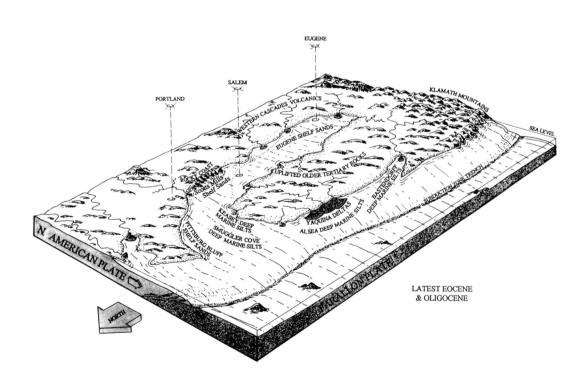

Late Eocene and Oligocene marine environments of western Oregon [after Orr and Orr, 1996].

GEOLOGY OF THE OLIGOCENE OCEAN

Owing to the constriction of the time frame of the Oligocene, marine sediments of this epoch are more scarce in Oregon than those of the Eocene. Bracketting the time frame from 38 to 25 million years ago, this was a period marked by the early emergence of the Coast Range from the ocean with uplift of the old forearc basin. Cascade volcanoes became increasingly active as the Farallon plate continued to slide beneath North America from the west, and the Willamette Valley, hemmed in between coastal uplifts and the Cascades, became a shallow seaway. The shoreline ran along the east side of the valley where it is delineated by the Scotts Mills Formation in Marion County. Northward from Lincoln to Columbia counties, parts of the Alsea, Yaquina, Pittsburgh Bluff, and Smuggler Cove formations represent the same marine setting.

The recognition of what strata should be assigned to the Oligocene on the West Coast and in Oregon was being argued at the turn of the century. Washburne and others believed the Willamette Valley was above water during what would be the Oligocene epoch and then submerged to Eugene during the Miocene. Much of the ensuing debate was between Bruce Clark of Berkeley and consulting geologists Ralph Arnold and Harold Hannibal. A University of Oregon student who went to Berkeley, Carroll Wagner discussed this controversy. "Dr. Clark is determined that I take up the problem of the [Oligocene] correlation left by Arnold and Hannibal ... Several men down here have worked in Oregon and they admit that it is impossible to get satisfactory results by examination of strata alone but certainly it must be done before the sequence of beds will be determinable."

A strong advocate of the presence of Oligocene strata on the West Coast, Clark described hundreds of Tertiary invertebrate species from California, comparing them to those from Oregon in his efforts to establish Oligocene boundaries. Even though he was sometimes charged with careless scientific errors, Clark's research added considerably to information on the Cenozoic. Because of the controversy surrounding his work and in spite of his many significant contributions, even as Clark was dying in the mid-1940s, efforts by his colleagues failed to obtain a promotion to full professor for him.

In 1918 the exhuberant Henry Howe waded into the ongoing debate. Leaving the University of Oregon to work on a PhD at Stanford, Howe found that Clark was "working on Hannibal's collection and told me I'd have to wait until he got done ... says it will take him 3 more [years] at least." Howe was then to do Oregon's marine stratigraphy but "that also interfered with his [Clark's] work" - as did the Miocene Empire Formation, so Howe was restricted to looking at the Coos Conglomerate, at that time assigned to the Pliocene. "I had a suspicion before I came down here that Clark thought he had a morgage [sic] on the whole of the Tertiary of the Pacific Coast."

The Oligocene debate emerged again for a time in the 1960s when a book by F.E. Eames and coauthors on global middle Tertiary stratigraphy suggested in an oblique way that there might not even be Oligocene on the North American West Coast. That notion was ultimately laid to rest by Jere Lipps who restudied microfaunas from this time period in California for his PhD in 1966 at the University of California, Los Angeles. Lipps was able to demonstrate a clear correlation between Oligocene rocks and those in Europe by comparing the cosmopolitan planktonic [open ocean] foraminifera from both areas.

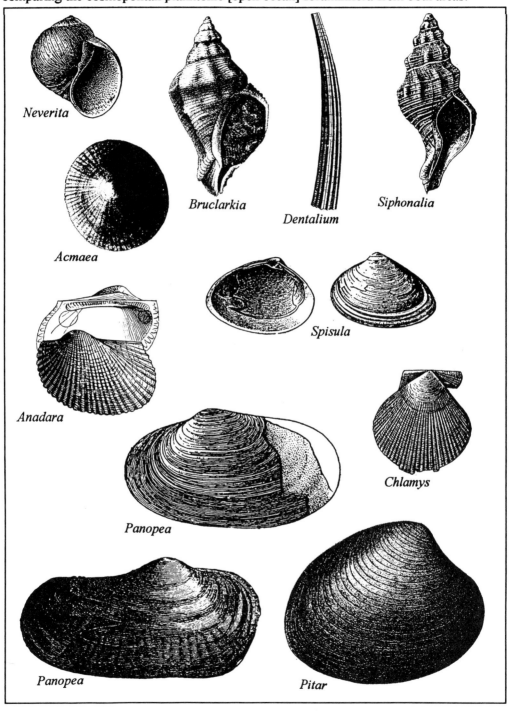

Oligocene invertebrates [from Gabb, 1869; Grabau and Shimer, 1910; Zittel, 1913].

At the Eocene-Oligocene boundary, 800 feet of sandstones and siltstones of the Pittsburg Bluff and almost 1,500 feet of mudstones, tuffs, and sandstones of the Smuggler Cove display a remarkable variety of environments from upper shelf marine to intertidal and terrestrial. Much of the Pittsburg Bluff is obscured by thick mature soils and dense vegetation, and scarce exposures can only be found in road cuts and stream beds.

The first detailed examination of the Pittsburg Bluff was made by a field party of the U.S. Geological Survey led by Joseph Diller and his assistant Frank Anderson. Leaving Forest Grove, the wagon train crossed the Coast Range on the Military Road over Saddle Mountain to Astoria, stopping to collect fossils on the Nehalem River and at the now abandoned community of Pittsburg in Columbia County. Returning to Forest Grove, the party was disbanded, and, as Diller wrote in his *A Geological Reconnaissance in North-western Oregon* in 1896, they "gave up camping to live with the people", reflecting the wild conditions of the countryside. Diller sent his megafossils to the Smithsonian where they were identified by William Dall as *Callista, Dentalium, Diplodonta, Macoma, Molopophorus, Mya, Neverita, Nucula,* and abundant *Solen.* In 1903 and 1909 papers, Dall used the clam *Callista* and the small stout snail *Molopophorus* to assign the Pittsburg Bluff to the Eocene. On the basis of a more extensive examination of the molluscs, which commonly occur within concretions, Bruce Clark reassigned the formation to the Oligocene in 1915. Then in 1981 John Armentrout placed it right at the Eocene-Oligocene boundary.

The most recent and definitive work on the paleontology of this formation was that of Ellen James Moore who described 48 species of molluscs, 13 of which are very common and 14 of which are extremely rare. For her 1976 monograph Moore carefully recollected from the known Columbia County localities in addition to examining specimens housed in the Smithsonian and at several universities in California. Moore suggests that the Pittsburg Bluff ocean was somewhat warmer than present day coastal waters and that the fauna represents three habitats - middle shelf water about 300 feet deep, moderately shallow water about 60 feet in depth, and very shallow nearshore to intertidal conditions. Clams and snails in the upper half of the formation typically inhabit sandy mudflats and embayments today, whereas local coal and plant fragments in the lower part suggest an advancing sea. Even though the fauna is well-preserved and abundant, it is marked by few species overall. The assortment of molluscs is peculiar in that the shells are broken and show signs of having been transported, yet most display little or no evidence of beach wear. Moore interprets this as evidence of storms catastrophically sorting the shells up on beaches from ocean depths of 75 to 100 feet. In some fossiliferous slabs accumulated in this way, up to 50% of the matrix is calcium carbonate shell fragments. Sand dollars and fish remains - including the ear bones [called otoliths] of conger eels and rat tails as well as shark teeth representing seven genera - are recorded from this formation.

Within the same basin, silty mudstones of the Smuggler Cove Formation includes molluscs, trace fossils, and foraminifera reflecting rapid deposition in a deep continental marine slope environment. Trace fossils are particularly abundant, especially the arcuate to spiraled *Phycosiphon* and *Zoophycos* - resembling a rooster tail. In 1985 Alan and Wendy Niem changed the name of this formation from the Oswald West mudstone and suggested it might be the outer edge of the Pittsburg Bluff delta. Several of Professor

Niem's students at Oregon State University have divided the Pittsburg Bluff into separate members, and Jeffrey Goalen's Masters thesis utilizes Ellen Moore's expertise for mollusc identifications.

OLIGOCENE INVERTEBRATES OF THE WILLAMETTE VALLEY

Thomas Condon's assessment of the Willamette Valley, which he designated the Willamette Sound, was remarkably perceptive in view of the basin's long marine history. Even today, as the Coast Range rises, the valley is sinking, so that at some time in the future the ocean will reinvade from Portland southward. During the Oligocene a well-marked shoreline of the seaway was east of Salem at Scotts Mills. The earliest report of megafossils from these beds was by petroleum geologist Chester Washburne in his 1914 Bulletin on the oil prospects in Oregon along with his controversial opinions on stratigraphy and faulting.

From Eugene, Chester Washburne's professional career centered mainly on petroleum geology, which carried him around the world and brought him into contact with influential personalities as E. L. DeGolyer and Bailey Willis [photo courtesy G. and E. Washburne].

Born in 1883, Chester Washburne's forebearers were California goldminers before arriving in the southern Willamette Valley where they opened a department store in downtown Eugene. At one time Thomas Condon's student and field assistant to Joseph Diller, Washburne took an A.B. and was awarded an honorary Doctor of Science from the University of Oregon. He went on to become an eminent authority on petroleum geology, his career, interests, and demand as a lecturer carrying him world wide. Addressing a letter to the Condon Club from Australia in August, 1925, Washburne's sense of humor is evident: "I am going around the World. That means four weeks across the Pacific, already accomplished, thank goodness. Most of the time is spent in sweating under Tropical skies, with a bunch of tourists who do not know what to do with themselves..." A notably independent thinker, his ideas were frequently controversial. While he viewed the dissent and arguments with humor when young, the continued conflicts ultimately led him to withdraw from the profession. Presenting one of his favorite theories about faulting to the Royal Geological Society in Sydney, "it received some hard hammering from the half dozen geologists entitled to argue with me." Leaving professional life, he took up residency in New York after World War II, but gave occasional talks until his death in 1971.

Throughout the 1980s and early 1990s a group of sedimentary rocks in Marion and Clackamas counties, named the Butte Creek Beds, were examined for plant and invertebrate fossils and formally designated as the Scotts Mills Formation by William Orr and his students at the University of Oregon. Representing the final retreating seaway in the Willamette Valley and Western Cascades during the late Oligocene, Scotts Mills sediments depict a variety of settings from nearshore swampy conditions to basalt headlands making up an irregular rocky coastline of seastacks, embayments, and steep submarine slopes. Orr and his student Paul Miller were also able to recognize and map storm deposits or tempesites here, whereas Robert Linder's Masters thesis and subsequent 1988 paper showed that this marine setting was the boundary between the warm-temperate and subtropical climate zones on the Pacific Coast during this epoch. Both the Scotts Mills strata and similar limestone lenses can be followed and mapped easily by the incidence oak forests that grow on the carbonate-rich soil above these rock formations. Linder also demonstrated that the tiny dime-size sand dollar *Kewia* from this formation was remarkable in that it selected and accumulated heavy minerals [magnetite] within its flattened crown [body]. The deliberate injestion of sand-sized heavy minerals, known in modern sand dollars as a type of "weight belt" strategy that these animals evolved for living in the high energy surf zone, was previously unrecorded in the fossil record.

Kewia

Salenia

Arbacia

The presence of both cool and warm water sea urchins and sand dollars in the Scotts Mills Formation places it at mid to low latitudes during the late Oligocene [photo courtesy R. Linder].

156

A professor at the University of Oregon for 30 years, William Orr's research has been diversified between planktonic foraminifera and Pacific Northwest Tertiary stratigraphy. Born in 1939 in Sioux Falls, Orr travelled continuously as part of a large military family which finally settled in Oklahoma. After his undergraduate degree at the University of Oklahoma and graduate work in California, his PhD on microfossils of the Gulf of Mexico was awarded at Michigan State University in 1966. In addition to his teaching role at Eugene, Orr has been Director of the Condon Museum of fossils for two decades. In this capacity he has evaluated fossil remains from throughout the Northwest.

Known for his rapid-fire style of lecturing and undecipherable handwriting, William Orr taught paleontology and oceanography at the University of Oregon. [photo courtesy W. Orr].

GEOLOGY OF THE MIOCENE OCEAN

By the end of the Oligocene epoch, 25 million years ago, widespread seas across western Oregon had diminished, and the Miocene ocean occupied a narrow strip only slightly east of the present coast. Uplift and eastward tilting of the Coast Range and concurrent depression of the Willamette Valley were well underway by the end of the Miocene interval, around 5 million years ago, so that the present geographic outlines were well-established.

Marine Miocene strata in the state are exposed intermittently in Coos, Curry, Lincoln, Tillamook, and Clatsop counties, where faunas inhabited shallow coastal basins. From Newport in Lincoln County to Tillamook the oldest formation is the Nye Mudstone which was covered in turn by Astoria rocks. Middle and late Miocene strata are the Tarheel, the Floras Lake Sandstone, and the Empire Formation in the vicinity of Coos Bay.

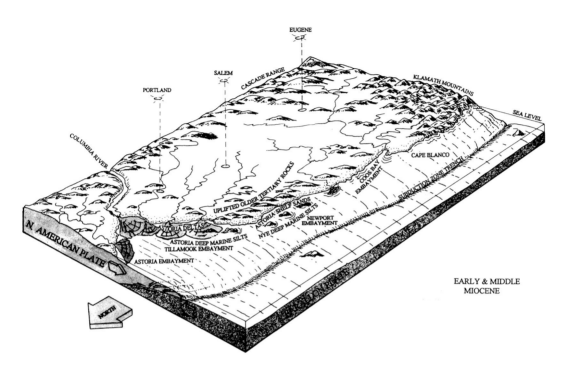

Miocene marine landscape of Oregon [after Orr and Orr, 1996].

MIOCENE INVERTEBRATES OF THE CENTRAL COAST

From Yaquina Bay and Newport northward the 4,000-foot thick Nye Mudstone tapers to less than 500 feet where it terminated against the rapidly growing Yaquina submarine fan and delta 23 million years ago. Here the Nye, with an abundance of deepwater microfossils, fish scales and vertebra, has only a meager count of molluscs, which are often crushed and distorted. This fauna suggests the cool temperatures of slope water depths, while south of Newport Nye strata with well-preserved molluscs reflect shallow water.

Fossils of the Nye have received considerable attention since Thomas Condon and his family spent their summers at a cottage on Nye Beach. Searching up and down the coast, Condon added considerably to the invertebrate shells at the Museum in Eugene. Molluscs from the vicinity of Yaquina were part of a collection loaned to the Smithsonian in 1871 and 1873 then transferred to Othniel Marsh at Yale University, where they were never unpacked from storage. Finally, on June 5, 1906, the new director of the Yale Museum, Charles Schuchert, wrote to Condon "...I now ask how and by what route we shall send [this material] to you."

Condon's faunal count was augmented by Charles Weaver and Harold Vokes. Weaver's exhaustive 1942 volume on Tertiary marine paleontology of the Pacific Northwest gives a complete listing of the megafossils, and Harold Vokes, a member of a mapping project near Newport and Waldport, provided a faunal inventory in 1949. In Nye sediments, the diminutive clam *Acila packardi* is cited as the most frequent mollusc.

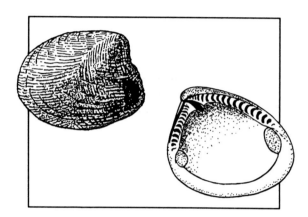

***Acila packardi*, the small clam, has a distinctive chevron-like pattern on the shell.**

Microfossils from this formation have been studied by several paleontologists. Weldon Rau examined foraminifera from surface exposures as well as in cores taken by the Army Corps of Engineers for their harbor exploration project at Yaquina Bay. Issued in conjunction with Parke Snavely of the U.S. Geological Survey in 1964 and 1969, Rau assigned foraminifera of the Nye to the early Miocene and estimated the paleo-environment to be cold water at depths of 1,000 to 2,000 feet. In 1972 Professor Jere Lipps and his student Dan McKeel at Davis corroborated the early Miocene age in their study of foraminifera. In these rocks they found few species overall, and less than 10% of the total assemblage was planktonic [open ocean] foraminifera. These characteristics of modern day cool waters led to the conclusion that during the middle Tertiary a temperate ocean and southward flowing current were in existance off the Oregon coast.

MIOCENE INVERTEBRATES OF THE NORTHWEST COAST

By far the most widely distributed and famed marine Miocene strata in the state is that of the Astoria Formation. Astoria rocks occur in a coastal strip from Clatsop County south to Yaquina Bay. Where it overlies the Yaquina and Nye formations near Newport, the formation reaches thicknesses up to 2,000 feet. Sandstones and siltstones, with carbonized wood, fossil-rich lenses of molluscs, small concretions with scallop shells or crabs, and large concretions with marine vertebrates remains inside attest to the shallow water paleosetting of the Astoria.

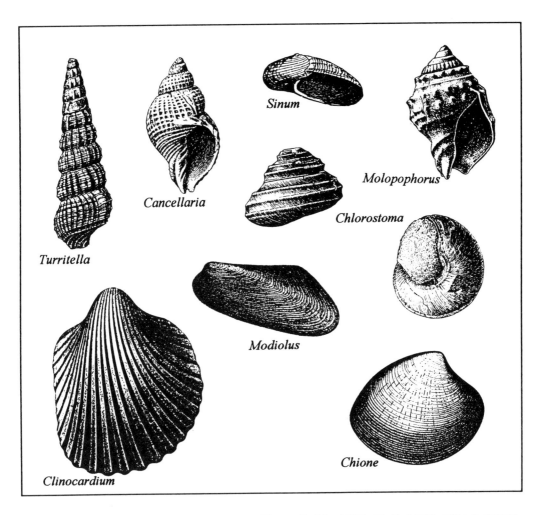

Miocene invertebrates - northwest coast [from Gabb, 1869; Dall, 1909; Zittel, 1913].

Although first named for sedimentary rocks in and around the town of Astoria, the thickest exposures are in coastal sea cliffs from Lincoln to Tillamook counties. The original sites - where fossils were first discovered - have been covered by city buildings and wharfs in the town of Astoria and by sand dredged from the Columbia River channel, posing ongoing problems for subsequent investigators. Difficulties in finding original collection locals have been further complicated by the renaming of streets and even by the complete elimination of man-made structures used as reference points. An interesting afternoon can be spent with an article and map by a native Astorian Betty Dodds, in which she attempted to pinpoint old fossil sites based on historic records. Ellen Moore's 1963 Professional Paper and book *Fossil Shells from Oregon Beach Cliffs* give a well-researched look into the history, providing more of a geologic picture at the same time.

This formation has enjoyed a lengthy past of scientific scrutiny. Shells around the Astoria fur trading post were initially collected between 1834 and 1837 by a Quaker ornithologist and physician John K. Townsend, sponsored by the Academy of Natural Sciences of Philadelphia. When Townsend visited the old trading post at Astoria it was already crumbling, and his *Narrative* recounts that he was "very anxious to procure the skulls" of Indians from a local cemetery rather than shells. Geologist James Dana, who was with the U.S. Exploring Expedition led by Captain Charles Wilkes collected from rock exposures along the water's edge in 1841. These government funded expeditions were to satisfy scientific curiosity about the west and evaluate it for economic gain. Seven mollusc specimens were collected in the late 1840s or 1850s by George Gibbs, an ethnologist who had been appointed to the Port of Astoria during President Filmore's administration. Townsend's and Dana's shells were sent to Timothy Conrad, associated with the Philadelphia Academy, who initially assigned them to the Miocene, an assessment he later changed to Eocene.

Thomas Condon, who named the "Astoria shales", spent the summer of 1868 walking the beach at Astoria, looking for shells by breaking open concretions. He sometimes cracked several hundred to reap only two or three worthwhile specimens. On previous visits Condon examined fossils in street excavations as well, but, although he never published his collection, the Museum catalog at the University in Eugene lists *Aturia, Fusus, Glycimeris, Lima,* and *Rostellites* as well as fish scales and bones.

William Dall's summation of the Astoria followed his visit in 1890. Even then many of the limestone concretions on the beach had been collected and burned for lime, while buildings, wharfs, and storehouses on piles out over the fossil layer cut it off from examination. Travelling from Seattle, Dall reached Eugene in early September. Here fortunately he was able to inspect Astoria fossils from Condon's original localities, suggesting that Astoria rocks spanned the Oligocene to Miocene boundary.

The first important contribution to the Tertiary paleontology of the Pacific Coast was in 1909 by Dall, who covered Miocene invertebrates, vertebrates, and microfossils at Astoria and Coos Bay. Born in 1845 in Boston, Dall brought unusual organizational abilities, dedication, and energy to a career that began as the naturalist on an 1865 expedition to Alaska for Western Union International Telegraph. From that time until his death in 1927, his lifework was tied to Alaskan and Pacific Coast explorations as a member of the U.S. Coast and Geodetic Survey then with the U.S. Geological Survey. He concentrated on Cenozoic and living molluscs and relied heavily on the facilities of the Smithsonian where he spent hours organizing their collections as well as his own. He was so devoted to his work on molluscs that during meals, whenever his wife left the room, Dall would turn his attention to a small table covered with shells - which he examined until his wife returned with the next course for dinner. In all he named a staggering 5,427 genera, sub-genera, and species of fossil and recent molluscs and brachiopods.

161

The obsessive William Dall, who didn't even take time away from his shells for meals, always kept a notebook at hand to record meticulously all expenses, even five cents for shoelaces [photo courtesy Archives, U.S. Geological Survey Denver].

Since Dall's early efforts, Astoria sediments have been evaluated repeatedly and the fossils locals visited by most West Coast molluscan paleontologists. Chester Washburne, in his reconnaissance of oil prospects, provides specific localities for Astoria molluscs as does Henry Howe in his PhD from Stanford in 1922 and in his follow-up 1926 paper. Howe wrote that he visited "every street cut in the city of Astoria in the summer of 1921", even checking the basements of several buildings. He noted that because the fossiliferous shales are steadily slumping and moving down the hillside toward the harbor, survey markers and even buildings must be reset constantly. The enthusiastic Howe took a bachelors degree in Humanities at the University of Oregon, did a stint at Yale Law School, and taught high school briefly in eastern Oregon before he settled on geology. His graduate research from Stanford University under eminent coral paleontologist James Perrin Smith focused on the Astoria of Lincoln County.

In a 1925 letter to Warren Smith, Howe forcefully took Dall to task for his assessment of the Astoria. "There is really no Oligocene ... at Astoria, and therefore the name Astoria will have to be abandoned for the Oligocene of the Northwest ... the story of how Dall got tangled up at Astoria is too long to relate, but actually he did no research himself there or collecting. He visited the place, said all the good localities were covered up, which was not true, and gave a list of nine species which he said were Oligocene ... His identifications of the nine species were practically all erroneous." Howe then revised the Astoria upward into the Miocene. Upon finishing his degree, Howe accepted a faculty

162

position at Louisiana State University where he built up the department from scratch, remaining there until retirement and death in 1973.

Because "Heinie" Howe's students received extensive training in micropaleontology, sedimentation, and stratigraphy, they were in great demand in the oil industry [photo courtesy Archives, Louisiana State University].

Harold Vokes' contribution to the cooperative mapping program with the State Department of Geology was the identification of invertebrates. His career in geology began with his PhD in paleontology and stratigraphy from the University of California in 1935. Initially working with molluscs at the Illinois Geologic Survey and at the American Museum in New York, Vokes' part time employment with the U.S. Geological Survey from 1943 to 1945 provided critical identifications of Tertiary invertebrates from the Willamette Valley and coastal Oregon. Maintaining his position at the Survey, he subsequently taught at Johns Hopkins and is now at Tulane University.

The most thorough treatment of Astoria molluscs to date is a Professional Paper by Ellen James Moore in 1963. She also examined bryozoa, corals, echinoderms, fish, crabs, plant remains, brachiopods, marine mammals, and foraminifera as well as compiling an exhaustive comparison of fossil localities beginning with Townsend's in 1834. Because the original Astoria Formation sites were no longer accessible, Moore recounts her dilligent attempts to find and compare those molluscs collected by Townsend and Dana, at the same time pointing out the fate that may await fossils, even those placed in prestigeous museums. Of Townsend's 14 Astoria specimens, published and illustrated by Conrad in 1848 and deposited in Philadelphia at the Academy of Natural Sciences, only three could be found: *Cytherea, Loripes,* and *Solen.* Dana's publication on results of the Exploring Expedition featured specimens that had been identified and written up by Conrad, but illustrated by Dana and placed in the U.S. National Museum. Moore encountered many difficulties because Dana's drawings might not agree with the specimen, because catalog numbers may have been changed or erroneously copied into a newer catalog, or because more than one specimen may have been given the same number. All of Conrad's original labels were missing, and ultimately Moore was obliged to re-illustrate and re-assess Conrad's species.

As part of her research, Moore counted 97 species and 73 genera of molluscs, presently housed in the Smithsonian. Of these, most are still present today along the Pacific Coast, but seven are extinct. She noted that the Astoria is exceptional as a few of its species occur in phenomenal numbers. These shells, frequently in sandy layers that can be traced for miles, are *Anadara devincta, Katherinella angustifrons,* and *Patinopecten propatulus.* Most of the clams have their valves still together and closed, showing little wear or abrasion and suggesting they had not been carried far before burial. This is typical of a fauna living on a soft muddy, non-rocky seafloor at moderately shallow depths around 500 feet. The Miocene ocean water was warm to temperate and compares particularly well to the present coast of Japan in the pathway of the mild Kuroshio Current.

Species of *Aturia, Katherinella, Anadara,* and *Patinopecten* are characteristic of the Astoria Miocene.

Microfossils of this formation were initially summarized in 1938 by Robert Kleinpell of Berkeley and ten years later by Roscoe and Katherine Stewart in conjunction with Joseph Cushman. The Stewarts and Ewart Baldwin had taken samples of the shales at the northwest corner of 10th and Harrison streets in Astoria, a frequent collecting spot for fossils. The foraminifera were then published by Doc Stewart in 1951, whose microfossil work was used to subdivide the Astoria into stratigraphic divisions for a 1963 University of Oregon Masters thesis by Kenneth Dodds.

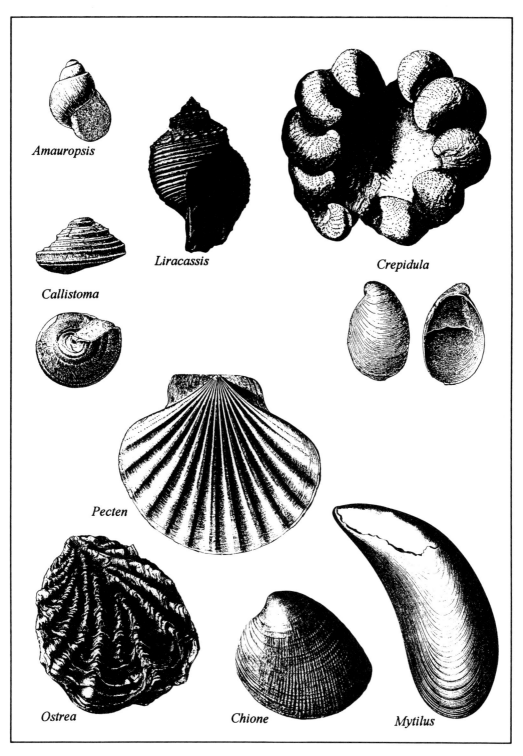

Late Miocene invertebrates - southwest coast [Gabb, 1869; Zittel, 1913].

165

In another graduate thesis from Eugene, mollusc populations from Astoria strata at Beverly Beach State Park in Lincoln County were utilized by Sharon Colbath to interpret predation by snails. For her 1981 thesis and later paper, Colbath enumerated a fauna that consists of 19 gastropod species, 15 pelecypods, and one scaphopod. She was specifically concerned with members of the Naticidae and Muricidae families, boring gastropods preying on molluscs by drilling a hole in the shell to rasp out the soft internal tissue. *Cryptonatica*, belonging to the Naticidae, had drilled most of the shells. By counting the frequency, size, and location of the holes in shells from two molluscan communities, one dominated by *Dentalium* and the other by *Acila* and the clam *Macoma,* Colbath found the Naitcidae preferred the clams over snails two to one, and *Macoma albaria* above all others. Perhaps this was due to *Macoma*'s shallow habitat or slow response to predators. The size of the shell was also a factor, and curiously the extremely small or large molluscs were not attacked by the shell-drilling snails. Snails apparently target the highest point on their prey, the hump or umbo, for drilling.

MIOCENE INVERTEBRATES OF THE SOUTHWEST COAST

Middle Miocene strata in the vicinity of Coos Bay were unknown until 1949 when molluscan-rich siltstones were brought to the surface and piled up in a disposal area during dredging operations in the Coos Bay channel. At that time Professor Baldwin from the University of Oregon, accompanied by his Masters candidate Ellen James, was giving a lecture at the Marine Biology station in Charleston when personnel from the Army Corps of Engineers mentioned the fossils. Expecting fossils belonging to the Empire Formation, which were to be the subject of Ellen James' [later Ellen Moore] thesis, she and a colleague went out in a boat to inspect the dredgings. "It was assumed that they would be Empire as no Astoria was then known to be exposed in the area," she related. When reaching the locality, Moore recognized the fossils as Astoria and "dropped to my knees and started collecting and didn't quit until we had to head back." Since the Astoria was unknown at that time in Coos Bay, Moore had to convince others this was the case. Specimens for Moore's thesis were well-preserved and free of any rock matrix, but since they were scattered over the surface of the piles, contamination was possible, and she speculated that in the future waves washing the dredgings might carry away the megafossils. In her 1950 thesis Moore provided extensive faunal descriptions as well as an evaluation of foraminifera by Doc Stewart.

Ellen Moore was one of the few woman majoring in geology at Oregon institutions during World War II, completing her degree from Ewart Baldwin once that conflict ended. As a young girl in Portland, Moore was exposed to geology by her mother, Mildred James, who took her to meetings of the Geological Society of Oregon Country and during this time she took an extension class in the subject from Edwin Hodge. Once she had a Masters, Moore wrote a number of institutions for job opportunities. Yale University responded that "our department is completely manned." The curator of another museum responded, "Will be glad to take you out for dinner but can't hire you." She accepted a position in Portland with the Army Corps of Engineers, but most of her career was at the U.S. Geological Survey. Today Moore and her husband, geologist George Moore, live in Corvallis.

Ellen Moore began her formal education in geology at age 16 when she took an evening extension class taught in Portland by Edwin Hodge, a professor from Oregon State University. Even though she was too young to enroll, Hodge told her to sit in the front row and "he wouldn't notice" [photo courtesy E. Moore].

In 1961 John Armentrout, another of Baldwin's students, visited Coos Bay to collect the fossils described by Moore, only to find there were no shells in the debris piles southeast of the channel but a plentiful supply along North Spit. In the summer of 1966 he returned to do field work for a thesis on the Empire Formation when he discovered rock outcrops, similar to those in the dredge piles, between Pigeon Point and the old Sitka Dock. He designated this rock as the middle Miocene Tarheel Formation, named after a local reservoir. Fossils were sparce in the outcrop but unworn and well-preserved. Approximately 70% of the fauna was the clam *Dosinia whitneyi*, also found at Astoria in Clatsop County and at Scotts Mills in Marion County. A total of 18 genera were recovered. Of these *Bruclarkia* and *Katherinella* are extinct, and *Dosinia* is extinct locally. *Patinopecten oregonensis cancellosus* is the most common pelecypod found in concretions here. On the basis of molluscs, Armentrout suggested the Tarheel was a basin of warm to temperate marine waters at shallow to moderate upper shelf depths reaching to 180 feet. The lack of brackish or fresh water shells indicates the basin was not part of an estuary or directly adjacent to land.

167

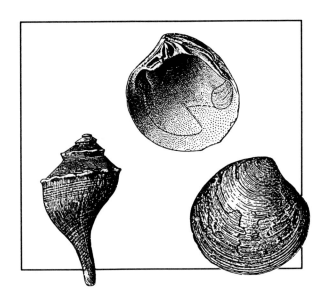

The gastropod *Bruclarkia* and clam *Dosinia* were common inhabitants of the southwestern coast during the late Miocene.

Born in 1942, in Portland, John Armentrout graduated from high school there before completing Bachelors and Masters degrees from the University of Oregon. These were followed by a PhD from the University of Washington on molluscan paleontology and biostratigraphy of the Lincoln Creek Formation of southwest Washington. As a graduate student with a natural flair for education, Armentrout organized and ran the Oregon Museum of Science and Industry summer course at Camp Hancock during the years 1967 to 1970. It was under his energetic direction that permanent buildings were finally established as part of the field station there. Since graduation, Armentrout has worked for Mobil Oil Company in Dallas. His unlimited enthusiasm and research interests in molluscan paleontology and biostratigraphy have made him a major player and authority on refining West Coast Tertiary stratigraphy for almost three decades.

In addition to several landmark papers on northwest stratigraphy and paleontology, John Armentrout's contribution has been as a mentor to younger scientists [photo courtesy J. Armentrout].

Above the Tarheel at Coos Bay, the Empire Formation stretches to Cape Blanco in Curry County. At South Slough the formation forms prominent cliffs and consists of around 3,000 feet of sandstones, containing concretions over a foot in diameter. The fossil-rich Coos Conglomerate lense at Fossil Point is part of the same strata. The Empire had been placed in the Pliocene until the Tertiary epochs were revised in 1983, and the base of the Pliocene boundary was moved upward from 10 to 5 million years before the present.

Joseph Diller in both his 1896 reconnaissance of northwest Oregon and his classic Coos Bay Folio reports on the Empire Beds between Pigeon Point and Fossil Point. At Fossil Point he found "the most remarkable fossiliferous rock seen anywhere on the coast" This was the Coos Bay Conglomerate seen today at low tide only in a patch less than one acre at Fossil Point. The conglomerate lense is beach material eroded from shallower layers of the Empire Formation and redeposited downslope as fill in a narrow submarine trough. Most of the shells in the deposit show the wear and abrasion of transport, and scattered bone fragments of marine vertebrates such as whales, sea lions, and seals are not uncommon within shell layers. Even though the Coos Conglomerate was long considered as a separate unit, Armentrout was able to demonstrate its origin as an integral part of the Empire Formation.

In 1902 the Empire Formation was first described in detail by William Dall of the Smithsonian Institution when he visited the village, which, he remarked, had the "ambitious title of Empire". Dall went on to relate that the tough matrix made fossils difficult to extract, and, in order to obtain a number of specimens for the U.S. Geological Survey, he purchased items from a local resident, B.H. Camman. Camman, a retired merchant of "advanced age" and without "scientific training", had collected fossils for 15 years while on daily strolls along the beach between Empire and South Slough. He accumulated piles of fossils in an abandoned warehouse, among which were bushels of *Pecten coosensis* and *Chione securis*. Many had been thoroughly cleaned of the surrounding material. The Camman collection included vertebra and rib bones of whales, seals, and sea lions as well as fossilized wood fragments bored by "shipworms" [a clam called *Bankai*]. Dall's published list totalled 90 species. Henry Howe compared species from various collections of Empire material in 1922, and almost twenty-five years later Charles Weaver's reexamination of the Empire fauna produced 112 species of marine pelecypods and gastropods.

John Armentrout's 1967 Masters degree from Ewart Baldwin at the University of Oregon reassessed the Empire Formation, the first such attempt after Weaver. Armentrout recorded 72 genera and 129 species of molluscs. Of these, 50 genera and 38 species still living along the West Coast prompted him to conclude that the late Miocene climate of Coos Bay varied little from that of today. Preserved intact, colonies of the slipper shell, *Crepidula princeps*, indicate an embayment of calm shallow water approximately 180 feet deep. Molluscs inhabiting this warm to temperate basin were abundant compared to other invertebrates, microfossils, and vertebrates.

The Empire Formation is also found at Cape Blanco, and in mapping this area for the U.S. Geological Survey near the turn of the century Joseph Diller sent fossils from Floras Lake and Blacklock Point in Curry County to William Dall. Dall placed the molluscs in the Miocene. However, the first complete inventory of megafossils from the Floras Lake sandstone was published by Ralph Arnold and Harold Hannibal in 1913 in their notable paper on the marine Cenozoic of the Pacific Northwest. These two authors became acquainted when Arnold, who left the Survey in 1909 for private consulting, sponsored Hannibal, a graduate student at Stanford. The reclusive Hannibal was not overly popular with his peers, but Arnold recognized Hannibal's rare ability as a stratigrapher and fossil collector. Arnold had visited a number of localities prior to 1911, and he funded Hannibal's spring and summer field expenses through 1912 along the Pacific Northwest coastline.

Molluscs from the lower and upper sections of the Empire Formation at Cape Blanco were lumped together in Arnold and Hannibal's samples, so their middle Miocene date continued to be controversial until 1953 when J. Wyatt Durham, from the University of California at Berkeley, identified a gap or unconformity in the local Miocene strata here. The formation was subsequently divided by Warren Addicott of the U.S. Geological Survey and described in the 1980s. Addicott named the lower portion the Sandstone of Floras Lake, but he retained the designation Empire Formation for the upper 300 feet.

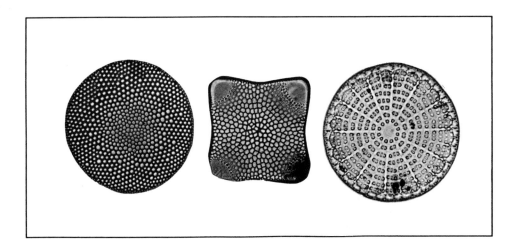

Rocks mapped as Empire Formation in beach cliffs just south of Bandon are unique in that they contain the only known marine diatomite in the state. First described by William Orr and university student Judi Ehlen in 1971, the claystones have a rich temperate flora of diatoms dominated by *Coscinodiscus, Trigonium,* and *Arachnoidiscus.*

One of the most influential contemporary workers in southwestern Oregon paleontology has been Warren Addicott. Addicott received his PhD from Berkeley in 1956, and in his long career with the U.S. Geological Survey he supervised West Coast paleontology, specializing in Cenozoic marine molluscs. When funding became tight, Addicott moved to the International Geology Branch where he taught himself Spanish and represented the Survey on Spanish-speaking projects. His work on Pacific Coast molluscs includes a number of exceptional papers. Several, such as his review of the literature of molluscan paleontology from 1840 to 1969, his historical overview, and his biographical sketches of paleontologists are quite unique. Of particular note are papers on molluscan stages and zones that fit these invertebrates into the West Coast standard stratigraphic chart.

Addicott demonstrated that contrasting molluscan faunas characterize the upper and lower Floras Lake Sandstone layers. The lower section has only a few species, but a dramatic increase in faunal diversity is notable toward the top. The pelecypod *Mytilus*, the barnacle *Balanus,* and the gastropod *Nucella* in the lowest section indicate a wave washed tidal setting close to a rocky shoreline. However, the appearance of the snail *Bruckarkia* and the clams *Macoma* and *Spisula* toward the middle, followed by the scaphopod *Dentalium*, the pelecypods *Katherinella* and *Patinopecten,* and gastropod *Liracassis* near the top reflect water deepening to 60 feet. At the highest level the sandstone contains scattered *Dentalium* and unbroken specimens of *Spisula*.

Paleontologist and stratigrapher, Warren Addicott retired to Ashland, where he presently teaches at Southern Oregon State University [photo courtesy W. Addicott].

PLEISTOCENE INVERTEBRATES OF THE COAST

Late Miocene and Pliocene sediments have not been recorded from the central and northern Coast Range of Oregon, and Pleistocene exposures are limited to the extreme western margins. Sea level history along the Pacific Ocean is complicated because of at least three independent geologic processes. During Pleistocene glacial advances, sea levels dropped off profoundly as water was locked up elsewhere as ice. Simultaneously, the coastline, topped by discontinuous terraces, has been elevated in stages because of tectonic plate subduction. Today, for example, the coast at Cape Blanco is being raised as much as one inch every three years, whereas globally sea levels rise about 1/32 inch per year as

171

glaciers melt. In yet another geologic phenomenon, periodic catastrophic earthquakes have dropped whole sections of the coast by several feet over intervals of hundreds of years.

The Pleistocene saw sheets of continental glaciers that projected from Canada southward into Washington as well as almost continuous ice caps across the higher mountain ranges. When the glacial ice melted, large regions of the shelf were submerged providing new habitats for invertebrates. The most significant Pleistocene shell deposits occur at Cape Blanco, which takes its name from their profuse whiteness. Here terrace deposits form the crest of a sequence that begins with Port Orford sediments, covered in turn by the Elk River Formation.

Ewart Baldwin designated the name Port Orford Formation for sedimentary rocks lying between the Empire Formation and Elk River beds at Cape Blanco. Coarse sandstones and conglomerates near the base grade upward to silts at the top. Only scattered trace fossils of burrows and molds of shells along with sparce foraminifera have been found in these beds.

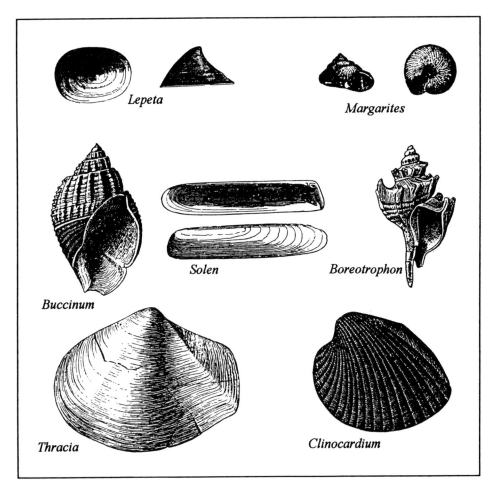

Pleistocene invertebrates - southwest coast [Grabau and Shimer, 1910; Zittel, 1913].

One of the first studies of megafossils at Cape Blanco was by Orville Bandy. For his 1941 Masters degree under Earl Packard's direction at Oregon State University, Bandy recorded foraminifera, molluscs, crab remains, barnacles, and ostracods [*Cytheretta*] in Pliocene and Pleistocene strata here. After the stratigraphy had been revised, Bandy published separate faunas from the Port Orford and Elk River formations in 1950, noting that the shallow water foraminifera *Elphidium hannai* was the most common species. At the base of the terrace deposits - where the terraces merge with the Elk River beds below - the microfossil fauna is dominated by cool water species.

Generally mild-mannered and affable, Bandy once took over command of an oceanic research vessel where he was chief scientist when disharmony arose between scientists and crew. His decision was later reaffirmed [photo courtesy University of Southern California, Archives].

Orville Bandy's family moved from Iowa to Corvallis, Oregon, in 1921, when he was 4 years old. It was here that he developed an interest in Cenozoic stratigraphy and paleontology, completing bachelors and masters degrees at Oregon State University in 1940 and 1941 under Professor Earl Packard. After military service during World War II, he worked under J.J. Galloway at Indiana University for a PhD. The result was his now classic study of Eocene and Oligocene foraminifera of Little Stave Creek, Alabama. Joining the faculty at the University of Southern California, he developed the reputation as a tireless researcher, who wrote copiously on foraminifera - boiled from their matrix and steaming up his tiny office known as "Bandy's broom closet". Internationally recognized as a micropaleontologist, Bandy produced a group of remarkable students before his unexpected death in 1973.

Above the Port Orford, the Elk River Formation, by contrast, has an exceptional fauna of fossil molluscs. These shell-rich conglomerates and sandstones have been variously assigned to the Pliocene and Pleistocene since first described by Diller in 1902, but Ralph Arnold and Harold Hannibal in their 1913 summary of northwest Tertiary stratigraphy point out that the megafossils here consist almost entirely of species still living today.

The most thorough paleontologic study of this formation was a 1979 PhD dissertation from the University of California, Berkeley, by Barry Roth. Roth divided the formation into four members and identified 112 species including 56 gastropods, 40 pelecypods, 6 barnacles, 5 crustacea, a scaphopod, chiton, echinoid [sand dollar], bryozoa, and brachiopod, along with foraminifera, trace fossils, sponges [*Cliona*], fish, and mammal remains. While plant fossils at the base of the formation accumulated in what was probably a channel of the ancestral Sixes and Elk River drainages, invertebrates in the younger upper layers occupied the shallow water of a muddy estuary. The basin gradually shallowed to less than 100 feet deep as the land was elevated and dissected by coastal streams. *Clinocardium meekianum baldwini* was the most common mollusc encountered.

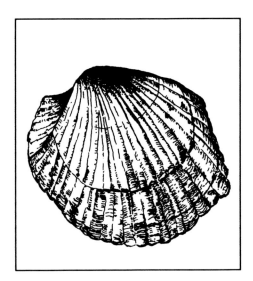

Clinocardium meekianum baldwini

North of Cape Blanco at Bandon, the Coquille Formation was deposited in an embayment at the mouth of the ancient Coquille River before the channel shifted southward during a final warming stage of the Pleistocene. In this last event, river entrances all along the coast were silted up. Similar deposits occur near Newport where, in 1950, Ewart Baldwin recorded the sparse fossils *Hinnites, Macoma, Thais, Schizothaerus,* and *Zirphea.*

COASTAL TERRACES

Elevated terrace deposits cap the older Port Orford and Elk River formations. Collision and subduction of the Juan de Fuca plate beneath the western edge of North America dramatically raised and tilted the Oregon coastal area to form step-like terraces that can be seen as discontinuous belts ranging from 20 to 50 feet in thickness and reaching elevations inland up to 1,600 feet. Because the rate of elevation varies from place to place, the age and relationship of terrace fragments to each other have been difficult to determine. More recently these surfaces have been very accurately dated by determining the uranium-thorium decay ratios in the skeletons of the corals *Celleporina* and *Heteropora* and the sea urchin *Strongylocentrotus.* Amino acid decay within shell calcite of the large clams *Mya truncata* and *Saxidomus giganteus* also provides precise dates, while oxygen isotopes yield paleotemperature information on the deposits. Although these methods of chemical paleontology are innovative and remarkably quantitative, they will not replace standard biostratigraphic techniques for dating because they involve expensive and time-consuming laboratory procedures.

Pleistocene molluscs from terrace deposits are meager in Oregon except for faunas at Cape Blanco in Curry County and Bandon in Coos County. This is in sharp contrast with the prolific occurrence of fossil invertebrates from terraces along the coasts of British Columbia, Washington, California, and Mexico. In 1964 paleontologist Warren Addicott reported an assemblage of 12 pelecypods, 24 gastropods, 5 barnacles, as well as echinoids, bryozoa, and foraminifera reflecting a sandy shallow offshore ocean setting preserved in sea cliff terraces at Cape Blanco. Water temperatures were cooler than today, as 20 of the fossil species are known only from regions considerably north of present-day Cape Blanco. Even though waves may have disturbed the shells in what was a very slow rate of deposition, abundant paired valves of the large clams *Saxidomus, Schizothaerus,* and *Tresus* in upright life position imply the shells were not moved a significant distance.

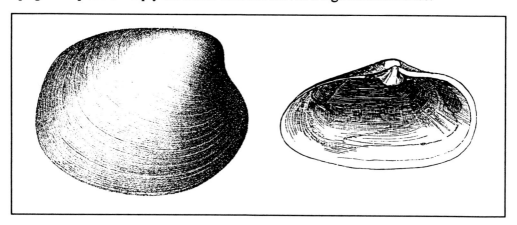

The large Pleistocene clams *Saxidomus* and *Mya* can be used for dating terraces [from Gabb, 1869; Zittel, 1913].

Associated with the California Academy of Sciences in 1969, Victor Zullo examined terraces at Bandon where he closely studied two pockets of Pleistocene invertebrates, one at Grave Point and the other at Coquille Point. Screening 100 pounds of material from Grave Point, Zullo noted high fossil concentrations representing 58 species. Plates and valves of *Balanus cariosus* [barnacles] were the most conspicuous by bulk but were exceeded in number by the pelecypod *Hiatella arctica*, gastropods *Fusitriton oregonensis, Margarites pupillus,* and *Oenopota tabulata,* as well as the bryozoa *Costazia* and *Heteropora*. At Coquille Point he identified 37 invertebrates, seven of which had not been seen at Grave Point. Today *Mya japonica* from Coquille Point is extinct in the eastern Pacific, and its presence here is the most southerly known to date. Zullo notes that although the Bandon shells are probably the same age as those from Cape Blanco, only 30% of the species are found in both sites because of varying habitats. Shallow water along a rocky coast at Bandon protected the molluscs from waves, while at Cape Blanco the shells accumulated and were sorted in the turbulent water by an advancing sea.

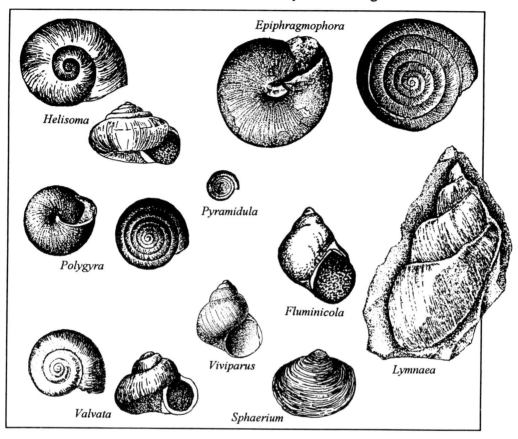

Land-dwelling and freshwater snails and clams [from Stearns, 1900; Zittel, 1913].

LAND-DWELLING AND FRESHWATER INVERTEBRATES

Even though freshwater and land-dwelling molluscs are known from several intervals of Oregon's fossil record, they are not represented in the same diversity and abundance as marine shells because their fragile shells seldom preserve well. Generally mentioned with fossil fish and bird localities, land-dwelling molluscs have been only sparingly treated.

Shells of freshwater clams are ordinarily thicker than those in the oceanic realm and are often composed entirely of the mineral aragonite in contrast to the calcite of marine shells. With burial and time, the aragonite shell, or "mother of pearl", is unstable and tends to recrystallize to calcite. In this degeneration process, the volume change and resulting fractures in the shell structure make it vulnerable to solution by groundwater. Even if the shells remain intact, the effects of recrystallization often cause them to flake and crumble as they are removed from the entombing rock matrix.

The oldest land-dwelling molluscs in Oregon are from Oligocene and Miocene deposits of the John Day and Malheur basins. The only other freshwater shells are those from Pliocene and Pleistocene lake deposits in the Great Basin region across the southern part of the state.

Molluscs in John Day strata were first noted by Robert Stearns of the Smithsonian around the turn of the century when he reported on collections made by Thomas Condon, Edward Cope, and John Merriam. Condon visited the John Day valley from 1864 onward, where he collected fossil terrestrial snails although his main interest was plant and mammal remains. He never published these finds, but turned over a small collection to the U.S. Geological Survey. About the same time, Jacob Wortman was hired by the Academy of Natural Sciences, Philadelphia, to search for vertebrate fossils in eastern Oregon. Wortman uncovered a small number of mollusc shells in the same site where Condon had found vertebrates, and in 1885 these were turned over Stearns. Comparing them to Condon's collection, Stearns noted an unusually small variety for what was supposed to be a lake deposit. He identified five members of the gastropod family Helicidae, which are land-dwelling, and one freshwater clam *Unio,* naming a new species *Unio condoni.*

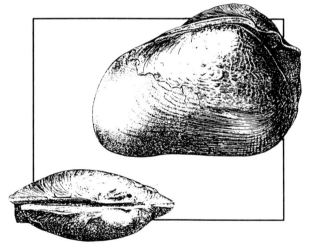

**The freshwater clam,
Unio condoni was an inhabitant
of eastern Oregon lakes during
the Miocene [White, 1885].**

Stearns also examined shells assembled by California paleontologist, John Merriam, who had conducted an expedition to central Oregon in 1899. Most were land-dwelling snails of the same genera as those living today in this area. Stearns speculated that the limited distribution and small size of the modern snails in this region may be due to extraordinary climate changes at the end of the John Day interval. Listed were *Ammonitella, Epiphragmophora [Helix], Polygyra,* and *Pyramidula.* Present in Merriam's collection were large numbers of *Unio condoni* and a pond snail *Lymnaea.*

A native of Boston, Massachusetts, where he was born in 1827, Robert E.C. Stearns led a very eclectic life as an adult, changing jobs frequently for 40 years from 1854 until he took a position with the Smithsonian. Beginning as a paymaster and clerk at copper mines in Lake Superior, he later farmed in Norfolk, Massachusetts. In California he was with a publishing house in San Francisco, then a secretary on the Board of the State Harbor Commissioners, a deputy clerk of the Supreme Court, a farmer, and finally secretary on the Board of Regents. In Florida he collected biological specimens and ultimately was appointed as an honorary associate in zoology at the Smithsonian from 1892 onward. His varied interests included the geographical distribution and variation in molluscs, descriptions of new jellyfish, sea anemones, and corals, as well as forestry.

During the Civil War Robert Stearns took over as editor of a popular religious journal in California, enthusiastically advocating the Union cause and influencing the decision of that state to adopt an anti-slavery policy [photo courtesy Smithsonian Institution, Archives].

Condon's shell collection from the John Day, housed in the Museum in Eugene, was not published in detail until 1920 when G Dallas Hanna, Curator of Paleontology at the California Academy of Sciences in San Francisco, identified 118 fossil specimens, 90 of which were the snail *Polygyra*. Of those remaining, *Gastrodonta*, *Helicina*, and *Rhiostoma* currently inhabit the tropics of Asia. Hanna found none of the pond-dwelling clams *Unio condoni*. Unfortunately the Museum catalog has no accompanying stratigraphic information, although Hanna dated the locality as Oligocene. Hanna, who completed a degree in paleontology and zoology at George Washington University, Washington, D.C., in 1918, spent his career on the West Coast. As a curator in California, he worked on almost all of the freshwater invertebrates known from Oregon. In his 51 years at the Academy, he published on fossil and living molluscs, diatoms, silicoflagellates, and foraminifera, compiling an impressive but unpublished *Index to West American Diatoms*.

Near Oregon's southeastern border, middle Miocene freshwater molluscs from the Juntura basin in western Malheur and Harney counties were found with a diverse mammal fauna. Three species of clams and six of snails suggest a perennial freshwater lake that

178

reached depths up to 30 feet between 15 to 10 million years ago. At that time in eastern Oregon, ponds and lakes were created by local lava flows that dammed streams. Noted in 1963 by Dwight Taylor, invertebrate biologist with the U.S. Geological Survey, the most common were *Carinifex, Fluminicola, Radix, Sphaerium,* and *Viviparus.* Taylor has since retired to Eugene.

After his family moved to Kansas when he was seven years old, G Dallas Hanna became interested in rocks and his natural surroundings during a mile-long walk to school each day [photo courtesy California Academy of Sciences].

Increased precipitation and lowered temperatures during the Pleistocene created vast lakes across the Great Basin. In southern Oregon, invertebrates from these ancient bodies of water are found at Fossil and Summer lakes, near the small lakes in the Warner valley, and from Harney Lake to the Snake River.

Snail shells litter the surface around Fossil Lake where they whiten the sand in accumulations blown together by the wind. Even though no specific studies have been completed on the molluscs, they have frequently been noted where they occur with vertebrate remains. Edward Cope, who visited here in 1879, remarked on the white shell *Carinifex newberryi.* Mapping for the U.S. Geological Survey at the turn of the century, Israel Russell collected *Gyraulis, Helisoma, Limnophysa, Pisidium, Sphaerium,* and *Valvata* that, he observed, are all still living. In his classic monograph on Fossil Lake, Ira Allison, a professor at Oregon State University, summarized previous work completed at this site. Allison also looked at the fauna from nearby Summer Lake in his overall 1982 environmental study of pluvial Lake Chewaucan - present-day Summer Lake, the Chewaucan marshes, and Lake Abert. He found that in the eastern part of the Summer Lake basin thin beds of shells and shell fragments make up an astonishing 90% of the strata. Wells drilled to depths over 700 feet penetrated layers of compacted molluscs indicating a much longer history of occupation by Pleistocene lakes than previous believed.

The Museum at Eugene houses freshwater clams and snails of this same time frame from Warner lakes, between Crooked River and Harney Lake, and in the Snake River valley. Assembled by Condon while on a trip to Lake County in 1876, the shells from near Harney Lake were so thoroughly compressed, crushed, and cemented together they were hard to extract and identify. These were evaluated in a 1922 paper by Dallas Hanna, who found that only the shell of a robust *Viviparus* was preserved, while other the gastropods, *Carinifex, Parapholyx, Valvata, Vorticifex,* and the clam *Pisidium* were preserved as casts without shells.

The freshwater snail *Carinifex* and clam *Pisidium* can be used to trace Ice Age lake and river drainages.

A relic of the Pleistocene epoch, the freshwater clam *Pisidium ultramonatauum,* living today in northeastern California and southcentral Oregon, was more widely distributed during the Ice Ages. According to Dwight Taylor, *Pisidium* lived over a region extending to southeast Idaho and adjoining Utah during the Pliocene and Pleistocene. The distribution pattern of *Pisidium,* the snail *Carinifex,* and a freshwater sucker *Chasmistes* show that a previously connected chain of lakes and drainage basins reached for hundreds of miles from Nevada and the Pit River in California to Klamath and Fossil lakes and the Malheur basin in Oregon, ultimately stretching to the Snake River and beyond. Based on this faunal information, Taylor concluded that the present course of the Snake River is relatively young and that at one time the Snake flowed into the Pacific Ocean somewhere between the Columbia and Sacramento drainage systems.

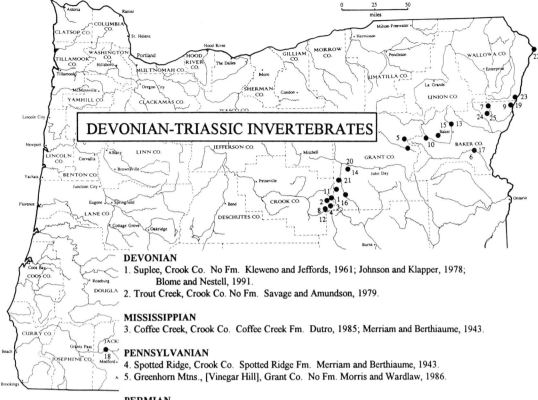

DEVONIAN

1. Suplee, Crook Co. No Fm. Kleweno and Jeffords, 1961; Johnson and Klapper, 1978;
    Blome and Nestell, 1991.
2. Trout Creek, Crook Co. No Fm. Savage and Amundson, 1979.

MISSISSIPPIAN

3. Coffee Creek, Crook Co. Coffee Creek Fm. Dutro, 1985; Merriam and Berthiaume, 1943.

PENNSYLVANIAN

4. Spotted Ridge, Crook Co. Spotted Ridge Fm. Merriam and Berthiaume, 1943.
5. Greenhorn Mtns., [Vinegar Hill], Grant Co. No Fm. Morris and Wardlaw, 1986.

PERMIAN

6. Burnt River, Baker Co. Burnt River Schist. Morris and Wardlaw, 1986.
7. Eagle Creek, Baker Co. Clover Creek Greenstone. Shroba, 1992.
8. Grindstone Creek, Crook Co. Coyote Butte Fm. Cooper, 1957; Murchey and Jones, 1994;
    Wardlaw, et al., 1982.
9. Homestead, Baker Co. Hunsaker Creek Fm. Vallier, 1967.
10. Sumpter, Baker Co. Elkhorn Ridge Argillite. Blome, et al., 1986; Bostwick and Nestell, 1967.
11. Suplee, Crook Co. Coyote Butte Fm. Merriam, 1942; Stevens and Rycerski, 1983.
12. Twelvemile Creek, Crook Co. Coyote Butte Fm. Blome and Nestell, 1991; Cooper, 1957;
    Murchey and Jones, 1994.
13. Granite Boulder Creek, Grant Co. Coyote Butte Fm. Blome, et al., 1986; Morris and Wardlaw, 1986;

TRIASSIC

14. Aldrich Mtns., Grant Co. Aldrich Mtn. Gr. Blome, 1984; Blome, et al., 1986.
15. Baker, Baker Co. Elkhorn Ridge Argillite. Blome, et al., 1986; Pessagno and Blome, 1986.
16. Beaver Creek, Grant Co. Begg Fm. Blome, et al., 1986; Dickinson and Vigrass, 1965.
17. Durkee, Baker Co. Burnt River Schist. Morris and Wardlaw, 1986.
18. Gold Hill, Jackson Co Applegate Gr. Irwin, et al., 1983.
19. Homestead, Baker Co. Grassy Ridge Fm. Vallier and Brooks, 1970.
20. John Day River, South Fork. Grant Co. Brisbois Fm. Dickinson and Vigrass, 1965.
21. Morgan Mtn., Grant Co. Rail Cabin Mudstone. Dickinson and Vigrass, 1965; Pessagno and Blome,
    1986.
22. Pittsburg Landing, Wallowa Co. Doyle Creek/Wild Sheep Creek Fms. White, 1994.
23. Spring Creek, Hells Canyon, Wallowa Co. Martin Bridge Fm. Newton, et al., 1987; Stanley and
    Whalen, 1989; Senowbari-Daryan and Stanley, 1988.
24. Summit Point, Baker Co. Martin Bridge Fm. Stanley and Senowbari-Daryan, 1986.
25. Wallowa Mtns., Wallowa Co. Hurwal/Martin Bridge Fms. Newton, 1987; Smith and Allen, 1941;
    Stanley, 1986.

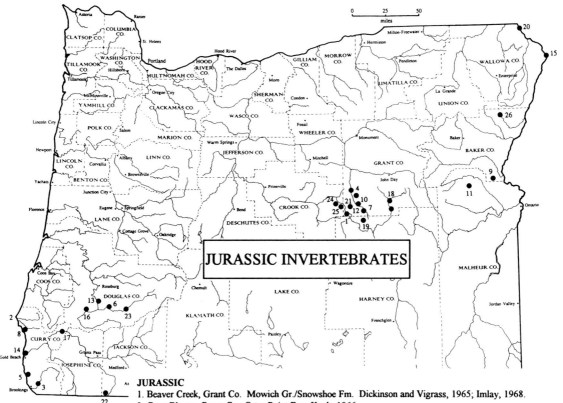

JURASSIC

1. Beaver Creek, Grant Co. Mowich Gr./Snowshoe Fm. Dickinson and Vigrass, 1965; Imlay, 1968.
2. Cape Blanco, Curry Co. Otter Point Fm. Koch, 1966.
3. Chetco River, Curry Co. Dothan Fm. Ramp, 1969.
4. Cow Creek, Grant Co. Mowich Gr. Dickinson and Vigrass, 1965.
5. Crook Point, Curry Co. Otter Point Fm. Koch, 1966.
6. Days Creek, Douglas Co. Riddle Fm. Imlay, et al., 1959.
7. Flat Creek, Grant Co. Snowshoe/Trowbridge Fm. Dickinson and Vigrass, 1965.
8. Humbug Mtn., Curry Co. Otter Point Fm. Koch, 1966.
9. Huntington, Baker Co. Weatherby Fm. Imlay, 1973, 1986.
10. Izee, Grant Co. Mowich Group/Snowshoe/Trowbridge Fms. Imlay, 1968, 1981;
      Pessagno and Blome, 1982; Pessagno, et al., 1986; Smith, 1980.
11. Juniper Mtn., Malheur Co. Weatherby Fm. Imlay, 1986.
12. Morgan Creek, Grant Co. Graylock Fm. Dickinson and Vigrass, 1965; Imlay, 1986.
13. Myrtle Creek, Douglas Co Riddle Fm. Imlay et al., 1959; Koch, 1966.
14. Otter Point, Curry Co. Otter Point Fm. Koch, 1966.
15. Pittsburg Landing, Wallowa Co. Coon Hollow Fm. Imlay, 1981, 1986; White, et al., 1992.
16. Riddle, Douglas Co. Riddle Fm. Diller and Kay, 1924; Imlay et al., 1959.
17. Rogue River, Curry Co. Galice/Rogue Fms. Dott, 1966; Pessagno and Blome, 1990.
18. Seneca, Grant Co. Mowich Gr./Snowshoe Fm. Dickinson and Vigrass, 1965;
      Imlay, 1973, 1986.
19. Silvies River, Harney Co. Donovan Fm. Lupher, 1941.
20. Snake River Canyon, Wallowa Co. Coon Hollow Mudstone. Stanley and Beauvais, 1990.
21. Suplee-Izee, Crook and Grant Cos., Mowich Gr./Snowshoe/Trowbridge Fms.
      Imlay, 1981, 1986; Pessagno., et al., 1986; Taylor, 1982.
22. Turner-Albright Mine, Josephine Co. Josephine ophiolite. Pessagno, et al., 1993.
23. Umpqua River, Douglas Co. Riddle Fm. Imlay, et al., 1959.
24. Wade Butte, Crook Co. Snowshoe Fm. Imlay, 1973; Lupher, 1941.
25. Warm Springs, Grant Co. Mowich Gr. Imlay, 1986; Lupher, 1941; Smith, 1980.
26. Wallowa Mtns., Wallowa Co. Hurwal Fm. Follo, 1994; Imlay, 1968; Smith and Allen, 1941.

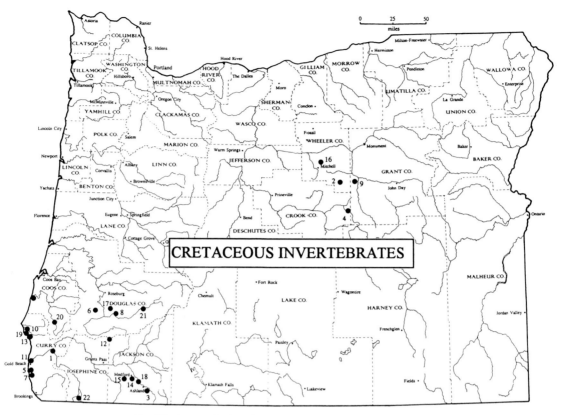

The following are selections of Oregon fossil invertebrate localities and authors who list faunas from them.

CRETACEOUS

1. Agness, Curry Co. Days Creek Fm. Popenoe, et al., 1960.
2. Antone, Wheeler Co. ?Hudspeth Fm. Jones, 1960; Popenoe, et al., 1960.
3. Ashland, Jackson Co. Hornbrook Fm. Nilsen, 1984; Popenoe, et al., 1960.
4. Beaver Creek, Crook Co. Bernard Fm. Dickinson and Vigrass, 1965; Popenoe, et al., 1960.
5. Cape Sebastian, Curry Co. Cape Sebastian Fm. Howard and Dott, 1961.
6. Cow Creek, Douglas Co. Days Creek Fm. Imlay, et al., 1959.
7. Crook Point, Curry Co. Cape Sebastian Fm. Howard and Dott, 1961.
8. Days Creek, Douglas Co. Days Creek Fm. Imlay, et al., 1959.
9. Dayville, Grant Co. Hudspeth Fm. Jones, 1960; Popenoe, et al., 1960.
10. Elk River, Curry Co. Days Creek Fm. Popenoe, et al., 1960.
11. Gold Beach, Curry Co. Hornbrook Fm. Bourgeois and Leithold, 1983; Nilsen, 1983.
12. Grave Creek, Jackson Co. Hornbrook Fm. Jones, 1960.
13. Humbug Mtn., Curry Co. Humbug Mtn. Congl./Rocky Pt. Fm. Koch, 1966.
14. Jacksonville, Jackson Co. Hornbrook Fm. Anderson, 1958; Nilsen, 1984.
15. Medford, Jackson Co. Hornbrook Fm. Nilsen, 1984.
16. Mitchell, Wheeler Co. Hudspeth Fm. Jones, 1960; Kleinhaus, et al., 1984.
17. Myrtle Creek, Douglas Co. Rocky Pt./Days Cr.Fm./Humbug Mtn.Congl. Imlay, et al., 1959; Koch, 1966.
18. Phoenix, Jackson Co. Hornbrook Fm. Anderson, 1958; Popenoe, et al., 1960.
19. Port Orford, Curry Co. Rocky Pt. Fm./Humbug Mtn. Congl. Diller, 1903; Koch, 1966.
20. Powers, Coos Co. Days Cr. Fm. Popenoe, et al., 1960.
21. Umpqua River, Douglas Co. Days Cr. Fm. Imlay, et al., 1959.
22. Waldo, Josephine Co. Days Cr. Fm. Imlay, et al., 1959; Popenoe, et al., 1960.

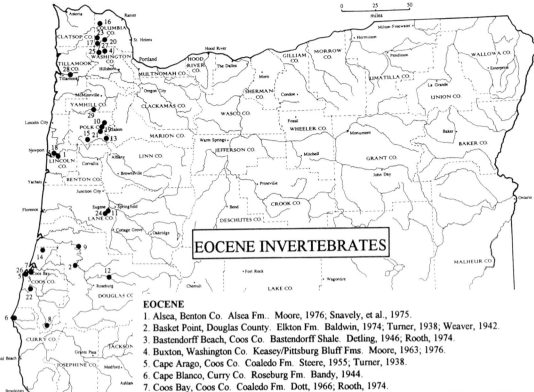

EOCENE

1. Alsea, Benton Co. Alsea Fm.. Moore, 1976; Snavely, et al., 1975.
2. Basket Point, Douglas County. Elkton Fm. Baldwin, 1974; Turner, 1938; Weaver, 1942.
3. Bastendorff Beach, Coos Co. Bastendorff Shale. Detling, 1946; Rooth, 1974.
4. Buxton, Washington Co. Keasey/Pittsburg Bluff Fms. Moore, 1963; 1976.
5. Cape Arago, Coos Co. Coaledo Fm. Steere, 1955; Turner, 1938.
6. Cape Blanco, Curry Co. Roseburg Fm. Bandy, 1944.
7. Coos Bay, Coos Co. Coaledo Fm. Dott, 1966; Rooth, 1974.
8. Coquille River, Coos Co. Roseburg/Lookingglass/Flournoy Fm. Baldwin, 1973; Miles, 1977.
9. Elkton, Douglas Co. Elkton Fm. Baldwin, 1974; Bird, 1967; Thoms, 1965.
10. Ellendale Quarry, Polk Co. Siltez River Volcanics. Baldwin, 1964; Thoms, 1965.
11. Eugene, Lane Co. Eugene Fm. Hickman, 1969; Schenck, 1923; Washburne, 1914.
12. Glide, Douglas Co. Lookingglass Fm. Miles, 1977; Turner, 1938; Weaver, 1942.
13. Helmick Hill, Polk Co. Spencer Fm. Baldwin, 1964; Cushman, Stewart and Stewart, 1947.
14. Johnson Creek, Coos Co. Tyee Fm. Allen and Baldwin, 1944.
15. Little Luckiamute River, Polk Co. Yamhill Fm. Warren, Norbisrath, and Grivetti, 1945.
16. Mist, Columbia Co. Keasey Fm. Hickman, 1980; Moore, 1976; Schenck, 1936.
17. Nehalem River valley, Columbia Co. Keasey/Cowlitz/ Pittsburg Bluff Fms. Mumford, 1988; Warren, Norbisrath, and Grivetti, 1945; Weaver, 1942.
18. Newport, Lincoln Co. Tyee Fm. McKeel and Lipps, 1971; Snavely, et al., 1969.
19. Oregon Portland Cement Co., Polk Co. Yamhill Fm. Baldwin, 1964; Hickman, 1976; Schenck, 1936.
20. Pittsburg, Columbia Co. Pittsburg Bluff Fm. Moore, 1976.
21. Rickreall, Polk Co. Siletz River Volcanics. Allen and Baldwin, 1944; Baldwin, 1964; Schenck, 1936.
22. Riverton, Coos Co. Coaledo Fm. Weaver, 1942.
23. Rock Creek, Columbia Co. Cowlitz/Keasey Fms. Mumford, 1988; Steere, 1957; Warren and Norbisrath, 1946.
24. Spencer Creek, Lane Co. Spencer Fm. Vokes, Snavely, and Meyers, 1951.
25. Timber, Washington Co. Cowlitz/Keasey Fm. Hickman, 1976; 1980; Weaver, 1942.
26. Tunnel Point, Coos Co. Tunnel Point Sandstone. Baldwin, 1973; Moore, 1976.
27. Vernonia, Columbia Co. Keasey/Pittsburg Bluff Fm. Hickman, 1976; Moore, 1976; Moore and Vokes, 1953.
28. Wilson River, Tillamook Co. Nestucca Fm. Warren, Norbisrath, and Grivetti, 1945.
29. Yamhill River, Yamhill Co. Nestucca Fm. Baldwin, et al., 1955.

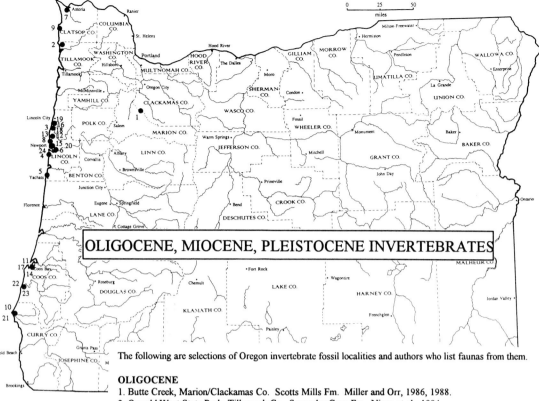

The following are selections of Oregon invertebrate fossil localities and authors who list faunas from them.

OLIGOCENE

1. Butte Creek, Marion/Clackamas Co. Scotts Mills Fm. Miller and Orr, 1986, 1988.
2. Oswald West State Park, Tillamook Co. Smuggler Cove Fm. Niem, et al., 1994.
3. Otter Rock, Lincoln Co. Yaquina Fm. Steere, 1954; Vokes, Norbisrath, and Snavely, 1949.
4. Seal Rock, Lincoln Co. Yaquina Fm. Vokes, Norbisrath, and Snavely, 1949.
5. Yachats, Lincoln Co. Alsea Fm. Snavely, et al., 1975.
6. Yaquina Bay, Lincoln Co. Yaquina Fm. McKeel and Lipps, 1972; Snavely, et al., 1964.

MIOCENE

7. Astoria, Clatsop Co. Astoria Fm. Colbath, 1981; Dall; 1090; Moore, 1963.
8. Beverly Beach, Lincoln Co. Astoria Fm. Colbath, 1981; Moore, 1963.
9. Cannon Beach, Clatsop Co. Astoria Fm. Moore, 1963.
10. Cape Blanco, Curry Co. Empire/Floras Lake Fms. Addicott, 1983.
11. Coos Bay, Coos Co. Empire/Tarheel Fms. Addicott, 1980, 1983; Armentrout, 1967; Moore, 1963.
12. Depoe Bay, Lincoln Co. Astoria Fm. Daugherty, 1951; Moore, 1963; Steere, 1954.
13. Fogarty Creek, Lincoln Co. Astoria Fm. Moore, 1963.
14. Fossil Point, Coos Co. Empire/Tarheel Fms. Armentrout, 1967; Dall, 1909.
15. Newport, Lincoln Co. Astoria/Nye Fms. Moore, 1963, 1971; Snavely, McLeod, and Rau, 1969.
16. Otter Rock, Lincoln Co. Astoria Fm. Moore, 1963.
17. Pigeon Point, Coos Bay, Coos Co. Empire/Tarheel Fms. Armentrout, 1967.
18. Schooner Creek, Lincoln Co. Astoria Fm. Moore, 1963.
19. Spencer Creek, Lincoln Co. Astoria Fm. Moore, 1963.
20. Yaquina Bay, Lincoln Co. Nye Mudstone. McKeel and Lipps, 1971; Snavely, et al., 1964; Stewart, 1956; Weaver, 1942.

PLEISTOCENE

21. Cape Blanco, Curry Co. Elk River/Port Orford Fms. Addicott, 1964; Roth, 1979.
22. Coquille Point, Coos Co. Zullo, 1969.
23. Grave Point, Coos Co. Zullo, 1969.
24. Newport, Lincoln Co. Coquille Fm. Baldwin, 1950.

Burrows for both feeding and habitation have thoroughly plowed up these small tracts of shallow water marine sediments [photos courtesy W. Orr].

OREGON TRACE FOSSILS

Trace fossils - also called ichnofossils or Lebensspuren, meaning a trace of life - have assumed increased importance in paleontology during the past decade. A trace fossil is an impression such as a track or burrow that records the activity of an organism. Many ichnofossils are made by varieties of marine worms either as permanent burrows or scavenging tracks when they forage across the sea floor.

Because the animal is only rarely found with its track, most trace fossils can't be related directly to a specific animal. Sometimes, however, the animal is found preserved in its burrow. This is the case with shipworm-bored wood where the shell of the pelecypod, *Teredo*, is often present. Unless it periodically molts, an organism ordinarily leaves one fossil, but trace fossils are invariably more common than a skeleton or shell since they can be left by the thousands from a single animal. For the vast numbers of soft bodied animals that lack a skeleton or shell, trace fossils are the only preserved record.

In just a few cases are trace fossils useful for geologic dating, but they do have advantages over fossilized body parts. Often found in sandstones where animal remains are rare, trace fossils are not altered by geologic processes. Because traces are made through sediments, they have not been moved and are thus valuable in interpreting paleoenvironments. Paleontologists, for example, are able to distinguish shallow water traces from similar but distinctive deep water burrows of crabs and worms.

Although trace fossils are abundant in both marine and nonmarine sediments in Oregon, they are rarely noted individually but are generally treated with invertebrates. Trace fossils figure in reports on the Hornbrook Formation in Jackson County, the Keasey in Columbia County, on the coast from Astoria to Newport, and inland on the Scotts Mills Formation in Clackamas County.

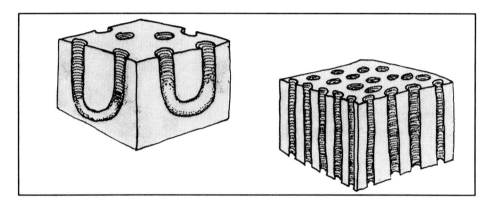

U-shaped burrows of *Arenicolites* characterize a firm sea floor, while rounded tubes of *Skolithos* indicate soft sediments.

The oldest rocks with trace fossils are Cretaceous sediments in southern Oregon. Tor Nilsen's 1984 *Geology of the Upper Cretaceous Hornbrook Formation, Oregon and California* notes that horizontal, vertical, and U-shaped burrows of *Skolithos* and *Glossifungites* are found in abundance. Depending on their diversity, identity, and numbers, trace fossils denote several ecologic settings from a wave tossed coastline to quieter estuaries.

Oluwafeyisola [Sylvester] Adegoke, who received a PhD at the the University of California, Berkeley, in 1966, looked at Keasey fossil collections from deep water Eocene intervals at the famous Mist local. Examining specimens collected by J. Wyatt Durham, professor at Berkeley, Adegoke noted over 20 specimens of elongate, cylindrical, segmented tubes, which he interpreted as the burrows of pogonophoran worms. In the 1980s attention was focused on modern pogonophorans, when they were discovered living in and around deep water submarine volcanic vents near the Galapagos Islands. Adegoke named the Keasey specimens for their discoverer *Adekunbiella durhami*. Upon completing his degree, he returned to Nigeria, where he became professor of geology at Ife University.

Eocene pogonophoran worms from the Keasey Formation, like their modern day counterparts, are typically found at bathyal and abyssal depths.

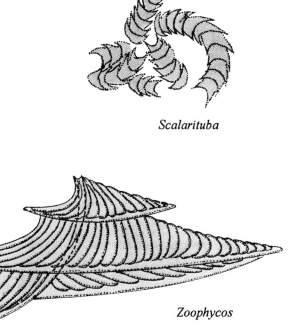

Scalarituba

Zoophycos

Cylindrichnus [on the left] displays wrinkled clay sheaths around a central sand filled tube, whereas *Zoophycos* and *Scalarituba* are more worm-like. [Diagrams after C. Kent Chamberlain, who is responsible for much of the present-day trace fossil paleontology].

Trace fossils are present in several marine intervals of the Oligocene. At Oswald West State Park in Tillamook County, Oregon State University Professor Alan Niem recognized that trace fossils could play a role as depth indicators. Swirrling rooster tail-like burrows of *Zoophycos* suggest slope environments and *Teichichnus* a shelf setting, however, the fecal ribbon *Scalarituba*, the tubular *Taenidium*, and the multi-branched *Chondrites* occur in various habitats. Here these ichnofossils are found with foraminifera and invertebrates in the Smuggler Cove Formation. Oligocene trace fossils, preserved in an upright position, have been designated *Cylindrichnus* by William Orr and his student Paul Miller from the University of Oregon. These tall, cone-shaped layered sand and clay sheaths surrounding a central sand-filled tube have a maximum diameter of three inches. Located in fossil-rich strata of the Scotts Mills Formation, *Cylindrichus* may represent the vertical burrows of an invertebrate.

Along the Oregon coast, the Miocene Astoria Formation provides examples of two different kinds of burrows from near Astoria and Newport. Until late 1960 the trace fossil *Tisoa* was unknown in North America. However, in 1969 individual tubes of about one half inch in diameter and up to three inches long were assigned to the genus *Tisoa* by Robert Frey and John Cowles. These tubes were first discovered inside concretions from the Lincoln Creek Formation in Washington, but a year later the same authors reported *Tisoa* from near Astoria. The tubes are both straight and branching or even U-shaped. The borrowing animal often lined the tube with organic secretions that later reacted chemically to precipitate sulfide minerals such as pyrite in the walls. Frey, a professor at the University of Georgia, and Cowles, a resident of Rainier, Washington, interpret scratch marks in the burrow as made by a shrimp-like arthropod, even though none of the tubes to date contain arthropod remains. Specializing in the habitat of living and fossil invertebrates and their traces, Frey taught from 1968 until his death in 1992. During his career he wrote and edited several books on ichnofossils and was founding co-editor of the journal *Ichnos*.

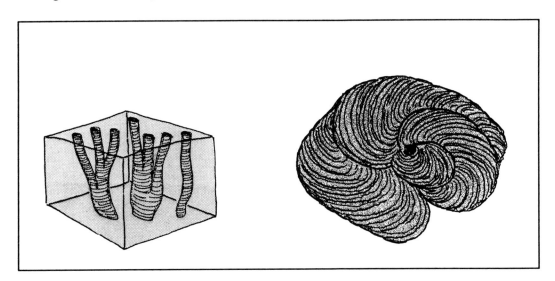

The internal structure of *Tisoa* is made up of parallel and branching tubes, whereas the deep water *Zoophycos* is sweeping traces of burrows.

Fossil burrows picked up on Moolack Beach in Lincoln County by Guy Rooth, professor at Western Oregon University, were also thought, at first, to have been made by a small shrimp. The pair of seven inch-long tight spirals, identified by Rooth as *Gyrolithes,* are preserved as internal fillings in sandy muds of the Astoria Formation. Even though it is not known with certainty what animal produced the burrows, studies of present-day tidal flats initially showed that a scavenging soldier crab, in digging downward, would rotate its body producing screw-shaped tubes. However, a later interpretation suggests the burrows were made by a shallow marine polychaete worm, an elongate segmented member of the phylum Annelida. The most familiar annelids are, of course, earthworms and leeches.

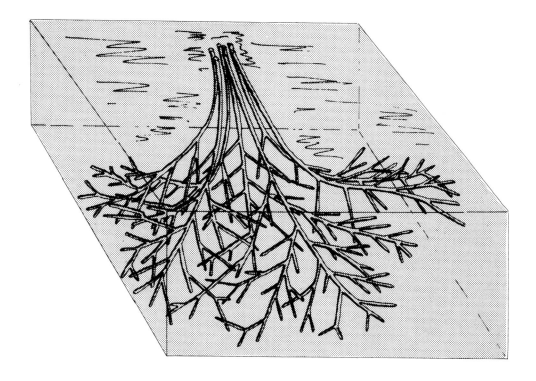

Feeding on sediments the animal that created the trace fossil *Chondrites* would stretch its body to mine the substrate.

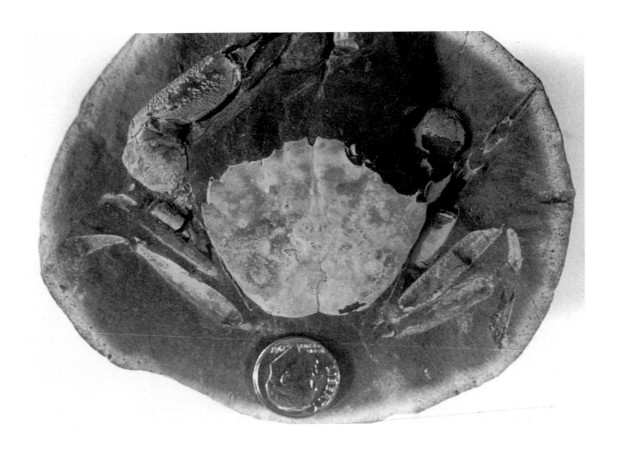

Crabs are often preserved inside concretions where they are found with legs and cara-pace intact [photo courtesy W. Orr]

OREGON FOSSIL ARTHROPODS

The vast array of living arthropods includes, among others, crabs, shrimp, lobsters, barnacles, scorpions, spiders, and insects. Of the many different joint-legged arthropods from the Oregon fossil record, most are present in the same strata as marine mollusc shells. Trilobites and insects, which are also arthropods, have each been found in single localities in the state. In 1967 arthropod remains from the Permian Coyote Butte Formation were identified as a trilobite by David Bostwick, who was unable to name them specifically because of their fragmentary condition. Insects have only turned up in the Oligocene John Day Formation.

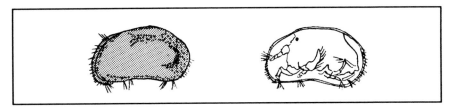

Ostracods, or "bean bugs", are the smallest of arthropods, measuring less than 1/24 inch in length.

Similar to a flea in appearance and size, ostracod microfossils are arthropods that come equipped with a defensive a clam-like shell of paired valves. The valves are hinged at the top, and living forms can withdraw their multiple appendages into the valves and snap them tightly shut. Other than passing mention of their presence, they have not been described from Oregon, even though they occur in both marine and freshwater sediments. Because of their uniform size and calcareous shell, ostracods, which are more common and diverse in marine deposits, routinely turn up in the extraction process for foraminifera. In the North American Gulf Coast they are extensively used for age and paleoenvironment analyses in the petroleum industry.

Cirripeds, or barnacles, are sessile [attached] marine crusteacans, which have a circular wall of plates. Because they occupy shallow water, their plates are usually scattered and show beach wear. The distinctive grooved triangular plates are easily recognized and make up significant portions of some sediments. Commonly present with molluscs in Oregon Tertiary strata, barnacle plates comprise over 75% of the limestone lenses that characterize the

Because of their shallow marine habitat in the high energy surf zone, barnacle fossils are usually found as small badly worn plates [from Zittel, 1913].

Marquam member of the Scotts Mills Formation in Clackamas County. Northwest of Salem in deposits of the Eocene Eugene Formation, barnacles are clustered together on fossilized wood.

Shrimp, crabs, and sowbugs live in an assortment of environments from fresh and marine water to land. By far, the most common of these arthropods in the Oregon fossil record are the Decapoda, or lobsters, crabs, and shrimp. In the coastal waters today these ten-legged crustaceans are among the most diverse of the invertebrates. Crabs and lobsters occupy a great variety of ecologic niches, some as ocean bottom dwellers, where they scavenge for food, but many swim intermittently to feed on plants and small invertebrates. Decapods display a remarkable range of variations and may even sport a tail or legs modified for swimming. Most species are easily sexually differentiated by the body size or shape of the segmented tail that typically is thin and pointed on males and broad and rounded on females.

Crabs and shrimps go through molting or "ecdysis" stages as they grow and add segments. Each new growth stage is accompanied by peeling away the old shell and the hardening in place of a new one. The cast-off body armor or carapaces are often destroyed by wave action or by other scavengers but may be preserved as fossils. Their remains frequently occur in dense masses of sedimentary rock called "concretions". Concretions are a rounded discrete accumulation of cementing material where a particle like wood or shell acts as a center of cementation. The process of forming concretions is like making candles by repeatedly immersing a wick (the fossil) in hot wax (the cement). Cementing material such as calcium carbonate in solution moving through porous rock will accumulate around a crystallization point such as a fossil. Ordinarily concretions are harder than the entombing material and may collect as cobbles at the base of a slope when rock weathers and crumbles. To extract fossils, the concretions are split along the widest diameter with sharp blows of a hammer. Fossils preserved in concretions require little preparation, and in some cases a vibra-drill tool can be used to improve the exposure. In the case of crabs, all of the limbs and even the antennae may be present.

In spite of the fact that crabs are common and well-preserved, they are only occasionally the focus of individual research. The most ambitious work on crustaceans of the United States was by Mary Rathbun. Her career paralleled that of her oldest brother Richard, who became assistant Secretary of the Smithsonian Institution. Mary Rathbun finished high school in the Buffalo, New York, school system in 1878, ending her formal education even though she was awarded an honorary Masters in 1916 and a PhD 1917 for her study of *The Grapsoid Crabs of America*. Her fascination with seashore faunas began at Woods Hole, Massachusetts, where she accompanied her brother in 1881. Three years later she was employed at the U.S. National Museum to organize and catalog their huge collection of marine animals. Rathbun became involved in decapods from around the world, publishing 158 papers on crustaceans. Even though she maintained an association with the Museum, she relinquished her salary in 1914 so someone else could be hired. At age 66 she completed her monograph *The Fossil Stalk-Eyed Crustacea of the Pacific Slope of North America* but continued to work and write until her death in 1943.

One of the exceptional women in science at the turn of the century, Mary Rathbun was from a wealthy and distinguished New England family active in business, education, and civil affairs [photo courtesy Smithsonian Institution, Archives].

Another of the small number of paleontologists who specializes in fossil crabs is Rodney Feldmann of Kent State University. Feldmann's research on the paleoecology and biogeography of crabs even extends to those from the Antarctic. When examining crustacea at the Smithsonian Museum, Feldmann came across specimens placed there over 80 years earlier by

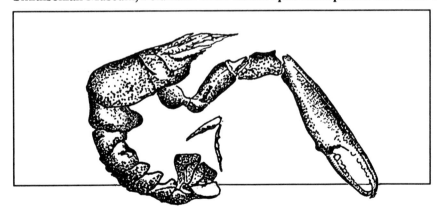

Hoploparia riddlensis, a new species of lobster from southwest Oregon.

Joseph Diller of the U.S. Geological Survey. Mapping near Agness and Riddle in Curry and Douglas counties during the late 1800s, Diller collected fossil lobsters that were later recognized by Feldmann as the earliest occurrence of the family Nephropidae in North America. From an examination of the carapace and appendages, Feldmann described a new species *Hoploparia riddlensis,* similar in size to a modern crayfish. In all, seven specimens from the museum collection were extracted from small limestone concretions within fine-grained sandstones and siltstones of the Cretaceous Days Creek Formation. Southward between Ashland and the southern Oregon border Hornbrook strata on Interstate 5 also yield shrimp-like arthropods. Even though smaller than those at Riddle, these are numerous, but usually poorly-preserved.

A native of North Dakota, Rodney Feldmann received his PhD in paleontology in 1967 from the University at Grand Forks. In addition to decapod biogeography and paleoecology, he has also published on Antarctic invertebrates [photo courtesy R. Berglund].

Crab carapaces and claws are present in Tertiary strata from many locals west of the Cascade Range, but in only a few instances are they found in the eastern part of the state. In the southwest near Agness the new species *Lophopanopeus baldwini* and *Zanthopsis rathbunae* were named by William Orr and his student Marilyn Kooser from the University of Oregon during the early 1970s. In the Eocene Lookingglass Formation here the crustaceans occur in concretions an inch or so in diameter, and the most common species, *Plagiolophus weaveri,* was usually intact. Specimens were cleaned with kerosene and a needle and housed at the Condon Museum.

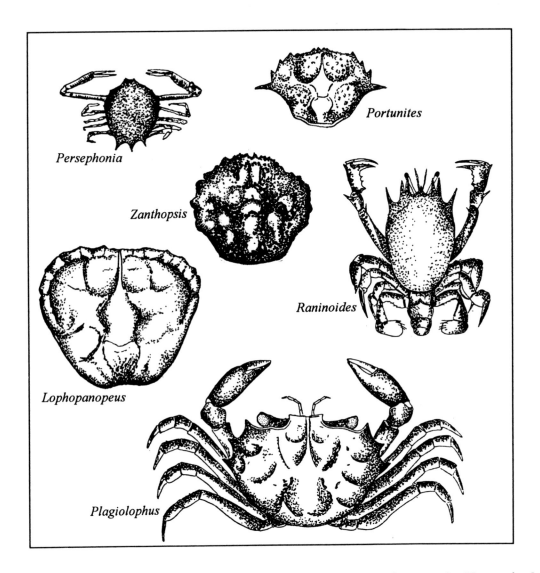

Eocene crabs from the Lookingglass Formation of southwest Oregon, the Keasey in the northwest part of the state, and the Eugene Formation in the Willamette Valley.

Yet another new ranid crab from the same location, *Rogueus orri*, was named by Ross Berglund and Rodney Feldmann. Superficially ranid crabs resemble crayfish but have spines on the front edge of the carapace, as in *Rogueus orri*, which is characterized by peculiar paired split spines. Fossil raninid crabs of this type are rare in deposits worldwide, because, as Berglund and Feldmann speculate, they often live offshore in deep water where chances of preservation are diminished. A retired Boeing engineer, Ross Berglund and his wife Marion have been interested in fossil crabs since the 1960s, systematically accumulating one of the finest collections of northwest decapods. Living on Bainbridge Island, Washington, the Berglunds first investigated crab remains at Cape Flattery. Receiving permission from the Indians, who owned the site, they found the fossil-impregnated concretions were being used to cover the adjacent landfill. From crab material obtained from here and elsewhere over a 30-year period, the Berglunds named close to a dozen new crab species.

Ross and Marion Berglund have worked on fossil crabs in the Northwest for years, and in 1994 he was presented with the Strimple Award for the best private paleontologist by the national Paleontological Society [photo courtesy R. Berglund].

When Mary Rathbun received a collection of Oligocene crabs from Washington and Vancouver Island, she began to assemble all Cretaceous through Pleistocene Decapod material in museums and private collections from Alaska to lower California. The accumulation yielded 91 species, of which 51 were new. The most prevalent were the extinct Oligocene crab *Zanthopsis vulgaris* and a freshwater crayfish *Astacus chenoderma* from eastern Oregon and southwest Idaho, which had been amassed at the Peabody Museum at Yale University. From Eocene and younger rocks, members of the Raninidae family were especially numerous.

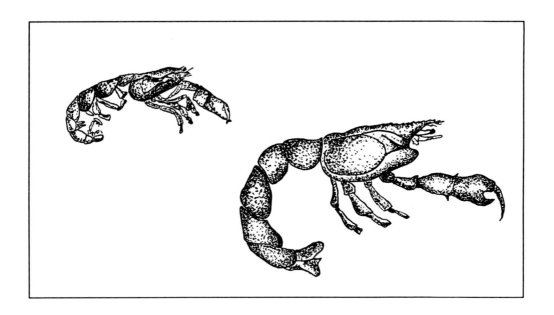

Miocene shrimp *Callianassa* and *Upogebia* from the Astoria Formation

In one of the earliest references to Miocene Crustacea, a single shrimp *Callianassa oregonensis* and barnacle fragments from the Astoria Formation were reported by James Dana accompanying the government-sponsored Wilkes Exploring Expedition from 1838 to 1842. Ellen Moore, in her classic paper on the Astoria, records the shallow-water mud shrimp *Upogebia*. This world-wide stalk-eyed crustacean, which inhabits rock burrows, has been found from the Jurassic to the present, but Moore's report from the Astoria is the first from Miocene rocks.

Miscellaneous Pleistocene barnacles and crabs were the subject of studies by Victor Zullo, geology professor at the University of North Carolina. In one unique occurrence, he noted the pea crab *Pinnixa faba* living in a symbiotic association within the valves of the pelecypod *Treseus capax*. Symbiotic relationships of this type are extremely rare in the fossil record because of dispersal by waves. The Cape Blanco clams, preserved upright in "life position" with valves intact, were apparently overcome and killed quickly before a rapid burial.

The tiny happy crab *Pinnixa* lived within the valves of a large clam.

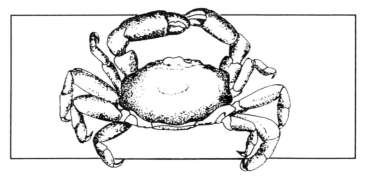

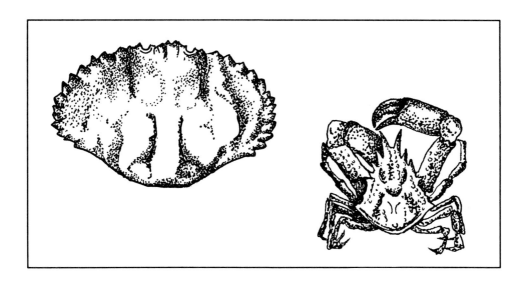

The dungeness crab *Cancer* as well as *Pugettia* were present on the southern Oregon coast during the Ice Ages, while crayfish as *Astacus* inhabited freshwater streams and lakes in eastern Oregon in the Pliocene.

Another of the arthropods, the isopods such as sow bugs or wood louse have invaded most environments and are found on land as well as in fresh and marine waters. In spite of their pervasiveness, the fragile carapace makes them exceedingly rare as fossils. A single fossil of a sow bug was reported in 1964 from the Eocene Keasey Formation by Sam Mercer, a 19-year old student at Longview, Washington. Mercer sent the specimen to H.K. Brooks, a specialist at the University of Florida for identification. Brooks named the new species after Mercer and wrote that "the specimens are the remains of isopods. No other fossils have been described from the United States though they are very common today ... Specimens have been reported from Mesozoic and Cenozoic of Europe." In a 1964 newspaper interview, Mercer related that his collection of over 900 specimens began in what was formerly his bedroom, but, as the number grew, Mercer was forced to change rooms.

The few known examples of fossilized insects in Oregon were recovered in Oligocene John Day deposits along with plants of the Bridge Creek Flora. The discovery of these arthropods is exceptional, and their past record, like that of snakes, toads, and frogs, could never match their original wide-spread presence and diversity. The best-preserved insects are often those captured and entombed in miniature tar pit-like environments by tree sap. All manner of airborne particles, most commonly pollen, are found in tree sap along with insects. In time, a process of slow drying chemically converts the sap to amber.

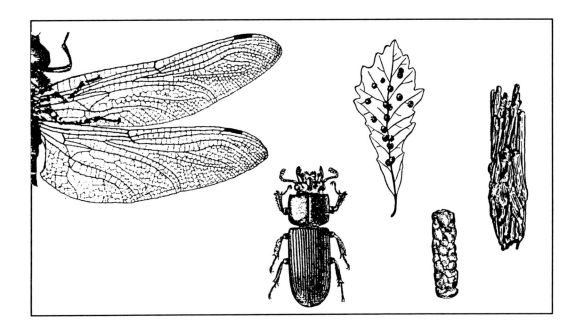

A dragon fly wing, sugar beetle, leaf galls, and caddis fly larva represent the total variety of insects in Oregon's fossil record.

There are no descriptions of insects in amber from Oregon, although rumors of amber here circulate occasionally. Gall midges on leaves of maple and alder, wings of dragon flies [Odontata], jaws of tropical sugar beetles [Coleoptera], and common midges [*Cecidomyia*] from Post in Crook County were sent by paleobotanist Ralph Chaney to Theodore D.A. Cockerell, who provided a short description. Cockerell's varied career began with private English schools in the late 1800s, before he worked at the British Museum and as a curator in Jamaica. Immigrating to America, he became a consulting entomologist specializing in scaled and winged insects and variations in plants and molluscs, especially slugs.

The only other account of an insect from the John Day was by a Yakima, Washington, student Joe Peterson. Working in the summer camps for the Oregon Museum of Science and Industry near Clarno, Peterson studied and collected fossils in his spare time. As part of an article on fossil plants of eastern Oregon, he described Trichoptera, caddis fly larval cases entombed in strata at Dugout Creek in Wheeler County. The tiny larval cylinders are frequently put together from leaves and pieces of *Metasequoia* [dawn redwood] needles.

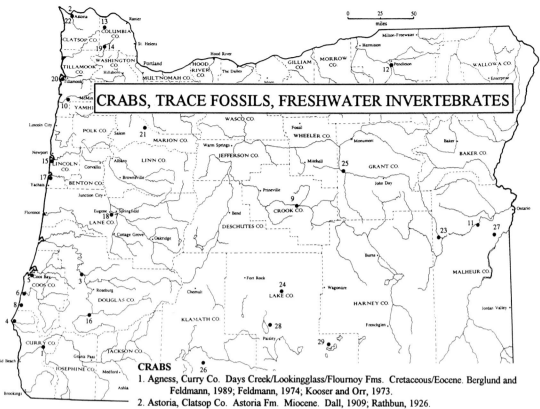

CRABS, TRACE FOSSILS, FRESHWATER INVERTEBRATES

CRABS

1. Agness, Curry Co. Days Creek/Lookingglass/Flournoy Fms. Cretaceous/Eocene. Berglund and Feldmann, 1989; Feldmann, 1974; Kooser and Orr, 1973.
2. Astoria, Clatsop Co. Astoria Fm. Miocene. Dall, 1909; Rathbun, 1926.
3. Basket Point, Douglas Co. Elkton Fm. Eocene. Rathbun, 1926; Weaver, 1942.
4. Cape Blanco, Curry Co. Pleistocene. Zullo, 1969.
5. Coos Bay, Coos Co. Empire Fm. Miocene. Weaver, 1942.
6. Coquille Point, Coos Co. Pleistocene. Zullo, 1969.
7. Eugene, Lane Co. Eugene Fm. Eocene. Hickman, 1969; Rathbun, 1926.
8. Grave Point, Coos Co. Pleistocene. Zullo, 1969.
9. Grays Ranch, 10 mi. east of Post, Crook Co. John Day Fm. Oligocene. Cockerell, 1927.
10. Hebo, Tillamook Co. Nestucca Fm. Eocene. Feldmann, 1989.
11. Little Valley, Malheur Co. Juntura Fm.? Miocene. Rathbun, 1926.
12. McKay Reservoir, Umatilla Co. McKay Fm.? Miocene. Rathbun, 1926.
13. Mist, Columbia Co. Keasey Fm. Eocene. Rathbun, 1926; Steere, 1957; Zullo, 1964.
14. Nehalem River valley, Columbia Co. Cowlitz Fm. Eocene. Warren and Norbisrath, 1946.
15. Newport, Lincoln Co. Yaquina Fm.? Oligocene. Rathbun, 1926.
16. Riddle, Douglas Co. Days Creek Fm. Cretaceous. Feldmann, 1974.
17. Waldport, Lincoln Co. Nestucca Fm. Eocene. Feldmann, 1989.

TRACE FOSSILS

18. Eugene, Lane Co. Eugene Fm. Eocene. Hickman, 1969.
19. Mist, Columbia Co. Keasey Fm. Eocene. Adegoke, 1967.
20. Oswald West State Park, Tillamook Co. Smuggler Cove Fm. Oligocene. Niem, et al., 1994.
21. Silverton, Marion Co. Scotts Mills Fm. Orr and Miller, 1984.
22. Youngs River, Clatsop Co. Astoria Fm. Miocene. Frey and Cowles, 1972.

FRESHWATER INVERTEBRATES

23. Black Butte, Malheur Co. Juntura Fm. Miocene. Taylor, 1963.
24. Fossil Lake, Lake Co. Pleistocene. Allison, 1966; Taylor, 1960.
25. John Day River Valley, Grant Co. John Day/Mascall Fms. Oligocene/Miocene. Hanna, 1920, 1922; Stearns, 1902, 1906.
26. Wilsons Quarry Pit, Klamath Co. Yonna Fm. Pliocene. Newcomb, 1958.
27. Mitchell Butte, Malheur Co. No Fm. Miocene. Taylor, 1963.
28. Summer Lake, Lake Co. Pleistocene. Hanna, 1922, 1963.
29. Warner Lake, Lake Co. Pleistocene. Hanna, 1922, 1963.

Earl Packard, a professor at Oregon State University, with the skull of a leatherback turtle from the Miocene Astoria Formation [photo courtesy Archives, Oregon State University].

OREGON FOSSIL AMPHIBIANS AND REPTILES

Amphibians and reptiles are treated together as they constitute the intermediary steps between fish and mammals. Although many amphibians such as frogs and salamanders live on land, they ordinarily lay their eggs in the water during an extended aquatic period when they breathe with gills. Despite the fact that the evolutionary stage between fish and amphibians is critical, fossil evidence of this event is virtually non-existent. This contrasts to the transition from reptiles to mammals, which is somewhat better documented. The Oregon record of both amphibians and reptiles is decidedly spotty and frequently overshadowed by the stellar remains of Tertiary mammals.

FROGS AND SALAMANDERS

Evidence of frogs and salamanders is scarce in Oregon's fossil record, and, of these, the salamanders most closely resemble the earliest primitive amphibians. Frogs and toads, on the other hand, are comparatively modern and did not appear until quite late in amphibian history. Even though they are key indicators of wetland paleo-environments, frogs are only mentioned in passing as at McKay Reservoir and in the John Day valley.

An early picture features a swimming reptile, a crocodile climbing through vegetation, and an ichthyosaur skeleton in the foreground [Fugier, 1891].

In contrast to frogs, accounts of salamanders are more complete. In spite of their fragile nature, which makes them among the rarest of fossils, there are several middle Tertiary salamanders from Oregon. The first of these was recovered from gray leaf-bearing shales of the Fisher Formation near the town of Goshen in Lane County. While he was searching for tropical leaves in 1951, George R. K. Morehead, a member of the Salem Geological Society, found a salamander, which ultimately made its way to Richard Van Frank at the Museum of Comparative Zoology, Harvard University. From there it went to the British Museum for study. Van Frank published a complete description of the new species, *Palaeotaricha oligo-cenica*, that was returned to Moorehead, who presented the well-travelled amphibian to the Condon Museum at Eugene. Although lacking a small part of the tail and a few other bones, the black carbonized five-inch long articulated skeleton is exquisitely preserved. Since that discovery, the Goshen local has yielded close to a dozen more specimens, but none are of the quality of Moorehead's find.

From John Day shales near Fossil in Wheeler County, a new species of salamander was collected in 1977 by L.A. Lindoe, curator of vertebrate paleontology at the University of Alberta. Named *Taricha lindoei* in a 1979 paper by Bruce Naylor in the Geology Department at the same institution, the salamander consists of a nearly complete skeletal impression around two inches in length. These amphibians are discovered with some regularity in the John Day Formation - usually in proximity to fossil leaves.

The rare Eocene salamander *Palaeotaricha*, discovered south of Eugene, took months of painstaking preparation with a needle and drill to expose the fragile intact skeleton [photo courtesy Condon Museum].

REPTILES

Reptiles are cold-blooded vertebrate animals which seem to share more similarities with birds than to frogs and salamanders. Unlike amphibians, most reptiles do well on land and breathe by lungs, and many, as snakes and lizards, have a long retractable tongue which provides an important organ for smell. During the Mesozoic era, dinosaurs, the largest of all reptiles, reached a remarkable size, second only to the blue whale in geologic history before they were extinguished along with ichthyosaurs about 66 million years ago. Reptiles diversified to an extraordinary degree in their long evolution, dominating terrestrial environments as well as successfully invading and populating the oceans as predators. Pterosaurian reptiles even solved the complicated equation of heavier-than-air flight by evolving splendid air foils [wings] for gliding.

Rocks with reptile remains in Oregon were often ocean environments where aquatic animals as ichthyosaurs, turtles, and crocodiles were entombed in a variety of settings from offshore deep water to shallow nearshore sands. The single snake, dinosaur, lizard, pterosaur, but more numerous turtles reflect dry land conditions in the state.

Despite current knowledge of modern marine turtles, sea turtles dating back to the early Cretaceous period are not well documented, and their fossils are even more rare than those of ichthyosaurs. An early report by Earl Packard of Oregon State University notes one of the very few finds of this large marine reptile. The well-preserved skull and fragments of a carapace [shell] were recovered in sandstones of the Astoria Formation by Henry Kuhl, a resident of Otter Rock, around 1940 and donated to the Horner Museum at Corvallis. The skull, described as *Psephophorus oregonensis*, is over a foot in length, which suggests the living animal may have been well over six feet. For years this skull served as a doorstop in the Oregon State University Geology Department. The carapace from the same locality is a mosaic of thick bony plates tightly fitted together. The family of this Miocene turtle, Dermochelydae, includes the modern leatherbacks, but the skull of the Oregon specimen is substantially more narrow and elongate than those of living counterparts. Today adult leatherbacks reach eight feet in length and weigh over half a ton. Many fragmentary marine turtles recovered from the Astoria, Nye, and Yaquina formations by private collector Douglas Emlong are now residing in the Smithsonian Museum awaiting study.

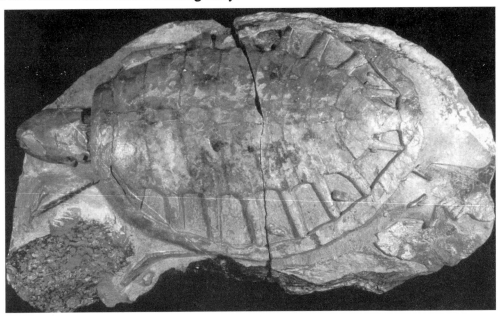

An ancient sea turtle from 50-million year old Coaledo sediments of the south coast is beautifully preserved [photo courtesy W. Orr].

The most recently discovered but oldest-known marine turtles from the state are from the Tyee and Coaledo formations of Eocene age. An 18-inch long carapace, skull, and breast plates [plastron] of a forerunner of green turtles, preserved in the 50-million year old Coaledo Formation at Coos Bay, were recovered by the private collector Ed Gory of Bandon. Gory removed the superb specimen from a cliff at Cape Arago in 1985, and, after it was identified by William Orr at the University of Oregon, generously donated it to the Condon Museum there. A decade later Forest Service personnel J.H. Steward, G.T. Schultz, and Carey Weatherly, inspecting a logging operation, recognized unusual markings on a rock near Scottsburg in the southern Coast Range. The specimen, also identified by Orr and acquired by the Museum, turned out to be another green turtle, this one from the Tyee Formation. Additional significance of this find is that as a submarine deep water fan the Tyee is notably poor in preserved fossils of any kind.

In eastern Oregon entire carapaces of freshwater pond and box turtles have been found in the Rattlesnake and Mascall beds. Breast plates and carapaces of *Clemmys* were described by Oliver Hay of the American Museum in 1903. Collected by parties under the charge of John Merriam in 1899 and 1900, the material was stored at the Berkeley Museum. In his monograph on the Mascall, California paleontologist Theodore Downs revised Hay's study on *Clemmys* and noted that only one of the four American species is completely aquatic, while the others as box turtles and terrapins are partially terrestrial. In 1959 this same material was reexamined by Bayard Brattstrom and Ann Sturn from the Department of Biology, Adelphi College in New York. They renamed Hay's *Clemmys hesperia* as *Clemmys marmorata* and added a new species *Clemmys owyheensis* from lakebed sediments at Rome in Malheur County.

Land turtles or tortoises, which have a vegetarian diet and are recognized by their large limbs, are fairly common in Tertiary sites where fossil bones and leaves are present, but only a few of these have been described. Fragments of land turtle skeletons have a distinctive shape but are difficult to identify with confidence unless most of the carapace or shell is present. In some cases, complete turtle shells have been recovered from the John Day Formation, although usually only small pieces of scutes or plates are found. Several entire shells up to two feet in length from the famous Turtle Cove local were named *Stylemys capax* by Oliver Hay in his *The Fossil Turtles of North America.* Hay's 1908 publication is still the most exacting treatise issued on this subject. The monograph is a beautifully illustrated large volume treating 266 species, almost one-third of which were previously unknown. Many of these were from the Cope and Marsh's expeditions to Oregon.

The presence of the shell of a giant tortoise from Gilliam County is an indicator of a frost-free climate in eastern Oregon during the Pliocene [from Orr, Orr, and Baldwin, 1992]

At three feet in length, two giant land tortoises from near Arlington rival those living in the Galapagos Islands today. In 1971 the massive nearly intact remains were found and described by Hanford worker Willis Fry from a Pliocene age pumice quarry in Gilliam County. The turtle was accompanied by logs and other plant fragments as well as the bones of horse, rabbit, deer, mastodon, and a mole. A mineralized carapace, limb bones, and lower breast plate, identified as possibly *Hesperotestudo orthopygia,* were donated to the Burke Museum at the University of Washington. Fry speculated that these huge turtles may have become extinct as the eastern Oregon climate cooled rapidly during the late Tertiary.

Lizards and snakes are the most widely distributed of the modern reptiles, and their ancestry can be traced as far back as the Permian and Triassic. However, owing to their fragile skeleton and poor environment for preservation, they have a scanty and incomplete record. Remnants of just one snake and one lizard have been reported in Oregon. Six vertebra of a snake *Ogmophis oregonensis* from along the John Day River were recovered by Jacob Wortman, who was employed as a collector by Edward Cope in the 1870s. After Cope's 1884 description, the bones were misplaced by the American Museum where they had been stored. The *Ogmophis,* whose modern-day equivalents are boas, is roughly the same size as those living in the area today.

A specialist in amphisbaenian reptiles, David Berman of the Carnegie Museum described a new genus and species of burrowing lizard from the Turtle Cove tuffs at Camp Creek in Crook County. Housed at the University of California Museum, eight specimens of *Dyticonastis rensbergeri* represent the first record of Tertiary amphisbaenians west of the Rocky Mountains. Members of the family Amphisbaenidae have a wedge-shaped skull and tightly bound bone elements that form the burrowing organ. Today similar lizards only live in the tropics and characteristically lack limbs giving them a worm-like body. During a decade of field seasons in the 1960s, University of Washington paleontologist John Rensberger collected a number of the tiny vertebra, ribs, and inch-long well-preserved skulls, one with the lower jaw intact. Rensberger pointed out that they were found in the same strata as large numbers of fossil borrowing gophers.

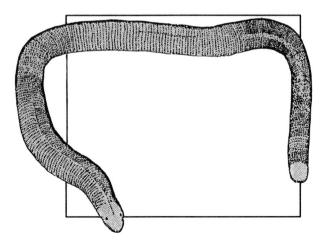

Legless lizards, resembling a worm, live today only in tropical areas as Florida, but about 25 million years ago they were present in eastern Oregon.

Because of their rich geologic record, crocodiles can readily be traced back to the middle Triassic, 200 million years ago, providing valuable clues about the relationship between reptiles and mammals. Ancient Jurassic crocodiles of the Teleosauridae family turned up frequently in European sediments but were unrecorded in North America until one of Earl Packard's 1930s finds from Suplee, Crook County, was examined by Eric Buffetaut. At Oregon State University, Packard had sent the skull, jaw, several vertebra, and long bones, still embedded in sandy limestone blocks of the Weberg Formation, to the Smithsonian. Here the Curator of Vertebrate Paleontology, Charles Gilmore, recognized their importance but never worked on them. Almost 50 years later, while on leave from the vertebrate paleontology laboratory at the University of Paris, Buffetaut came across the specimens, which he placed in the Teleosaurid family, but was unable to assign a generic name to the pieces. He characterized the shallow-water Weberg crocodile as six-feet long, heavily armored, with an elongate narrow snout studded by slender teeth. Specializing in reptiles and especially dinosaurs in worldwide locations, Buffetaut's talents also encompass writing children's books.

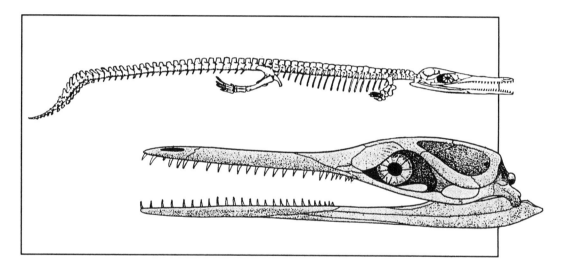

While fossil marine crocodiles frequently occur in Jurassic rocks of Europe and Africa, they are scarce in North America

Another small crocodile from the same formation was later collected by David Taylor of Portland State University. Even though this animal was similar to Packard's Teleosaurid, Taylor has assigned it to the Metriorhynichid family. Both of these Jurassic crocodiles are especially significant in that they were recovered from exotic terranes, which were deposited elsewhere then transported to Oregon by large-scale crustal plate tectonic mechanisms.

David Taylor, who was born in Portland, began his paleontology career by excavating most of a mammoth skeleton while still in high school. This interest led him to summers as a student at the Oregon Museum of Science and Industry camp in eastern Oregon and ultimately to a PhD on ammonite stratigraphy from Berkeley in 1981. He opened the Northwest Museum of Natural History in Portland in 1994, where he displays his own collection as well as fossils, rocks, and minerals from the Geology Department there.

A native Oregonian, Dave Taylor's paleontology interests developed when he was a student in summer field camps from Oregon Museum of Science and Industry. Here he is excavating a tortoise [*Geochelone*] near Jordan Valley during an OMSI camp in 1995 [photo courtesy D. Taylor].

At the time it was found in 1962, a crocodilian from the Eocene Clarno Formation was the first such fossil reptile discovered west of the Rocky Mountains. Almost 90% of the jaw and teeth of the beast was recovered when Jane Gray, paleobotanist at the University of Oregon, came across 35 bone fragments and 15 teeth while doing field work. The superb reassembled skull is housed in the Condon collection and has been identified as the aligator *Pristichampsus*. Unlike their modern counterparts, this reptile had long serrate teeth, similar to those of carnivorous dinosaurs.

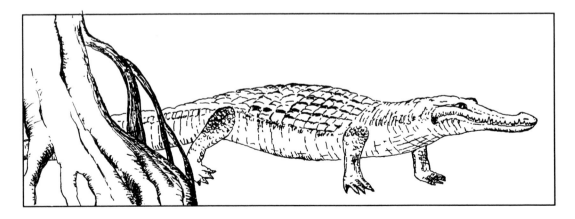

Alligators, such as this one from the Eocene of eastern Oregon, are exceptional.

212

Flying reptiles are certainly unique, and the late Cretaceous pterosaurs are the largest of all known airborne animals. The genus *Pteranodon* is thought to have had a wing span of almost 20 feet and a weight around 35 pounds. *Pterosaur* arm bones invariably display an unmistakable flange for muscle attachment, and the combination of a very light air frame with skeletal and muscle structure suggests these animals remained aloft by soaring rather than by flapping wings. Delicate limbs were highly adapted to gliding flight, and it is difficult to imagine them folded for locomotion on the ground. Three smaller toes positioned midway on the front of the wing may have assisted in walking or clutching onto trees or rocks.

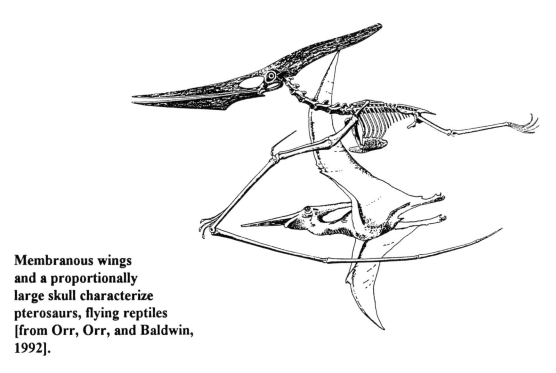

Membranous wings and a proportionally large skull characterize pterosaurs, flying reptiles [from Orr, Orr, and Baldwin, 1992].

A *Pteranodon* from Cretaceous marine sediments of the Mitchell Quadrangle, Wheeler County, adds to the scarce record of this animal in North America and is the only such find from Oregon. An upper arm bone [humerus] and neck vertebra [cervical], discovered by Earl Packard, were sent to Charles Gilmore curator at the Smithsonian Institution. Packard accompanied this material with a letter in September, 1927, to say the fossil bones were from the Hudspeth Formation, remarking that "The Oregon pterodactyl must have presented a re-markable appearance as it glided majestically through the air or suddenly darted to the surface of the Mitchell sea to spear some fish ... Its thin, translucent wing membrane must have been vary-colored and beautiful when outspread, but the animal surely presented a grotesque ap-pearance when resting with its enormous wings folded about its small body."

To date a single fragmentary dinosaur bone has been collected in the state. Working with a team of volunteers, David Taylor recovered a sacrum - the fused backbone pieces above the pelvis - of what appears to be an hadrosaur or duck-billed dinosaur from the southwest coast. The bones were imbedded in a very hard layer of the late Cretaceous Cape Sebastian Sandstone a few miles south of Gold Beach in Curry County. Since this formation is part of the Gold Beach terrane, which was displaced over 80 miles northward from California, the dinosaur may be one of the state's first emigrants.

Even though duck-billed dinosaurs were common elsewhere in North America during the Cretaceous, just one small piece of these reptiles has been found locally.

As pervasive as dinosaurs are in Mesozoic rocks elsewhere in the world, it is curious that the local record is so scanty. This may be because Triassic rocks from this era in both the Klamath and Blue mountains are almost exclusively volcanic or offshore continental shelf limestones and shales unlikely to entomb terrestrial dinosaurs. Similarly much of the Oregon Jurassic represents a marine deep water setting inhabited by open ocean-dwellers. Prime targets for locating dinosaurs in eastern Oregon would be sediments of the Coon Hollow Formation along the Snake River, from the Hudspeth Formation in Wheeler County, as well as from Cretaceous rocks in the Greenhorn area of Baker County. In the western part of the state, shallow water nearshore sands of Jurassic plant locals in Douglas County and sands and shales of the Cretaceous Hornbrook Formation in and around Ashland may eventually yield bones of dinosaurs. The virtual absence of dinosaurs in Oregon is undoubtedly due to the lack of a thorough search for them.

Common in Mesozoic oceans, ichthyosaurs reached their greatest diversity during the Jurassic period, 160 million years ago, before suffering extinction near the end of the Cretaceous. These reptiles, along with sharks, were frequently the top carnivore in the marine food chain. Their rows of sharp conical teeth set in a beaked jaw were well-adapted to feed on fish and swimming molluscs such as squids and ammonites. With a sleek streamlined body, most of these creatures were roughly similar in size to modern porpoises, but some giants attained a length of 60 feet.

Fascinating studies of the stomach contents of Jurassic ichthyosaurs from Great Britain have revealed thousands of tentacle hooks, sucker rings, and mouth parts of squid-like cephalopods. What makes this research all the more remarkable is that, with few exceptions, it is usually impossible to demonstrate predator-prey relationships in the fossil record. Complete Jurassic ichthyosaurs from Germany, which have premature or unborn young inside the body cavity, show that, unlike other reptiles, these animals were even liberated from the mode of egg laying, making them fully independent of the land.

In German legends, gnomes were practiced in excavating the skeletons of ichthyosaurs [Pouchet, 1882].

The first pieces of ichthyosaurs discussed in Oregon were too fragmentary for specific identification. In 1895 Othniel Marsh of Yale University mentions a vertebra from the Blue Mountains found with the shallow water clam, *Trigonia*. More than 30 years after this, Earl Packard extracted two ichthyosaur vertebra [centra] from Cretaceous strata of the Mitchell Quadrangle in Wheeler County. The bones had been placed in the Condon Museum at Eugene where Chairman Warren Smith wrote in a letter of 1937 that they were temporarily misplaced in "three or four partially filled trays of Suplee rocks". Once located, Packard shipped the material to the Smithsonian's Charles Gilmore. Gilmore and John Merriam of the University of California ultimately described the specimen, which they felt represented a genus new to North America, even though they did not designate a generic name.

It was to be another 30 years before Norman Peterson of the Oregon Department of Geology and Mineral Industries collected parts of the upper and lower jaw of an ichthyosaur from a coastal local at Sisters Rocks in Curry County. Belemnites, a bullet-shaped squid-like cephalopod, and molluscs are also found in the dark gray Jurassic mudstones of the Otter Point Formation that contained the reptile. The jaw, with a dozen teeth, had been crushed and deformed. Peterson gave these fragments to John Koch, who, at the time, was completing a PhD thesis from Berkeley in that area, and Koch, in turn, donated them to the University of California, Museum of Paleontology. Here they were identified by Charles Camp as comparable to *Ichthyosaurus californicus.* As with other Mesozoic rocks and fossils of the Klamath Mountains, Koch's ichthyosaur is especially notable since it was entombed in an exotic terrane that originated in California before being shifted to Oregon by faulting.

The 1978 geology summer field class from the University of Oregon found scores of articulated vertebra and ribs in the Triassic Martin Bridge limestone along Eagle Creek in the Wallowa Mountains. Large stone blocks encasing the bones were extracted and laboriously hauled to Eugene where the specimens were removed from the tough matrix. William Orr and a student Kurt Katsura identified the find as the ichthyosaur, *Shastasaurus,* here-to-fore known only from northern California.

A partial ichthyosaur skull was discovered at the same site on Eagle Creek several years later by Orr with a team of summer students from the Oregon Museum of Science and Industry. Although the specimen was badly distorted by metamorphic processes, it was intact enough to be assigned to the same genus. Shastasaurids from Oregon and California - quite unlike Triassic ichthyosaurs found elsewhere in North America - are additional evidence that the Wallowas are part of an exotic or accreted terrane.

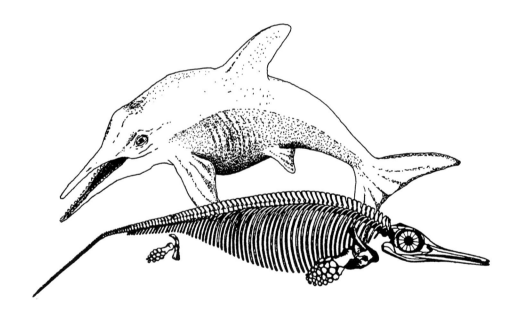

An extinct marine reptile, an ichthyosaur, from the Jurassic ocean [from Orr, Orr, and Baldwin, 1992].

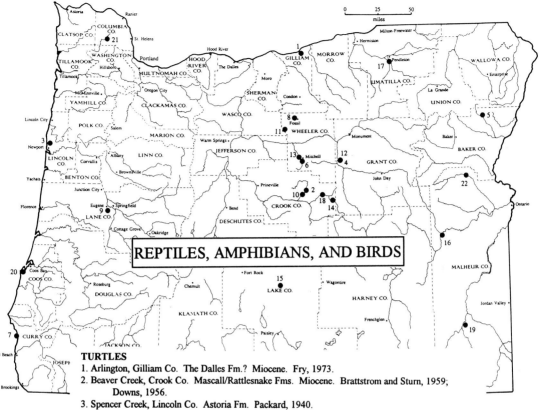

TURTLES
1. Arlington, Gilliam Co. The Dalles Fm.? Miocene. Fry, 1973.
2. Beaver Creek, Crook Co. Mascall/Rattlesnake Fms. Miocene. Brattstrom and Sturn, 1959; Downs, 1956.
3. Spencer Creek, Lincoln Co. Astoria Fm. Packard, 1940.
4. Turtle Cove, Grant Co. John Day Fm. Oligocene. Hay, 1908.

ICHTHYOSAURS
5. Eagle Creek, Baker Co. Martin Bridge Fm. Triassic. Orr and Katsura, 1985.
6. Mitchell, Wheeler Co. Hudspeth Fm.? Cretaceous. Merriam and Gilmore, 1928.
7. Sisters Rocks, Curry Co. ?Otter Point Fm. Jurassic. Koch and Camp, 1966.

SALAMANDERS
8. Fossil, Wheeler Co. John Day Fm. Oligocene. Naylor, 1979.
9. Goshen, Lane Co. Fisher Fm. Eocene. VanFrank, 1955.

SNAKE, CROCODILES, LIZARD, AND PTEROSAUR
10. Camp Creek, Crook Co. John Day Fm. Oligocene. Berman, 1976.
11. Clarno Mammal Quarry, Wheeler Co. Clarno Fm. Eocene. Hanson, 1996.
12. John Day River. Grant Co. John Day Fm. Oligocene. Cope, 1884.
13. Mitchell, Wheeler Co. Hudspeth Fm.? Cretaceous. Gilmore, 1928.
14. Suplee, Crook Co. Snowshoe Fm. Jurassic. Buffetaut, 1979.

BIRDS
15. Fossil Lake, Lake Co. Pleistocene. Howard, 1946; Jehl, 1967; Miller, 1911; Shufeldt, 1912.
16. Juntura, Malheur Co. Juntura Fm.? Miocene. Brodkorb, 1961.
17. McKay Reservoir, Umatilla Co. McKay Fm. Miocene. Brodkorb, 1958.
18. Paulina Creek Valley, Crook Co. Mascall Fm. Miocene. Shufeldt, 1915.
19. Dry Creek, Malheur Co. Juntura Fm.? Miocene. Brodkorb, 1961; Miller, 1944.
20. Sunset Bay, Coos Co. Coaledo Fm. Eocene. Miller, 1931.
21. Vernonia, Columbia Co. Keasey Fm. Eocene. Goedert, 1988.
22. Willow Creek, Malheur Co. No Fm. ?Miocene. Brodkorb, 1961.

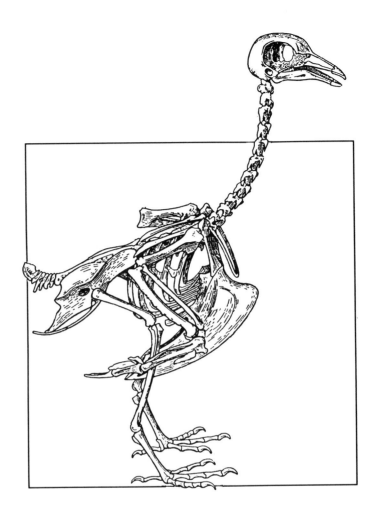

In a ratio of strength to weight, nothing exceeds the bird skeleton, as exemplified by this pigeon. The internal struts of a vulture wing are known in engineering parlance as a Warren's truss.

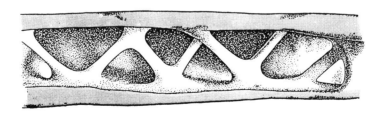

OREGON

FOSSIL

BIRDS

A scene of prehistoric birds by Robert Schufeldt, 1912.

Birds have been among the most intensely studied of modern vertebrates, but avian ancestry and relationships are incomplete because of their dismal fossil record. Even though birds had diversified by the end of the Cretaceous, 66 million years ago, and the counterpart of many living avian families can be traced foreward from the Eocene, the ancestry of birds is often unclear because their fragile air frame of hollow bones seldom preserves well. However, ongoing scrutiny of Cenozoic bird fossils has assisted in modern day classification sorting out avian relationships. Over the past two decades a considerable amount of attention has been focused on birds and avian paleontology when it was recognized that birds may be the only descendants of dinosaurs. The presence of feathers is the primary distinction birds possess over reptiles, but considering the unusual probability of feathers being preserved as fossils, it is clear that the ancestry of birds will be difficult to trace at best.

Across the state, fossil birds are randomly scattered throughout the Cenozoic. Only at Fossil Lake are bird bones abundant, even though fragmentary remains have been found on the coast at Coos Bay and near Vernonia as well as east of the Cascades in the John Day valley, near Arlington, and on the Owyhee Plateau.

Oregon's oldest bird fossils are leg bones from the Eocene Coaledo Formation at Sunset Bay in Coos County and in the Keasey Formation near Vernonia in Washington County. Imbedded in a matrix with an abundance of marine shells, the remains of an auk, *Hydrotherikornis oregonus*, were found by Francis Turner, a student from the University of California, engaged in field work during the summer of 1926. Alden Miller, professor at the same institution and son of the famous ornithologist Lloye Miller, regards the long-legged *Hydrotherikornis* as a diving and swimming near shore bird similar to living auks and murrets.

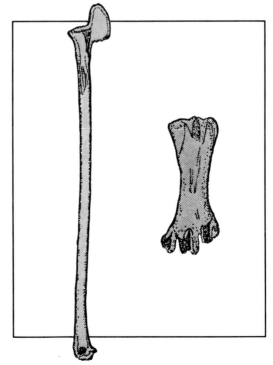

Left - the upper leg bone [tibiotarsus] of an auk [*Hydrotherikornis*] of the Coaledo Formation in southwest Oregon and right - the lower leg bone [tarsometatarsus] of a flightless *Phocavis* from the Keasey Formation in the northwest part of the state.

Another single bird find, a pelican-like *Phocavis maritimus* from the Keasey is represented by just a leg bone. James Goedert, a resident of Washington and Associate of the Los Angeles County Museum, who reported the specimen in 1988, notes that this is the oldest recorded member of the now extinct Plotopteridae family and the first known in Oregon. Goedert speculates that Plotopteridae may have become extinct because of the drop in numbers of fish or rise in pinnipeds concurrent with a middle Miocene global warming. Since fossils of the large flightless bird were found with molluscs that lived in 1,500 feet of water, it evidently operated a distance from shore.

During the winter of 1995 a sensational fossil bird egg from Keasey strata was recovered by James Leary of Cottage Grove. Somewhat smaller than that of a chicken and slightly crushed, the egg was examined and confirmed by examining its surface and a cross-section of its shell with an electron microscope at the University of Oregon. Details of the shell architecture compare best to members of the pelican family. Additionally a CAT scan of the intact egg revealed no internal embryo. Although known from several intervals in the geologic record, eggs are among the rarest of fossils because they are so fragile. When William Orr at the university confirmed the find, he remarked ruefully that "he had been looking at 'eggs' brought to him over a span of 30 years", and all but one turned out to be rounded stream pebbles or concretions.

The first clues that the Keasey egg was the real item were the shell thickness and the presence of pores in the surface. An unmistakable crystal pattern within the shell confirmed the identification [photo courtesy W. Orr].

Like the early Tertiary, Oligocene and Miocene sediments have only rare bird fossils. Few have turned up in the John Day Formation despite the richness of mammal faunas there. Isolated basins spotted across eastern Oregon 15 to 10 million years in the past were the sites of lakes and ponds during times of heavy rainfall. Under these conditions birds would gather around the waterways where today a handful of fossils might be the only evidence of their presence.

Drawing of a smiling double-crested cormorant [*Phalacrocorax*] by Robert Schufeldt, 1912.

In the process of examining all avian material collected by Othniel C. Marsh for Yale University, Robert Shufeldt came across rare leg bones from the John Day valley. He identified these as *Colymbus* [grebe] *Larus* [gull], *Limicolavis* [surfbird], *Phalacrocorax* [cormorant], and *Phasianus* [pheasant], a list that has yet to be expanded or updated.

A small collection of Miocene bird bones in the northern Great Basin of Oregon was made by field parties from California Institute of Technology in the 1920s and 1930s and further enhanced during the 1950s by the work of Arnold and Genevieve Shotwell with the Condon Museum. Old lake beds on the Owyhee plateau of Oregon and Idaho and at McKay Reservoir near Pendleton produce bird fossils close to the surface. Thirty bones from the Owyhee plateau, that had been placed in the Museum at the California Institute of Technology, were identified by Lloye Miller in 1944. The mineralized bones had been scattered across the ground and some even had lichens attached. The accumulation of storks, flamingos, ducks, cormorants, swans, teals, pheasants, and coots, along with beaver and otter suggested to Miller an ancient lake and marsh.

Miocene marshes and lakes were similarly depicted for Umatilla County by University of Florida biologist Pierce Brodkorb when he looked at a number of avian fossils from McKay Reservoir submitted to him by the Shotwells. Brodkorb determined that the fossils were duck

[*Nettion*], quail [*Lophortyx*], and sandpiper [*Bartramia*] - an assessment that fit Shotwell's environmental setting of a pond and neighboring grasslands.

From his first study of Pleistocene fossil birds at Rancho LaBrea, Lloye Miller went on to publish over 200 titles before retirement [photo courtesy Page Museum Archives, Los Angeles].

Avian paleontologists are almost as rare as the fossils themselves, and Lloye Miller is one of the few who devoted a lifetime to this field. Miller was born in Louisiana in 1874, where his earliest memories were of chasing a brilliant oriole through the woods on a spring morning. Because of their affiliation with the Confederacy, the family moved to Riverside, California, after the Civil War. Here Miller, his brothers, and sister could ramble through what was then an undisturbed country. Interested in many aspects of nature, Miller, however, focused on paleo-ornithology for a PhD in 1912 from the University of California, Berkeley. Miller's first contact with Oregon was accompanying vertebrate paleontologist John Merriam on an expedition to the John Day basin in 1899. Acting as Merriam's photographer-ornithologist, he left immediately after the trip for a teaching post in Honolulu. The journal he kept of his Oregon trip wasn't published until 1972, after it was edited by Arnold Shotwell. Miller retired from teaching at the University of California, Los Angeles, in 1943 but maintained an office and continued his research until his death in 1970 at 96 years of age.

By far the greatest number and assortment of birds inhabited the broad inland lakes of eastern Oregon during the cool moist Pleistocene epoch. The vast diversity of birds at Fossil Lake indicates that, as with Klamath and Malheur lakes today, these waterways were stop-overs for migratory birds, but the many remains of juveniles confirm that birds frequently nested here as well.

Historically the geographic usage of the terms Christmas Lake, Silver Lake, and Fossil Lake became confused, probably because the first geologic maps in 1884 by Israel Russell and Willard Johnson of the U.S. Geological Survey show only a single lake basin. Most of the vertebrate remains described from this vicinity at the turn of the century were probably from Fossil Lake.

A sketch of Silver Lake looking southeast drawn by E.D. Cope in 1889, and the same scene taken in May of 1998 [photo courtesy W. Orr].

Shiny jet black bones scattered across the expansive surface of dry Fossil Lake are strikingly prominent. Here in northern Lake County an optimum environment for burial and fossilization existed. Soft organic-rich mud of the lake bottom gently covered the carcasses, while subdued wave activity kept wear and abrasion to a minimum. Today drifting sands uncover thousands of bones of vertebrates, birds, freshwater fish, and shells. Although fish fossils far outnumber those of birds, the careful observer working on hands and knees can quickly make fossil finds without difficulty. Unfortunately the skeletons were separated and dispersed because of the slow sediment accumulation that characterized these inland waterways.

Fossil Lake became famous for its vertebrates in the 1860s and was the site of particular interest to early visitors such as Thomas Condon, Edward Cope, and Charles Sternberg. These travellers used ranches owned by George Duncan and Lee Button as headquarters. Postmaster at Silver Lake, Duncan frequently provided room and board and served as a guide to the "bone yard". Duncan's nearest neighbor, Lee Button, was a local hermit, who hosted visiting scientists in his log cabin a day's journey from Silver Lake. When he was away, Button buried the key to his door in a tin can to assist friends and keep away anyone who "abused his hospitality."

An imaginary scene depicts what could have been Pleistocene conditions in central Oregon [from Pouchet, 1882].

Thomas Condon made the first excursions to the "Fossil Beds" in 1877 when "the rarest and most valuable fossils ... were the eighty bird-bones which were unusually perfect and in a fine state of preservation." His explorations were followed shortly by those of Edward Cope, Philadelphia Academy of Sciences, and Charles Sternberg, his assistant and commercial collector. As soon as he came upon the fossils, Sternberg went down to his hands and knees, picking up bones and teeth and putting them in piles. In his autobiography he wrote "I did not find a single bone or tooth in its original position ... but that all were loose, detached, and scattered, and that [Indian] implements were lying about in the same way." Packing some of the teeth, arrowheads, and bones, he sent them off to Cope.

The bird bones gathered by Condon were loaned to Cope in 1879. Cope, in turn, gave them to Robert Shufeldt at the Smithsonian. A March, 1891, letter from Shufeldt to Condon promises to keep Condon's 80 specimens "quite distinct, and will return them to Prof. Cope when my labours are completed." In spite of later appeals from Condon asking for their return, the bird bones did not come back to Oregon until 1926 and then only through the persistent efforts of Rachel Husband. A graduate of the University of Oregon, Husband had worked in the Museum at Eugene before being employed at the American Museum in New York. Here she searched through the Cope collection to find those distinctively marked by Condon's colored numbers. Notifying officials, the specimens were returned to Condon's daughter, Ellen McCornack. Condon's bird fossils made another trek in 1942 when they were sent to Chester Stock at California Institute of Technology, who passed them on to avian paleontologist Hildegarde Howard at the Los Angeles County Museum. Precisely measuring the bones, Howard concluded in a 1944 letter that Shufeldt's "work seems to have been particularly bad and a number of glaring errors were made in the identification of these water birds." Howard returned the specimens two years later with new identifying slips.

Among the early-day biologists, Robert Shufeldt's passion for birds enabled him to develop a unique knowledge of their characteristics and habitats. As a child in the 1860s he accompanied his father, a Rear Admiral in the Navy, on his travels enabling the young Robert to indulge his interest in natural history. His room became a museum for his private collection of over 500 birds and mammals. Obtaining a medical degree from Columbia University, Shufeldt joined the army as an assistant surgeon. While serving on the western frontier, he continued his collections and scientific publications, writing over 150 books, memoirs, and monographs on the local fauna. In the late 1800s Shufeldt had to defend himself in court against the remarkable charge "whether an officer of the medical corps of the army could devote himself to scientific studies during his time of leisure." The decision was against Shufeldt, and he retired shortly thereafter. A long association with the Smithsonian brought an appointment as curator until his death in 1904.

Biologist Robert Shufeldt, who was fascinated with modern and fossil birds, married Florence Audubon, grandaughter of the famous ornithologist.

Probably Shufeldt's most consequential paper on Oregon was in 1913, but his 1912 *Prehistoric Birds of Oregon* is pleasingly illustrated and easy to read. In his reports on Fossil Lake he identified 51 species, 13 of which were new, from a total of 1,500 bone fragments. *Aechmophorus* [grebe], *Colymbus* [grebe], *Podilymbus* [grebe], and *Larus* [gull] were the most numerous. Of the water birds, ducks, geese, and swans were plentiful, but no loons or similar divers of the Alcidae family were found. A flamingo [*Phoenicopterus copei*], heron [*Ardea*], one shore bird [*Phalaropus*], two eagles [*Aquila*], a blackbird [*Scolecophagus*], and raven [*Corvus*] are now extinct.

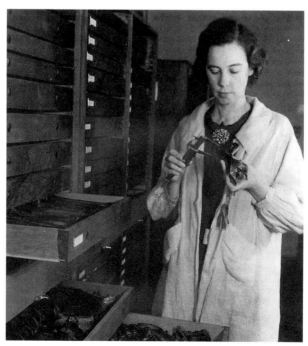

In determining that the humerus bone of a pigmy goose [*Anabernicula*] from Fossil Lake was a distinct species, the meticulous Hildegarde Howard examined and measured 300 skeletal parts from seven locations [photo courtesy Archives, Page Museum, Los Angeles].

Paleo-ornithologist Hildegarde Howard was born on the east coast in Washington, D.C., in 1901 but spent her professional life in California. After her undergraduate work at Berkeley, she worked part time at UCLA for Lloye Miller, who directed her toward the study of fossil birds. Receiving a PhD in Zoology in 1928 at the University of California, she was offered a curatorial position at the Los Angeles County Museum processing thousands of birds from Rancho La Brea. It was here on an assigment to clean up the mammal collection at Rancho La Brea, damaged during a flood, that she met Henry Wylde, her husband to be for 54 years. Howard retired in 1990, when, as she was fond of saying, two men were hired to replace her. She currently lives in southern California.

Vultures [*Coragyps*] are among the bird bones at 8,000-year old Indian sites near The Dalles [from Pouchet, 1882].

Twenty-five years after Howard's work here, Robert Storer used new methods of analyzing skeletal material to reach different conclusions than Howard. At the University of Michigan, Museum of Zoology, Storer compared the skeletons of recent *Aechmophorus occidentalis*, Western Grebes, from Canada to those from the Pleistocene of Fossil Lake to show that previous techniques of contrasting bone size between fossil and recent birds to determine new species might not be valid. Storer based his determinations on measurements of skeletons of 119 Western Grebes that had been frozen in Lake Newell, Alberta, in 1959 against those housed in museums in California and at the American Museum. He concluded that significant skeletal differences between the two groups could be attributed to geographic variations, post mortem wear, or preparation techniques, and not to genetic variations.

Avian paleontology was examined in depth in 1912 by Loye Miller when he looked at bird fossils from nine west coast locations including Fossil Lake to provide species lists and draw general conclusions on distribution, environment, and correlation among the different faunas. Discussing extinction of birds during the late Tertiary he proposed that while humans probably did not directly cause extinction, the demise of large mammals certainly contributed to the end of large carrion eating birds. Disease and climate changes are also suggested as causes for extinction. Miller recounts that in 1908 and 1909 thousands of sea birds, dying over a relatively short time span, when examined were found to be filled with intestinal worms. Diminished rainfall after the Ice Ages brought about a drying of lakes in the Great Basin, and temperature changes would have altered the composition of the forests - affecting bird populations. In more recent time, one of the consequences of El Nino weather systems has been sea bird mortality in fantastic numbers due to lack of food at tropical and mid latitudes.

Sea creatures frolicking in an imaginary ocean [Fugier, 1891].

OREGON FOSSIL MARINE AND FRESHWATER VERTEBRATES

Sharks, marine mammals, and bony fish from fresh and salt water are grouped here because of the similarity of their habitats. The remains of open ocean whales and porpoises are often found buried alongside nearshore animals such as seals, sea otters, and shore birds. Sharks, as marine scavengers, are invariably drawn to carcasses, and it is not uncommon to find their teeth still imbedded in the bones of bigger animals. Bony fish are easily one of the most successful and adaptive of all vertebrates, and their preserved skeletal debris is readily apparent in virtually all aquatic sediments.

In spite of the comparatively massive body size of many marine vertebrates, their fossil record is remarkably poor when compared to that of terrestrial animals, and their limited remains tend to be scattered and abraded. Several factors contribute to this. One is that there are not many living members of a marine population at any given time. Except for small fish, most ocean-dwelling vertebrates are at or near the top of food pyramids, which means that the environment can only support a few such individuals. Even if an animal is physically large, big populations are what really count with respect to being represented in the fossil record. If a whale is buried and preserved, it is much less probable that this single specimen will be discovered and collected than three to five thousand smaller animals of equal weight.

The marine setting itself acts as a deterrent to preservation of vertebrates. An impressive array of scavengers from sharks to crabs and fish await the opportunity of any carrion. With smooth efficiency, this clean-up crew rapidly strips the flesh then thoroughly disperses the bones across the ocean floor. Carcasses washing ashore as well as the bodies of coastal animals carried into the ocean are subject to intensive sorting, scattering, and abrasion by the high energy of the surf. In the terrestrial realm, there are specialized environments such as quicksand, tarpits, and bogs that trap, enmire, and bury animals to preserve them, often intact, but these situations seem to be lacking in marine settings.

In Oregon, aquatic vertebrates fall into four classes from the most primitive fish to mammals: sharks and rays [Chondrichthyes], fish [Osteichthyes], and otters, seals, sea lions, and whales [Mammalia].

Shark teeth from the Eugene Formation show beach wear as well as the darkened enamel typical of fossil teeth [photo courtesy Condon Museum].

SHARKS AND RAYS

Sharks and rays, whose lineages date back as far as the Devonian period over 350 million years ago, breathe through gill plates and have a flexible non-bony skeleton. The cartilaginous skeleton of sharks usually deteriorates too rapidly for preservation, while their many teeth are replaced continuously over a lifetime - thus almost all shark remains are teeth. The same is true for skates and rays, which are bottom-feeders with a pavement-like dental surface in the mouth adapted for crushing shells. In addition to the production of copious numbers of teeth, calcium phosphate of the tooth enamel is highly resistant to the geologic processes of wear, abrasion, and solution.

Shark fossils in Oregon, however, are known only from the Cretaceous through Tertiary periods. Of the 16 genera of sharks, skates, and rays inhabiting the coastal waters today, 10 are present in the fossil record, and, of these, teeth of the dogfish shark, *Squalus*, are most frequently encountered.

Fossil sharks were mentioned as early as 1849 by James Dana of the U.S. Exploring Expedition, but descriptions of cartilaginous fish are rare and generally included with accounts of invertebrates. At Stanford University, David Starr Jordan and Harold Hannibal turned their attention to sharks and rays of the Pacific coast in 1923. These had been collected by Hannibal in 1911 and 1912, but only three shark teeth - *Carcharias ornatus* from the Arago Formation and *Carcharias virgatulus* and *Isurus* from the Empire - are listed. Jordan's work in the 1920s, which provided the basis for future investigations of northwest fossil sharks, was succeeded by Bruce Welton's studies of the 1970s.

Bruce Welton became interested in paleontology because of his outdoor experiences as an Oregon Museum of Science and Industry participant. His first contact with fossils and sharks came during one of their trips to the Keasey Formation at Vernonia [photo courtesy B. Welton].

Bruce Welton is one of the few researchers who, over the years, has specialized in sharks and rays. Born in Portland, Welton attended summer camps organized by Oregon Museum of Science and Industry and subsequently Portland State University. As a student in 1972, he wrote a summary paper on shark teeth before going on to obtain a PhD in 1979 from the University of California, Berkeley, on Cretaceous and Cenozoic Squalimorphii, primitive sharks of the northwest Pacific Ocean. For his dissertation Welton records the squalimorphs *Chlamydoselachus, Echinorhinus, Heptranchias, Oligodalatias,* and *Squalus* in sediments of the Keasey and Pittsburg Bluff, Yaquina, Nye, and Astoria formations. The highest percentage is occurrences of *Squalus,* reflecting shelf or intertidal habitats. Welton currently works for Mobil Oil Company in Dallas, Texas.

In his 1972 paper, Welton ennumerated some of the difficulties in identifying sharks and rays from the teeth alone. The shape of the crown, root, position of nutrient canals, tooth size, serrations on the crown, and denticles are just a few of the characteristics that must be scrutinized to determine a genus or species. Diversity in the teeth of an individual jaw must be taken into account, and one of Weldon's most successful techniques has been to reconstruct entire "tooth sets" to show all variations within a species.

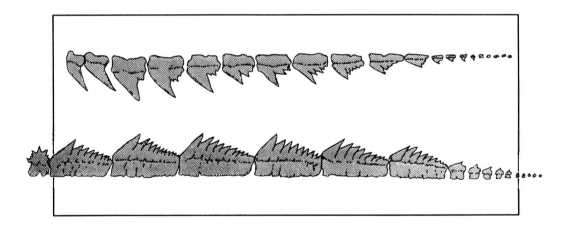

Complete tooth set of the shark *Hexanchus* showing the characteristic comb-like lower teeth.

Following an inventory of Oregon shark material housed in West Coast institutions, Welton listed one Cretaceous and seven Eocene formations that contain shark teeth. Of the three teeth from the Cretaceous Hudspeth Formation near Mitchell, Wheeler County, one was tentatively described as a Goblin shark, *Scapanorhynchus.*

234

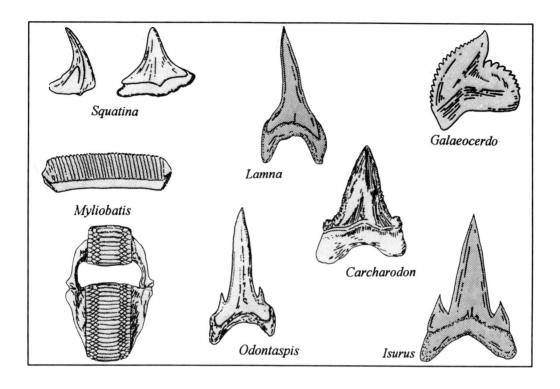

Squatina

Lamna

Galaeocerdo

Myliobatis

Carcharodon

Odontaspis

Isurus

Representative shark teeth from Oregon

At least 75% of all recorded shark teeth are from Eocene strata. Among these formations, the Coaledo at Shore Acres State Park in Coos County frequently yields fragments and complete teeth of the sand shark *Odontaspis*, the dogfish shark *Squalus,* and the eagle ray *Myliobatis.* The Coaledo has the most *Myliobatis* material of any in the state and the highest variety of sharks and rays - *Aetobatus, Carcharias, Galeorhinus, Heterodontus, Isurus, Lamna, Rhinoptera, Scyliorhinus, Squalus,* and, *Squatina.* By carefully washing and screening a thin lense of Spencer Formation sediment - less than one-foot thick - Welton was able to isolate over 2,000 teeth, 95% of which belong to *Odontaspis macrota.* Spencer strata at Helmick Hill in Polk County is one of the few localities where the teeth are affected by detrimental conditions. Here they display beach wear and leaching by groundwater, actions that smoothed and rounded sharp edges.

Even though shark remains, other than teeth, are rarely encountered, 22 vertebra, "patches of hollow cubes" of calcified cartilage, and a single tooth of a sand shark were collected by Department of Geology and Mineral Industries geologists in 1967. From dark gray marine shales of the Yamhill Formation, the material was sent to the Los Angeles County Museum where it was examined by their vertebrate paleontologist, Shelton Applegate. Comparing the fossils to living sharks, Applegate identified the peculiar-shaped cubes as components of the skull, jaws, gill and fin supports. The tooth associated with the skeletal remains was assigned by Applegate to the species, *Odontaspis macrota,* whose modern equivalent is the sandshark *Odontaspis taurus,* a somewhat sluggish predator, capable of short bursts of speed. Today it is found on shallow ocean bottoms along the coastline of the eastern United States, Europe, and the Mediterranean.

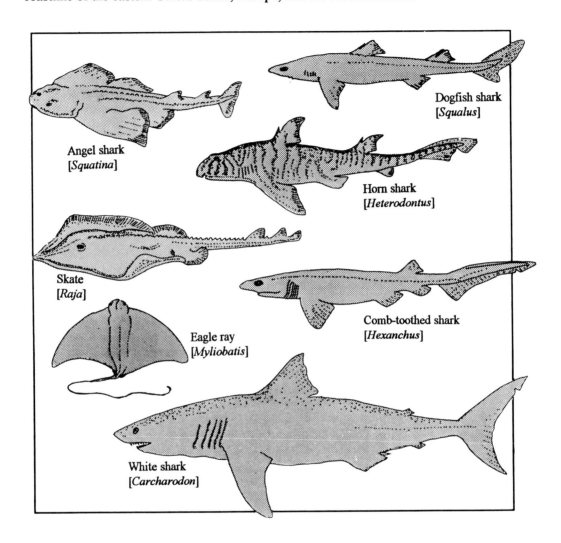

Reconstructed fossil sharks

BONY FISH

As with sharks, bony fish also date back to the Devonian period where they were extremely diverse. Modern bony finned fish such as haddock, cod, trout, and perch, numbering more than 25,000 species, dominate marine and fresh waters. The oldest fossils of marine fish in Oregon are Eocene, 40 million years in age, and most are from Tertiary marine sediments of the Coast Range. Brown to amber scales, ribs, vertebra and skull fragments often appear in microfossil samples processed foraminifera. A single landmark paper by Lore Rose David in 1956 specifically treats fossil marine fish.

While working for Richfield Oil Company in California, David was able to set up a precise chronology of fish scales that was utilized by the petroleum industry exploring deep water intervals of the Los Angeles basin. Since fish scales are more readily visible than microfossils of foraminifera and radiolaria, but more compact than most molluscs, they are easier to handle. One of David's innovations was to glue chips of rocks containing the flat scales to one end of wooden tongue depressors then record data on taxonomy and stratigraphy of the scale on the other end of the stick. Ultimately she built a sizeable catalogue of easy-to-use fossil scales. David's collection is now housed at the Los Angeles County Museum.

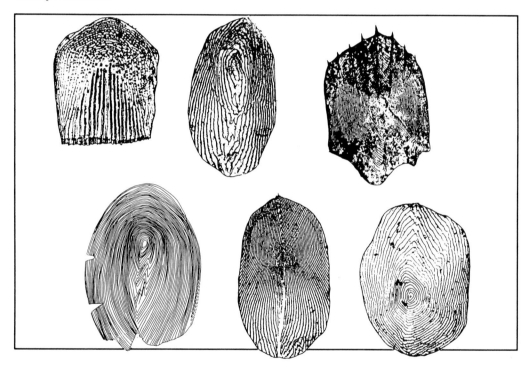

A distinctive pattern of growth lines, spines, and wrinkles on fish scales clearly identifies each species [after David, 1956].

For her studies, David examined the scales of deep water fish from Eocene through Pliocene intervals of California, Oregon, and Washington. Most of these belong to the Gadiformes, living hake and cod, a group known as "herrings of the deep sea" because of their abundance in deep ocean waters. The scales, recovered from oil well cores in the Eocene Nestucca and Keasey formations and Oligocene Yaquina and Nye sediments of western part of the state, have a fingerprint-like pattern of grooves and ridges on the face that are unique and reliable for positive identification of species. By comparing her fossil assemblages to modern fish, David was able to list characteristic fish scales from several paleo-ocean depths. In Pacific Coast faunas she identified four paleoenvironments: shallow shelf [upper neritic], deep shelf [outer neritic], slope [bathyal], and slope base to 10,000 feet [abyssal]. Inhabitants of this milieu were *Calilepidus, Probathygadus, Paleobathygadus, Promacrurus, Pyknolepidus,* and Macrouridae.

A quiet self-contained person, who retained a heavy German accent, Lore Rose David's work on fossil fish scales remains unique to this day [photo courtesy J. Jorgensen].

David's scientific career centered on paleoichthyology. Born and educated in Germany, she received a PhD in biology at the University of Berlin in 1931. From there she moved to Belgium as ichthyological curator in the Museum at Tervuren before immigrating to the United States. From 1938 to 1947 she worked in laboratories at California Institute of Technology and Richfield Oil Company. Following a career change in 1954 she served as a librarian at private and public institutions until retirement from the Santa Clara County library system. David died in San Jose in 1985.

FRESHWATER FISH

During the Cenozoic, freshwater fish occupied the lakes and streams of eastern Oregon, a wetlands environment that today yields evidence of their presence. These remains are rarely preserved in an unbroken condition, and most have been scattered across the surface of old lake beds. Some of the better-known occurrences are from Eocene and Oligocene sites in Wheeler County, Miocene from Malheur County, along with Pliocene and Pleistocene from Klamath, Jefferson, and Lake counties.

Work on freshwater fish has been very sporadic since Edward Cope first investigated them in the Great Basin during the late 1800s. A member of the Academy of Natural Sciences in Philadelphia, Cope's paper *"On the Fishes of the Recent and Pliocene Lakes of the Western Part of the Great Basin..."* listed species and localities in Oregon as well as in adjoining states. Many of his paleoenvironmental interpretations are still valid, but his generic names have changed. After that effort, a gap of around 50 years lapsed before work in this area was carried foreward by Carl Hubbs and Robert Miller. This was followed by research conducted by Miller's student Gerald "Jerry" Smith, all at the University of Michigan. Hubbs, who was also Miller's father-in-law, had studied at Stanford with David Starr Jordan and was the driving force to get paleoichthyology going in the west. Their classic 1948 paper shows how ancient lake and river systems can be traced by the distribution of freshwater fish. Miller's interest also extended to river drainages in the Coast Range, and he wrote to Ewart Baldwin at Eugene in 1950 "It might interest you to know that ... [fish] distributions strongly suggest connections of some sort between the Willamette and these coastal streams ..." In 1963 Miller and Jerry Smith summarized the late Cenozoic fish record for North America, pulling together information on species, age, and localities as well as providing comments on the validity of each; then in 1981 Smith compared fossil and recent fish evolution in North America, updating and documenting the past environments.

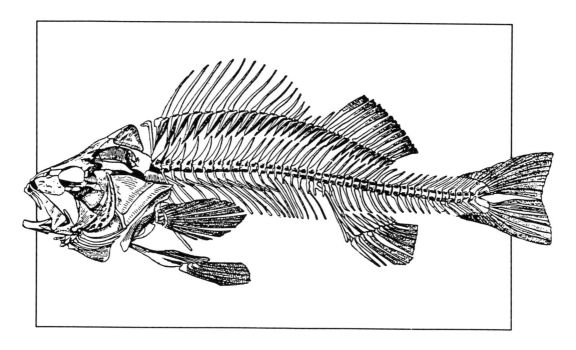

Perch [Perca], a typical teleost fish, is made up of dozens of loosely [articulated] bones.

Another paleoichthyologist Ted Cavender, who began a life-long interest in fish remains from the state during the 1960s, was from Tuxedo, New York. Cavender took a graduate degree from the University of Chicago in 1963 on the scale histology of palaeoniscoid fishes, then taught at the University of Michigan for six years before taking a position at Ohio State University. Cavender's research centers on the evolution of fish, especially palaeoniscoids [a very early primitive bony fish] and freshwater teleosts such as perch and goldfish, and his *"Revision of the History of North American Freshwater Fish"* in 1986 is a compilation of research 100 years after Cope.

Eocene fish scales, vertebra, and skulls, long noted in Clarno sediments at Ochoco Pass, were collected by Margaret Steere, geologist with the Department of Geology and Mineral Industries, who loaned her specimens to Cavender for examination. In August, 1966, a field party, led by Cavender, visited the site, adding to the fish inventory at the University of Michigan. Steep roadcuts at Ochoco Summit in Wheeler County yield a diversity of fish remains, which are younger than the famous middle Eocene Green River fish of Wyoming but older than several other middle Tertiary faunas in western North America. Bowfins [*Amia*], mooneyes [*Hiodon*], catfish [Siluriformes], and suckers [Catostomidae and *Amyzon*] are the most abundant from these dark shales that have been interpreted by Cavender as a lake. A rich accumulation of plant impressions accompany the fish as do occasional broken beetle wings. Thick elongate bowfin scales are distinctive and are usually preserved intact. In their evolutionary history, bowfins are a particularly

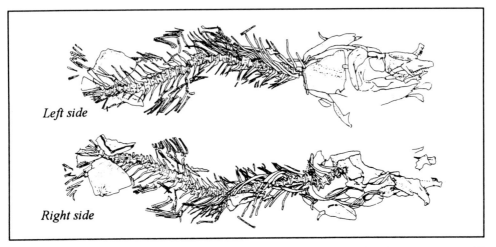

Left side

Right side

Small in size and obscure in habits, the mudminnow *Novumbra* is rarely seen alive and is even more scarce in a preserved state [after Cavender, 1969].

conservative group, having changed very little in 70 million years from their first appearance during the Cretaceous. Of the four fossil groups, only the Catostomidae live in the same region today. Mooneyes, catfish, and bowfins no longer inhabit the Columbia River basin, but catfish are known from late Tertiary sediments of ancient Lake Idaho in the western Snake River valley.

Calm waters of pond and lakes, that characterized the John Day Formation of central Oregon 36 to 23 million years ago, provided for the accumulation and preservation of fish long after the region had become dry and arid. Several exceptional specimens of an Oligocene mudminnow, *Novumbra oregonensis*, were found at two different locations of this formation in Wheeler County. Around four inches in length, living mudminnows inhabit the muddy bottoms and dense aquatic vegetation of quiet lowland streams. Mudminnows can endure considerable variation in temperature and dissolved oxygen but have a somewhat limited tolerance for strong currents and changes in salinity.

In 1964 high school students Edward Frazer and William Prince, while participating in an Oregon Museum of Science and Industry camp, collected remains of *Novumbra* at Knox Ranch, and in 1966 a group led by local resident Lee Jenkins and Ted Cavender found additional material at Allen Ranch. Skull and jaw fragments were picked up by the party. The *Novumbra* from Knox Ranch was complete except for a missing caudal fin, while the second superb specimen was virtually intact as well. Plant fossils from both locals belong to the Bridge Creek flora, and other freshwater fish from the same strata were identified by Cavender as pikes or pickerels [Esocidae]. Previously, in 1927, paleobotanist Ralph Chaney sent fragmentary fish remains from Bridge Creek shales at Gray Ranch, Crook County, to David Starr Jordan at Stanford. These were too poorly preserved to name them with any certainty, but Jordan thought one might be related to a primitive perch and a second to *Pholidophorus*, an ancient fish that had eyes surrounded by bony plates and the large teeth of an active predator.

The Miocene of eastern Oregon was ushered in by renewed volcanic activity, empounding numerous lakes. One of the largest of these was ancient Lake Idaho backed up in the Snake River Plain from Vale and Baker, Oregon, to Twin Falls, Idaho, between 15 to 5 million years ago. Fish and mammal remains in the lake deposits have been utilized by paleoichthyologists Peter Kimmel and Gerald Smith to sketch the ancient setting.

Scattered, broken fish bones from silts and sands of the Deer Butte Formation, a middle Miocene interval of Lake Idaho, were accumulated by field parties from the University of Michigan led by Miller and Smith. Subsequently examined by Kimmel, the diverse fauna boasts 24 species of salmon, sunfish, sculpins, and whitefish, showing high percentages of the catfish [*Ictalurus*], large salmon-like predators [*Rhabdofario* and *Paleolox*], bottom-dwelling omnivorous suckers [*Catostomus*], and mollusc-eating minnows [*Mylocheilus, Ptychocheilus,* and *Idadon*]. Jaws of these large minnows have characteristic blunt or rounded shell-crushing teeth which, at first glance, resemble those of a primate.

By careful geological and biological observations, Kimmel has been able to reconstruct a detailed paleoenvironmental picture for Lake Idaho, noting, for example, that the massive sands and siltstones interbedded with pure volcanic ash could point to either slow or rapid deposition during very intermittent volcanic activity. However, the presence of beautifully articulated fish and mammal bones and the incidence of conglomerate beds supports rapid deposition typical of a flood plain or the edge of a lake disrupted by swiftly flowing streams. The dimensions of some of the predatory fish, which include several close to three feet in length, further suggest a lake of considerable size.

Peter Kimmel spent his early years in the John Day fossil beds, but moved to Colorado with his family where he collected skark teeth near Milliken. A return to Oregon led to a graduate degree at Oregon State University and a subsequent PhD from the University of Michigan on fossil fish in eastern Oregon and Idaho. He currently lives in Virginia and works on government contracts [photo with his daughter courtesy P. Kimmel].

The most recent study of fish from this large body of water is by Gerald Smith on the Chalk Hills and Glenns Ferry formations, representing late Miocene and Pliocene intervals. Smith records very diverse fish faunas that evolved here during the late Cenozoic, and, on the basis of key species, he was able to set up three biostratigraphic zones. *Mylocheilus* [large minnow] characterizes the youngest zone, *Mylopharodon* and *Orthodon* [primitive minnows] typify the middle, and *Smilodonichthys* [salmon-like fish] the oldest zone. The drainage of this huge lake in late Pleistocene time brought about the extinction of almost half of the species.

Over thirty species of salmon inhabited western North America waters during the late Cenozoic time, but fossils of these fish are astonishingly rare. Some teeth, vertebra, and skull fragments of an extinct salmon turned up in California as early as 1917, but it wasn't until the mid 1950s to 1960s that more complete specimens from Oregon made description of a new species of Chinook Salmon *Smilodonichthys rastrosus* possible.

Around 1950 Ann Brownhill, a student working for the Condon Museum, discovered numerous skeletal parts of a single large salmon near Gateway in Jefferson County. The fossil was then collected from what is strata of the Deschutes Formation by Arnold Shotwell the museum director. During the summer of 1964 the skull, jaws, and gill arches of a second specimen from the same area were recovered by Mrs. George Iiames and Scott McKail and acquired by the Museum. Further searching at Gateway over the past 30 years has yielded a steady stream of additional fragments, making the Brownhill specimen truly spectacular, consisting of over 100 skeletal pieces and a complete skull 17 inches in length.

Both paleoichthyologists at the University of Michigan, Jerry Smith and Bob Miller [holding the thirteen pound squawfish] have traced the ancestry of freshwater fish in North America [photo courtesy G. Smith].

By comparing the many pieces from the Pacific Northwest already placed in museums to new finds, Ted Cavender and Robert Miller were able to develop something of an ancestry for this giant. Estimated to reach eight feet in length, the size of this fish as well as details of its bone structure indicate that, like modern salmon, it was anadromous, splitting its life cycle between freshwater and the ocean. In addition to its massive size, there is evidence that the Oregon specimen was a breeding male and as such sported fang-like fighting teeth roughly 1.5 inches in length, hence the name *Smilodonichthys*, after the sabre-toothed cat. In spite of its fierce appearance and name, this great fish fed on plankton aided by a delicate and elaborate system of over 100 gill rakers in the skull that functioned as a sieve. *Rastrosus* is the Latin word for rakers.

Another locality at Worden in Klamath County produced the jaw of a young salmon along with parts of Cyprinidae [minnows] and Catostomidae [suckers] from sandstones of the Pliocene Yonna Formation. These were discovered in 1968 in an abandoned railroad cut by Norman Peterson of the Oregon Department of Geology and Mineral Industries. Land mammal bones and those other fish from here were haphazardly thrown together when the sands were deposited.

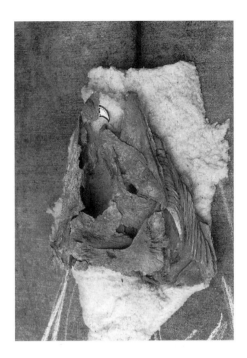

Assembled from bits and pieces over several years, the skull and skeleton of the salmon *Smilodonichthys* reached a length totalling eight feet. Shown here with noted fish artist Ray Troll of Ketchikan, Alaska [photo courtesy W. Orr].

The state's most famous Pleistocene fish locality is in northern Lake County at Fossil Lake. Even though terrestrial vertebrate remains are also known from this site, fish are by far the most common fossil. Fish bones litter the fine sands of what was a large lake during the late Tertiary and Pleistocene. The lack of fine-grained clays across much of the old lake surface has largely precluded the preservation of fragile scales, but skull bones, vertebra, and ribs abound and are easily collected. The turbulent shallow environment of the lake has thoroughly scattered the individual fish, and no articulated remains are reported.

In 1883 Edward Cope described several freshwater minnows and suckers from Fossil Lake, and David Starr Jordan revised the list in 1907, adding a giant salmon. Similar to the present-day King salmon, it is represented by numerous skull bones, jaw, teeth, and vertebra from this and other sites. Salmon bones in Lake and Klamath counties indicate that former Fort Rock Lake, a much larger water body encompassing the present day areas of Fossil Lake, Christmas Lake, and Silver Lake, may have overflowed through an outlet to the Pacific Ocean as late as Pleistocene time. Some salmon apparently adapted and remained in the lake even after it became an isolated body of water.

As a result of his studies on fish, David Starr Jordan named over 1,000 genera and more than 2,500 species of fish from regions throughout the world [photo courtesy Archives, Stanford University].

David Starr Jordan was among the miniscule number of scientists specializing in the study of fish during the late 1800s. Born in New York in 1851, Jordan's educational direction was influenced by both parents, who were teachers, and by the faculty at Cornell University, where he took a Masters degree in botany and zoology in 1872. Inspired to enter the fledgling field of ichthyology by the famous geologist Louis Agassiz, Jordan's research and publications from the late 1800s onward dominated the field. He wrote several books on fish classification as well as the *Manual of Vertebrates.* A parallel career in higher education led to the chancellorship at Stanford University.

MARINE MAMMALS

Historically, Oregon marine mammals have received sporatic attention, in part, because of their fragmentary nature. Since the 1970s renewed interest can be attributed to the description and close scrutiny of new material by several researchers such as Lawrence Barnes and Ed Mitchell at the Los Angeles County Museum, Clayton Ray at the Smithsonian, Richard Tedford of the American Museum, Charles Repenning at the U.S. Geological Survey, and Annalisa Berta of San Diego State University. As a result, knowledge of the evolution and taxonomy of marine vertebrates has reached the stage where today it is advancing very rapidly.

One of the now classic papers by Edward Mitchell is *"Faunal Succession of Extinct North Pacific Marine Mammals"* in 1966. In his paper, restorations of the mammals by science illustrator Bonnie Dalzell, based on skeletal material, are both creative and artistic. A special issue of *Systematic Zoology* in 1977, edited by Repenning, focused on marine mammals and contained such articles as *"Fossil Marine Mammals of Oregon"*, a paean to Douglas Emlong by Clayton Ray. Since then, Repenning and Tedford produced *Otariid Seals of the Neogene* in 1977, Barnes and coauthors added the *Status of Studies on Fossil Marine Mammals* in 1985, and in 1994 Annalisa Berta published *"Pinniped Phylogeny "* as well as edited *"Contributions in Marine Mammal Paleontology."*

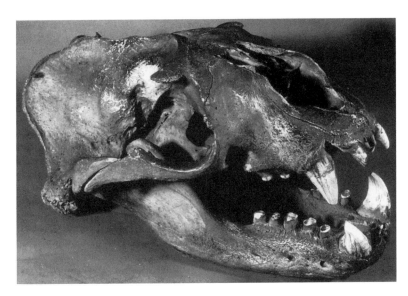

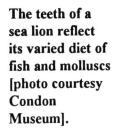

The teeth of a sea lion reflect its varied diet of fish and molluscs [photo courtesy Condon Museum].

Marine mammals can be broadly grouped into the otters, seals, sea lions, and walruses [Carnivora], the whales and porpoises [Cetacea], manatees and dugongs [Sirenia], and unique hippopotamus-like creatures called Desmostylia, lacking modern representatives. Marine mammals range from awkward-looking nearshore herbivores to torpedo-shaped open ocean predators. Despite their diversity, they all share characteristic mammalian features such as hair and warm-blood physiology.

Marine carnivores comprise the families Mustelidae [sea otters], Phocidae [true seals], Otariidae [sea lions and fur seals], and Odobenidae [walruses]. As thriving predators on land, it was inevitable that carnivores would invade and diversify in the marine environment as well.

Of the Tertiary carnivores, mustelids were clearly distinguishable by the early Oligocene. Modern mustelids are familiar as weasels, skunks, mink, and river otters, but less well-known as sea otters. These animals are generally slender, with powerful muscles and an irritable disposition. The only mustelid from the marine environment of Oregon is a single fossil sea otter, an *Enhydra*. From the Pleistocene Elk River Formation at Cape Blanco, the fossil is identical to the modern *Enhydra lutris*. Two *Enhydra* femurs, described by Sanford Leffler, were found here in 1960 during a paleontology field trip from the University of California and are the earliest record of sea otters in North America. After death, this animal apparently washed up into a quiet embayment where it was preserved along with the remains of an eared seal and tapir.

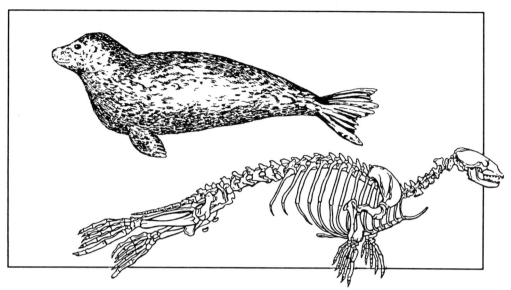

The modern-day harbor seal is similar to those living on the Oregon coast during the Pliocene and Pleistocene.

Seals and sea lions first appeared in the middle Miocene - phocids in the Atlantic and Mediterranean and otariids in the Pacific basin. True seals in the Phocidae family and eared seals and sea lions in the Otariidae are often known as pinnipeds. Although somewhat dated, the term is still usefully descriptive of carnivores with webbed or pinnate feet. During the late 1800s these animals were further divided into the "walkers" and the "wrigglers". Seals which were able to flex their back legs and walk on shore are the otariids, while those that wriggled across the land on their stomach with their hind legs splayed behind them are called phocids. In 1977 Charles Repenning and Richard Tedford attribute the comparatively poor fossil record of pinnipeds more to sampling than to actual frequency. "As much as anything this seems to be the result of mammalian paleontology stopping at the water's edge ... pinniped remains frequently have been ignored or described as more or less isolated curiosities."

At Cape Blanco, the Pleistocene Port Orford Formation has produced Oregon's only true seal, a phocid. This marginal record is consistant with that for phocids elsewhere. Lawrence Barnes and Edward Mitchell described skull fragments from a small young female seal, *Phoca vitulina,* that was collected about 1960 by Copeland MacClintock. Comparing the fossil fragments to living seals inhabiting the Pacific Northwest coastline today, they found that both are similar and speculate that *Phoca vitulina* became extinct during the Ice Ages after being isolated by advancing ice. At the same time modern phocids, by contrast, were becoming established.

Three exceptional otariids from the Oligocene and Miocene - *Enaliarctos, Pteronarctos,* and *Desmatophoca* - along with the Pleistocene *Eumetopias* are part of the

247

Oregon past. Coastal rocks are the richest source for marine mammals in the state, yielding two unique extinct animals, an *Enaliarctos* and *Pteronarctos*. These aquatic bear-like creatures are the most primitive of the pinnipeds. Using material from the Emlong collection, the classification of enaliarctid pinnipeds was revised by Annalisa Berta. Berta's 1991

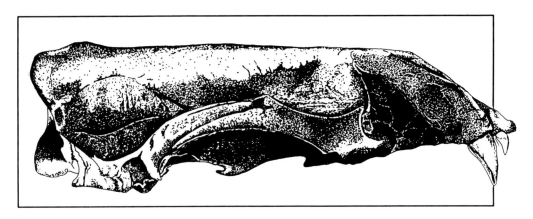

Skull of *Pteronarctos,* a primitive bear-like aquatic animal [after Barnes, 1990]

contribution distinguished between new Oregon species, *Enaliarctos barnesi, E. emlongi,* and *E. tedfordi,* and one previously described, *E. mitchelli,* all from Lincoln County between Newport and Waldport. The skulls were from three successive formations, the Oligocene Yaquina Formation and Miocene Nye Mudstone and Astoria strata. Even though carefully comparing characteristics of well-preserved skulls, Berta was unable to resolve the relationships between the three enlaliarctid species. She felt, however, there are hints of a common ancestry.

A new genus and two new species *Pteronarctos piersoni* and *Pteronarctos goedertae* have turned up in the Astoria Formation of Lincoln County. *Pteronarctos* shares several characteristics with modern true sea lions, fur seals, and primitive fur seals. A complete skull with canine teeth, lying among loose boulders on Moolack Creek, was found in April, 1983, by the private collector, Guy Pierson. Later acquired by the Los Angeles County Museum, the specimen was described in 1990 by their Curator Lawrence Barnes. The second species *Pteronarctos goedertae,* similarly described by Barnes in 1989, was found at Nye Beach by Los Angeles County Museum assistant, Gail Goedert, a resident of Knappton, Washington. Barnes noted that *Pteronarctos* was the first new pinniped genus from the Pacific Northwest coast since Condon's description of *Desmatophoca* in 1906.

Born in Portsmouth, Virginia, Lawrence Barnes received most of his education in California, completing a PhD from Berkeley in 1972 in vertebrate paleontology and mammalogy. Holding concurrent appointments at the Los Angeles County Museum and the Berkeley Museum of Paleontology, Barnes specializes in marine mammals of the Tertiary.

As much as anyone, Larry Barnes has probably been responsible for the volume of recent work on marine vertebrates of the Oregon coast [photo courtesy Archives, Page Museum, Los Angeles].

Astoria strata near Newport also yielded the skull and humerus of an extinct sea lion, *Desmatophoca oregonensis*, initially discovered and described by Thomas Condon. Ten years after Condon's work, John Merriam wrote to Warren Smith at the University of Oregon on behalf of his graduate student Remington Kellogg, who wanted to examine the specimen. Kellogg was then working on Tertiary seals and sea lions of the Pacific Coast. Since only the upper side of the skull was exposed in Condon's illustration and the under-side was still enclosed in martix, Merriam proposed to have the specimen sent to Berkeley for cleaning, or pay "for the preparation of the under side of the skull at your museum." To prepare and study the specimen, Kellogg ended up coming to Eugene.

A brief note in Mitchell's 1966 paper and restoration by Dalzell shows *Desmatophoca* to be about the size of living sea lions, with a long slender head and sharp teeth. In 1987 Barnes' presented the first in depth treatment, which fully addresses the status of this pinniped. The discovery of a second skull, *Desmatophoca brachycephala* by Gail and James Goedert near Knappton, Washington, as well as a partial skull and canine collected north of Newport by Donald Martel triggered Barnes' study. To date, *Desmatophoca* is known only from the northeast Pacific margin. *Desmatophoca* and *Pteronarctos* inhabited a warm-temperate ocean on an open shelf at moderately shallow depths. Both pinnipeds occupied coastal Oregon during the Miocene, but without more specimens Barnes could not determine whether they lived here during different seasons or migrated simultaneously to the same beaches.

An extinct marine pinniped, *Desmatophoca* **lived on the Oregon coast in the Miocene.**

Remains of only one sea lion, *Eumetopias,* have been reported in the state. While working for the Department of Geology and Mineral Resources, Ewart Baldwin found the radius [lower arm bone] of a sea lion in Pleistocene sediments of the Port Orford Formation near Cape Blanco. Baldwin turned the material over to Earl Packard at Oregon State University, who concluded it was similar to those living on the coast today. Modern day *Eumetopias* first appeared as far back as two million years ago near Japan.

Walruses of the Odobenidae family are among the largest of the carnivorous marine mammals, attaining a weight of up to 1.5 tons on a diet of shrimp, starfish, and molluscs. Just one fossil walrus has been found in Oregon, and the identification of the skull was not determined until approximately 70 years after discovery. The skull and rib fragments of what was thought to be a sea lion were extracted from a sandstone bluff at Fossil Point by a local merchant Harry Camman. The late Miocene Empire Formation here produces a wealth of invertebrates as well as bones of fish and marine mammals. A visitor to Camman's residence in the late 1800s, Smithsonian paleontologist William Dall noted that the German store owner was "without any scientific training, books, or knowledge of paleontology except ... from an old edition of Webster's Dictionary ... Seeking some occupation for his hours of leisure" Camman had become fascinated by the many fossils he found on the beach during his daily strolls. By patrolling after storms, Camman accumulated quite a number, which he stored in a warehouse. Among his shells were vertebra and rib fragments that Dall hesitantly identified as the humpback whale *Megaptera* but declined to purchase because there was no accompanying stratigraphic information and identification was too uncertain. Dall did buy the skull of a carnivore, which the Smithsonian's Frederick True, concluded was a new species of otariid sea lion, *Pontolis magnus*. Over the years pieces of *Pontolis* appeared sporatically, but it was almost 50 years after Dall's publication that Professor Arnold Shotwell referred to part of a jaw from the same region, which likely represented this species. Further preparation and closer examination of Dall's specimen by Repenning and Tedford for their 1977 paper redesignated the bones as from a walrus.

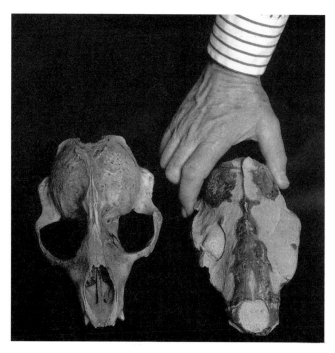

Comparison of the skulls of a primitive aquatic *Pteronarctos* [on the right] and modern seal [photo by Jack Liu; courtesy Condon Museum].

Yet another unique carnivore *Kolponomos newportensis,* of unknown affinity, was recovered in 1969 from strata of the Nye Formation. Somewhat similar to a sea otter, the partial skull, encased in a concretion, was found north of Newport, Lincoln County, by Douglas Emlong. Six years later he found a second part of the same concretion containing the remainder of the skull, mandible, and teeth. Included in a comprehensive volume on marine mammal paleontology in 1994, an article by Richard Tedford, Larry Barnes, and Clayton Ray characterizes the *Kolponomos* as a partially aquatic, near-shore animal whose molar teeth were suited to crushing the hard shells of mussels, limpets, and abalone after prying them off rocks with their incisors and canines. It's possible the creature had a large upper lip, as in modern day walruses, that was sensitive to the touch, enabling the *Kolponomos* to feel its prey in turbulent sea water when visibility was poor. The life style and habitat of *Kolponomos* most closely resembled that of modern sea otters. Since no remains of this mammal have been found in deposits younger than middle Miocene, *Kolponomos* may represent the end of a lineage.

Cetacea, or whales and porpoises, have fully adapted to the marine environment with a thick insulating cover of blubber and streamlined bodies, yet they retain a range of unmistakable mammalian features in their flesh and bone structure. These are the most abundant and varied of the marine mammals and are divided into the Archaeoceti or extinct primitive toothed whales, the Odontoceti or modern toothed whales and porpoises, and the Mysticeti or baleen "whalebone" whales. The first two are carnivorous predators occupying top positions in food chains. The Mysticeti, by contrast, have essentially regressed by eliminating several rungs in the food pyramid to feed directly on small plankton. Almost all modern large whales are Mysticeti, and their body shape readily distinguishes their life style and habitats. The frequency of Mysticete fossils suggests these whales lived in abundant populations off the West Coast during the Miocene epoch, much like their closest living relative, the gray whales.

Primitive toothed archaeocete whales first appeared over 50 million years ago during the Eocene epoch then disappeared before the end of the Oligocene after branching into modern toothed and baleen whales. There are gaps in the ancestry of whales, and their remains have yet to be located in several formations such as the Pittsburg Bluff where there are sharks and bony fish. However, in view of the wide range of paleoenvironments favorable for the preservation of marine vertebrates, the eventual discovery of new fossil cetaceans is inevitable.

Bones of whales from the Eocene through Pleistocene intervals are scattered on the coast from Cape Blanco to the mouth of the Columbia River and in the foothills of the Western Cascades. Most are from the Miocene Astoria Formation, but the oldest cetacean in the state is as yet undescribed vertebra from Keasey sediments.

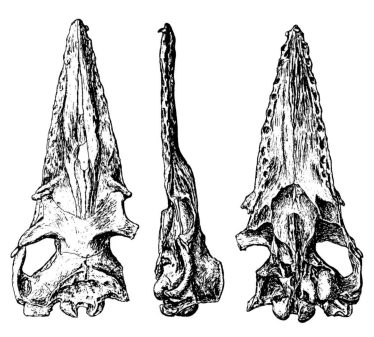

Views of the skull of the primitive whale *Aetiocetus* [after Emlong, 1966].

One of the most noteworthy finds is of the primitive 12-foot long toothed whale from the Oligocene Yaquina Formation in Lincoln County. *Aetiocetus* was initially discovered just north of Seal Rock State Park by Douglas Emlong in March, 1964. After excavating the 30-million year old specimen, he prepared the bones under the supervision of Arnold Shotwell at the Condon Museum in Eugene. Shotwell provided Emlong with a research appointment, guidance, work place, and limited financial support. Benefitting from advice by both Shotwell and Remington Kellogg of the Smithsonian, Emlong described the new genus as an Archaeocete of the species *Aetiocetus cotylalveus* in 1966. The complete skull, teeth, and most of the vertebra of the *Aetiocetus* were so distinctive that Emlong even proposed a new family name Aetiocetidae for this unique creature - this despite the fact that the skeleton of the animal displays many characteristics of baleen whales [Mysticeti]. Wear on the tooth crowns along with numerous crab shells and fish remains at the same spot attest to the diverse diet of *Aetiocetus*. Emlong's classification, has since been disputed, and some paleontologists have assigned the whale to the mysticetes in spite of its multiple sharp teeth. The 1994 papers by Barnes and his co-authors summarize both sides of the controversy.

Other skeletal remains of *Aetiocetus* have turned up on the coast. Emlong mentions two well-preserved skulls and bones that are similar from the Yaquina and Toledo formations. Another nearly complete skull - also from near Seal Rock State Park - was found by Bruce Welton in 1969. The remainder of the skeleton, uncovered a few years later by Welton, Barnes, and assistants, was named *Aetiocetus weltoni* by Barnes in 1994.

Immediately after graduating from high school, Douglas Emlong opened a private museum on the coast at Depoe Bay where admission to see the collection was .50 cents [photo courtesy of Oregon Department of Geology and Mineral Industries].

Growing up on the Oregon coast, Douglas Emlong was fascinated with fossils from an early age, collecting his first marine vertebrate at Fogarty Creek when he was 14 years old. His enthusiasm and zeal were such that after school he would often have the bus drop him off at the sea cliff where he was extracting fossils, hiding his finds in bushes along the roadside until he could come back in a friend's car to retrieve them. Seeking to sell his fossils in 1967, he contracted with the Smithsonian Institution whose paleontologist

Clayton Ray, accompanied by Frank Whitmore and Charles Repenning of the U.S. Geological Survey, valued some 40,000 pounds of fossils at $30,000. In a letter, Shotwell asked the Oregon State Land Board to examine the collection to assure that no specimens had been taken illegally from state land. However, the Board unanimously decided that it "would take no action to assert an ownership interest in any part of the collection." Something of a recluse, Emlong suffered from emotional problems, and in 1980, while still a young man of 38, fell to his death at Devils Punch Bowl.

Since Emlong's description of *Aetiocetus*, similar fragmentary whale bones from the Scotts Mills Formation have come to light along Butte Creek in Marion County. This is the most easterly marine cetacean in Oregon, and several vertebra were discovered in the creek bed by residents Jake Fryberger and Glenn Slentz. A large slab containing the fossils was removed intact from the late Oligocene siltstones by William Orr's paleontology class during the summer of 1972. The presence of both juveniles and adults of *Aetiocetus* indicate a developing coastal population of these predators that are like modern Orca killer whales. After the recent discovery of *Aetiocetus* from middle Tertiary sediments in Japan, the geographic distribution of this primitive whale is beginning to emerge.

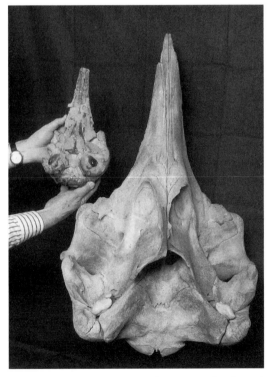

The skull of a long-nosed porpoise with tiny slightly hooked teeth - part of Guy Pierson's collection from the coast - is dwarfed by that of a modern toothed whale [photo by Jack Liu; courtesy Condon Museum].

The recovery of Oligocene whale remains in the Pacific Northwest is noteworthy as there was a pronounced drop in the number of cetaceans worldwide during this epoch. It is curious that although two new groups, Mysticeti and Odontoceti, appear for the first time during the Oligocene, this interval is marked by its limited populations and low diversity of cetaceans. This lull correlates well with a simultaneous global drop in plankton. Even though the baleen whales (Mysticeti) consumed enormous quantities of plankton, there can be little doubt of the key role of plankton in the food pyramids of toothed whales as well. Further evidence suggests that the waning plankton populations may have been set off by slow but profound changes in worldwide sea temperatures and ocean circulation. It is not uncommon for an environmental crisis to trigger the appearance of new and innovative life forms.

Toothed odontocete whales have not yet been reported from Oregon, but there are many porpoise skulls waiting to be described in the Emlong collection at the Smithsonian. Similarly Guy Pierson of Newport has collected and prepared undescribed porpoise remains having rows of tiny pointed teeth set in an elongate beak, most of which are from the Astoria Formation.

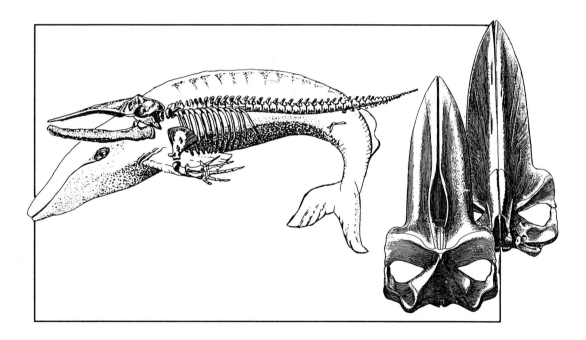

The baleen whale *Cophocetus* is the most frequently recovered fossil whale in Oregon. The spade-shaped skull is typical of cetaceans [from Orr and Orr, 1996; Packard and Kellogg, 1934].

Of all the skeletons and fragments of baleen whales along the coast, most are from Miocene Astoria strata, long known for its richness of vertebrates. Indeed, the first such whale to be recorded from Oregon was from the Astoria by James Dana, a geologist accompanying an expedition sent out by the U.S. government to explore the west. Commanded by Charles Wilkes, the party landed near Puget Sound in the Spring of 1841. Dana explored the coast south into Oregon where he collected vertebra and ribs of a whale along with fish, crabs, mollusc shells, and plants about 13 miles above the mouth of the Columbia River. Another explorer to the region from 1848 to 1860 was naturalist and geologist George Gibbs, who sent cetacean fossils from this same formation to his sponsors at the Academy of Natural Sciences in Philadelphia.

Following this, a new genus of a primitive baleen whale, *Cophocetus oregonensis,* from the Astoria was named by Earl Packard and Remington Kellogg. The skeleton, lying in a nearly horizontal position with part of the jaw and skull exposed, was found at Newport by Packard in 1920. Packard and his student Rachel Husband excavated the specimen, and, after transporting it to Eugene, Husband did most of the tedious preparatory work. John Merriam reported the find to Remington Kellogg, a cetacean expert at Berkeley. In 1932 Kellogg wrote to Packard that he would like to examine the specimen, so Packard obligingly send sketches and a preliminary manuscript. He advised Kellogg, who was to arrive by train, that "The specimen is in my Eugene office and you could begin its study even though I were not present."

A few years later another baleen whale was recovered by Eugene Callaghan, a geology student at the University of Oregon, while a third skull was collected about 1932 by J.C. Snyder, a store-keeper at Otter Rock. As is typical of Astoria fossils, several of the bones were encased inside large hard concretions. Packard befriended Snyder, who was described in a letter, as a man "who is also somewhat interested in fossils", and Synder consequently loaned his *Cophocetus* skull to Packard for preparation. In his role as state paleontologist after the death of Thomas Condon, Packard was routinely notified of fossils picked up on Oregon beaches, so that over the years he examined well over a hundred occurrences of whale fragments. Similarly, in ensuing years, Museum curators have identified dozens of whale remains from the coast, most of which turned out to be *Cophocetus.*

Many fossils are found by interested persons, who build large private collections. Often these are scattered or sold when the owner dies, but some find their way into museums. Such was the case with the collections of Alonzo Hancock and Andrew Sherwood. Around 1947 Hancock, from Portland, found a fine skull of a whale at Spencer Creek in Lincoln County, which was later sold to the Oregon Museum of Science and Industry as part of his extensive fossil inventory. Numerous whale vertebra and mandibles owned by Andrew Sherwood, a state geologist from the Pennsylvania Survey who retired to Portland, were ultimately donated to the Horner Museum at Oregon State University in 1934, but what became of the large J.C. Snyder collection isn't known. Much of Guy Pierson's superb pinnipeds, cetacea, and invertebrates obtained from the 1960s through the 1990s were donated to the Museum at Eugene.

Guy Pierson's interest in fossils began when he would gather up dinosaur bones as a young boy visiting relatives in Montana. Although educated as an economist, Pierson stated in a newspaper interview that he "fell back into my old ways" when he moved to Moolack Beach where he was "sitting right on the fossil beds." For many years Pierson gave talks about fossils to Portland schools and displayed his collection to visitors [photo courtesy S. Pierson].

South of Coos Bay, late Tertiary and Pleistocene whale bones, worked loose from the cliffs at Cape Blanco, included a miscellany of mandibles, vertebra, ribs, limbs, and skulls of the Empire Formation. When seen by Packard, some were too fragmented to be identified, but a dozen or so others, accessed into the Horner Museum, were later described. Among items donated by Maude Kohl of Port Orford, a unique specimen showing a carbonized impression of baleen plates of a Mysticete whale caught Packard's attention. Stiff at one end and fringe-like at the other, baleen is suspended in the mouth of a whale to screen and filter its food. Unlike bone, baleen is of chitinous organic composition unlikely to be preserved without rapid burial to protect it from bacteria. The irregular water worn chitinous block, described by Packard, was 18 inches long, 11 inches wide, 4 inches thick, with a pattern of bristle-like fibers regularly spaced across the surface. The specimen was not collected in place, but rock matrix still adhering to the block confirmed it was from Empire strata.

One of the most recent whale finds, projecting from sediments of the Port Orford Formation, was recovered in 1988. Bones of an enormous baleen whale were noticed by a San Diego tourist, who alerted the Parks Department because the fossils were on state park land at Cape Blanco. The specimen was brought to the attention of paleontologist David Taylor from Portland State University. Taylor excavated vertebra, ribs, and portions of a fin, which now reside at the Northwest Museum of Natural History in Portland.

Remains of an enormous Ice Age baleen whale were excavated from near Cape Blanco [photo by D. Taylor; courtesy Oregon Department of Geology and Mineral Industries].

Traditionally the evolutionary lines of modern day dugongs and manatees [Sirenia] and extinct bizarre quadruped mammals [Desmostylia] have been linked to elephants, but this is no longer the case. Even though both were herbivores inhabiting the nearshore to intertidal region, they are currently regarded as in separate lineages.

Sirenians first appeared during the Eocene, but their single presence in Oregon is in early Miocene sediments of the Nye Mudstone. A partial skull and jaw of the dugong, *Halitheriinae*, was found in 1984 by the private collector Guy Pierson and donated to the Smithsonian Museum. Enclosed in a concretion that had been drilled through by clams, the fragments were discovered at State Wayside Park south of Newport, Lincoln County. Daryl Domning at Howard University and the Smithsonian's Clayton Ray, who examined the Oregon specimen, concluded that *Halitheriinae* reached the West Coast from the Caribbean when the coastal waters were at their warmest.

The ancestry of Desmostylids, which inhabited coastal regions of the Pacific Ocean between 30 to 10 million years ago, is problematic, and, for this reason, *Desmostylus* has recently been treated separately.

Very few skulls of this peculiar extinct mammal have been found, and is is largely represented in the fossil record by its frequent and distinctive cheek teeth. The generic name *Desmostylus,* derived from the Greek *Desmos* [bundle] and *Stylos* [pillar/column], refers to the structure of these odd molars as a tightly packed group of tapering cylinders. One rare skull from Spencer Creek in Lincoln County was chiselled out of the Miocene Astoria sandstone by J.G. Crawford of Albany and sold to the Smithsonian in 1914. Several years later Oliver Hay, vertebrate paleontologist at the same institution, named the beast *Desmostylus hesperus.*

The distinctive molar teeth of *Desmostylus* are multiple cylinders [photo courtesy Condon Museum].

A research associate at the Museum of Paleontology, Berkeley, Vertress L. Vanderhoof studied all of the available desmostylian remains in 1937 assigning them to the sea cow [Sirenia] order of marine mammals. In attempting to come to some conclusions about the life-style of desmostylids, Vanderhoof noted that all known fossils occur in shallow water sediments and speculated that the omnivorous animals lived on a diet of molluscs, sea weed, and shore grasses. The solid enamel cyllindrical teeth were well-suited for crushing shells and "the shovel-like lower jaw, armed with formidable tusks, would have been an excellent scoop in a clam bed." He pointed out that the California locations where *Desmostylus* remains turn up are invariably shell beds.

A jaw, teeth, and tusk, sold to the Smithsonian by Douglas Emlong, was named as a new species of desmostylid, *Behemotops emlongi,* by Daryl Domning, Malcolm McKenna at the American Museum, and Clayton Ray. In a letter of March, 1977, shortly after the discovery, Emlong wrote to Ray that "I stopped at Seal Rock ... and found the most interesting thing of all - a giant desmostylian-like mandible ... The Oligocene specimen is far larger and heavier and I am sure it is a great find ... It may be related to that giant tusk ... from the Yaquina Formation, and is not far from that area." Emlong's collection has a substantial inventory of desmostylian material from the Yaquina, Nye, and Astoria formations.

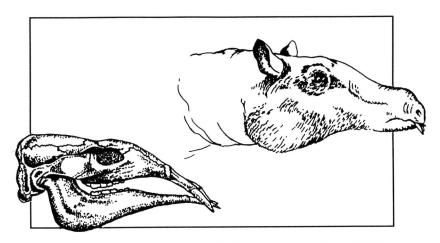

A reconstructed *Desmostylus* skull [from Orr and Orr, 1996].

Domning, Ray, and McKenna reexamined the earlier notion that *Desmostylus* was related to both Sirenia [sea cows] and Proboscidea [elephants]. Considering several lines of evidence, they concluded that while there was a common ancestor between elephants and desmostylids, Sirenia are a separate group. In addition, the resemblance of desmostylid body size, build, and jaw to the hippopotomus suggests similar lifestyles. Never straying from from salt water, these creatures may have fed on algae and other marine plants. Whereas Vanderhoof felt the projecting tusks were ideal for digging up molluscs, Domning notes the "incisors and canines ... seem well suited to forking up masses of vegetation, detatching plants from rocks ... or uprooting mats of rhizomes." Artistic restorations of *Desmostylus* by Bonnie Dalzell in Mitchell's 1966 paper prudently obscured the front feet and type of food eaten by this strange animal.

As work proceeds on Oregon's fossil aquatic vertebrates, a more complete picture will emerge to complement the present knowledge.

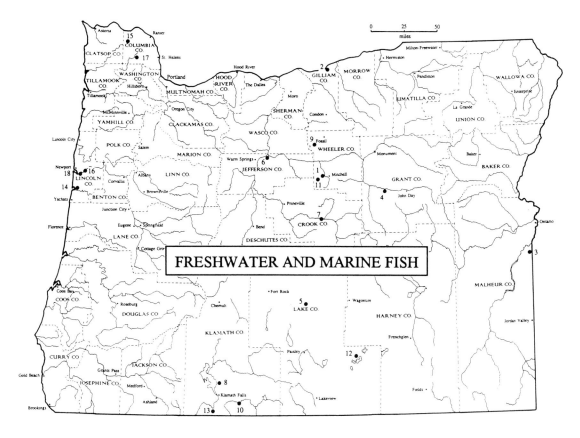

FRESHWATER FISH

1. Allen Ranch, west of Mitchell, Wheeler Co. John Day Fm. Oligocene. Cavender, 1969.
2. Arlington, Gilliam Co. The Dalles Fm.? Miocene. Cavender and Miller, 1972.
3. Blackjack Butte, Malheur Co. Deer Butte Fm. Miocene. Kimmel, 1975.
4. Dayville, 13 mi. east of. Grant Co. ?Mascall Fm. Miocene. Cope, 1883; Uyeno
   and Miller, 1963.
5. Fossil Lake, Lake Co. No Fm. Pleistocene. Allison, 1966; Cope, 1883; 1889.
   Uyeno and Miller, 1963.
6. Gateway, Jefferson Co. Deschutes Fm. Pliocene. Cavender and Miller, 1972.
7. Grays Ranch, 10 mi. east of Post, Crook Co. John Day Fm. Oligocene. Chaney, 1927.
8. Klamath Lake, Klamath County. Pliocene/Pleistocene. Uyeno and Miller, 1963.
9. Knox Ranch, 6 mi. east of Clarno, Wheeler Co. John Day Fm. Oligocene. Cavender, 1969.
10. Lost River, Klamath Co. Pleistocene. Jordan, 1907; Uyeno and Miller, 1963.
11. Ochoco Mtns., Wheeler Co. Clarno Fm. Eocene. Cavender, 1968.
12. Warner Lake, Lake Co. Pleistocene. Cope, 1883.
13. Worden, Klamath Co. ?Yonna Fm. Pliocene. Cavender and Miller, 1972.

MARINE FISH

14. Alsea Bay, Lincoln Co. Yaquina Fm. Oligocene. David, 1956.
15. Mist, Columbia Co. Keasey Fm. Eocene. David, 1956.
16. Toledo, Lincoln Co. Nestucca Fm. Eocene. David, 1956.
17. Vernonia, Columbia Co. Pittsburg Bluff Fm. Oligocene. David, 1956; Moore, 1976.
18. Yaquina Bay, Lincoln Co. Nye Mudstone. Miocene. David, 1956.

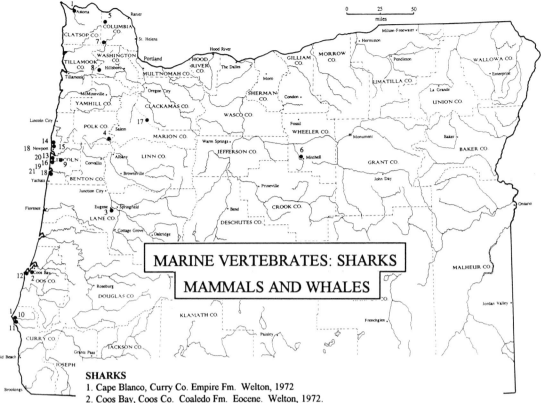

SHARKS

1. Cape Blanco, Curry Co. Empire Fm. Welton, 1972.
2. Coos Bay, Coos Co. Coaledo Fm. Eocene. Welton, 1972.
3. Eugene, Lane Co. Eugene Fm. Eocene. Welton, 1972.
4. Helmick Hill, Polk Co. Spencer Fm. Eocene. Welton, 1972; 1979.
5. Mist, Columbia Co. Keasey Fm. Eocene. Welton, 1972; 1979.
6. Mitchell, Wheeler Co. Hudspeth Fm. Cretaceous. Welton, 1972.
7. Nehlem River Valley, Columbia Co. Cowlitz/Pittsburg Bluff fms. Eocene. Steere, 1957; Welton, 1972.
8. Scoggins Creek, Washington Co. Yamhill Fm. Eocene. Applegate, 1968.
9. Toledo, Lincoln Co. Nestucca Fm. Eocene. Welton, 1972.

OTTERS, SEALS, SEA LIONS, WALRUSES

10. Cape Blanco, Curry Co. Empire Fm. Miocene. Packard, 1947.
11. Cape Blanco, Curry Co. Elk River/Port Orford Fms. Pleistocene. Barnes and Mitchell, 1975; Leffler, 1964; Packard, 1947.
12. Coos Bay, Coos Co. Empire Fm. Miocene. Dall, 1909; Tedford and Repenning, 1977.
13. Lost Creek, Lincoln Co. Nye Mudstone. Miocene. Berta, 1991.
14. Moolack Beach, Lincoln Co. Astoria Fm. Miocene. Barnes, 1990; Packard, 1947.
15. Newport, Lincoln Co. Astoria Fm. Miocene. Barnes, 1987, 1989; Tedford, Barnes, and Ray, 1994.
16. Seal Rock, Lincoln Co. Yaquina Fm. Oligocene. Berta, 1991.

WHALES

17. Butte Creek, Clackamas Co. Scotts Mills Fm. Oligocene. Orr and Miller, 1983.
18. Newport, Lincoln Co. Astoria Fm. Packard and Kellogg, 1934.
19. Seal Rock, Lincoln Co. Yaquina Fm. Oligocene. Barnes, et al., 1994; Emlong, 1966.

DUGONGS AND DESMOSTYLIDS

20. Lost Creek, Lincoln Co. Nye Mudstone. Miocene. Domning and Ray, 1986.
21. Seal Rock, Lincoln Co. Yaquina Fm. Oligocene. Domning, Ray, and McKenna, 1986.

A 1925 fossil collecting expedition to the John Day region from the University of California crossing the Columbia River by ferry between Roosevelt and Arlington [photo Archives, Page Museum, Los Angeles].

OREGON FOSSIL MAMMALS AND OTHER LAND VERTEBRATES

Land mammals first appeared in the fossil record during the Triassic period more than 200 million years in the past, about the same time that the dinosaurs emerged. These early mammals were small rat-size creatures that fed on insects and co-existed with dinosaurs for several million years before the demise of those large reptiles at the end of the Cretaceous period. After that time, about 65 million years ago, the smaller animals rapidly diversified to dominate terrestrial habitats.

Fossil mammals typically occur in nonmarine rocks such as wind blown dune sands, fine-grained lake deposits, and the coarse sands and gravels of streams and rivers. Normally oceanic strata are not a likely place for preservation of extensive terrestrial vertebrate remains, although occasional mammals other than whales or seals are found in marine rocks. Most Mesozoic rocks in Oregon - including the Triassic, Jurassic, and Cretaceous periods - are marine. Oregon's oldest rocks to have fossil mammals are 44 million year old nonmarine Eocene exposures in the eastern part of the state. Virtually all of the Eocene through Miocene intervals containing fossil land mammals are in eastern Oregon, whereas Pleistocene locations are scattered throughout the state.

During the 1980s several increasingly precise geologic time scales were published. A Cenozoic chronology of North American mammals stages was edited by John Armentrout in 1981.

M.Y.A.	EPOCHS	NORTH AMERICAN LAND MAMMAL STAGES	TERTIARY MAMMAL FAUNAS
	PLEIST.	RANCHOLABREAN	FOSSIL LAKE-CHRISTMAS LAKE-SILVER LAKE < 1mybp
		IRVINGTONIAN	
	PLIOCENE		YONNA Fm. 2.0mybp •
		BLANCAN	
5			McKAY/ARLINGTON FAUNAS, McKay Fm. 5.5-8.5mybp
		HEMPHILLIAN	RATTLESNAKE FAUNA, Rattlesnake Fm. 6.4mybp
			LITTLE VALLEY/JUNIPER CREEK FAUNAS, Chalk Butte Fm. 8.5mybp
			BARTLETT MTN./OTIS BASIN FAUNAS. Drewsey Fm. 8.5mybp
10			ROME FAUNA, 10.5mybp
		CLARENDONIAN	THE DALLES FAUNA, The Dalles Fm. 10.5mybp
			BLACK BUTTE FAUNA, Juntura Fm. 11.3mybp
	MIOCENE		
15		BARSTOVIAN	BEATYS BUTTE/QUARTZ BASIN FAUNAS, Deer Butte Fm. 15.0mybp
			SKULL SPRINGS/RED BASIN FAUNAS, Butte Creek Volcanic Sandstone 15.0mybp
			MASCALL FAUNA, Mascall Fm. 15.4mybp
		HEMINGFORDIAN	SUCKER CREEK FAUNA, Sucker Creek Fm. 16.7
			WARM SPRINGS FAUNA, John Day Fm. 18-19mybp
20			HAYSTACK VALLEY FAUNA, John Day Fm. 19-20
			KIMBERLY FAUNA, John Day Fm. 22.mybp
25		ARIKAREEAN	
	OLIGOCENE		TURTLE COVE FAUNA, John Day Fm. 28.6mybp
30		WHITNEYAN	
		ORELLIAN	
35			
		CHADRONIAN	
			CLARNO MAMMAL QUARRY, Clarno Fm. 38mybp
40			
		DUCHESNEAN	
45		UINTAN	CLARNO NUT BEDS, Clarno Fm. 44mybp
	EOCENE		
		BRIDGERIAN	
50			
		WASATCHIAN	
		CLARKFORKIAN	
55			
		TIFFANIAN	
	PALEOCENE		
60			
65			• m.y.b.p. (millions of years before the present)

266

GEOLOGIC DATING

Initially it was difficult to resolve the age of nonmarine rocks in North America with vertebrate fossils because there was no standardized biostratigraphic chart to use as a guide. When the geologic record was being delineated and refined in the 1800 s, research was carried out in marine basins of Great Britain and western Europe, so that time terms like "Eocene", "Miocene", and "Pliocene" were based on characteristic mollusc shells occurring there. A complete chronology for invertebrates was ultimately established, and these European time divisions were carried over to the major marine basins of North America. However, it was still impossible to correlate accurately nonmarine rocks which had mammal fossils because of the totally different environments.

In rare areas where marine rocks can be traced laterally directly into nonmarine strata of the same age, a prehistoric "strand" or shoreline between the old ocean and land has been crossed. In this case the marine and nonmarine layers interfinger, and nonmarine rocks can be dated by using molluscs in the adjacent marine deposits. For the most part, however, correlating or dating nonmarine strata by using mammal fossils was difficult and imprecise.

To remedy this problem, paleontologists established a separate chronology of "mammal stages" based on local North American vertebrate faunas. One characteristic of mammals is that they evolve rapidly and thus tend to have very short stratigraphic ranges. The duration, then, of mammal species in the geological record from first appearance to disappearance is notably short when compared to that of fossil plants and invertebrates, and the limited stratigraphic ranges pinpoint the age of the entombing rock particularly well. Later, by the use of radioactive decay techniques ("absolute dating") and magnetic stratigraphy, mammal stages were precisely tied in with the established European epochs. This more recent method of magnetic reversal stratigraphy is based on changes in polarity of the earth's magnetic field. Integrating these new time charts with the fossil records of vertebrates, molluscs, foraminifera, and plants into a single chronologic framework has provided a standard for comparison with worldwide time charts.

FOSSIL RECORD

In the fossil record not all animals are created equal. Because of their sizable populations and prolific reproductive rate, smaller mammals such as gophers, rats, mice and shrews produce far more fossil material than the less numerous ungulates or hoofed mammals. Ungulates, in turn, invariably leave a better record than the more rare predators. The environment also plays a role. Fossil remains of animals that lived in a lowland or plains region, where sedimentary deposition takes place, are invariably more numerous than those living in a hilly or mountainous region, where erosion predominates. If animal carcasses are transported in streams before being deposited, much of the skeletal material is lost or destroyed in transit.

Mammals are represented in the fossil record by their bones and teeth, and since they are the most durable part of the skeleton, teeth are most commonly preserved. A single vertebrate animal may leave over one hundred separate fossil bones, but the complexity of the mammalian skeleton is such that the various parts can be readily associated with a given species. Because of the appearance of the crown surface, the cheek or jaw teeth are highly distinctive and can be used for identification. The architecture of the enamel and dentine along with normal wear on the teeth produces a characteristic pattern for most species much like a fingerprint.

In addition to aiding in the identification of a given mammal, aspects of the skeleton reflect the animal's niche in the environment. For example, the high crowned teeth of pronghorn antelope indicate a diet of abrasive grass. The condition and frequency of fossil skeletal parts may provide insight to the environmental conditions at the time and place of burial and entombment. If a generous number of bones of a specimen are found at one site and if they show minimal wear, death and burial probably occurred at that location. However, most skeletal debris is badly degraded and dispersed by running water and scavengers.

An imaginary Tertiary landscape inhabited by tapirs, deer, a heron-like bird, and palm trees. [Pouchet, 1882]

ENVIRONMENTS

The Cenozoic era in Oregon was a time of almost continuous volcanic activity, which had dramatic effects on the environment while providing optimum conditions to preserve a record of ancient life. At the beginning of the Eocene epoch, 55 million years ago, Oregon's coastline lay along what is today the eastern side of the Willamette Valley. Volcanism, related to the subduction of massive earth crustal plates, produced vast amounts of lava and ash from local erupting vents. Mixing with water to form muddy lahars, this debris swept down, covered, and entombed plants and animals. Streams were plugged resulting in large ponds and swamps. In a warm moist tropical landscape the lush, heavy vegetation was the natural habitat to such animals as horses, camels, cats, oreodons, and larger herbivores like rhinoceros, unitatheres, and brontotheres. Crocodiles and aquatic turtles of formidable size completed the picture.

The end of the Eocene was marked by early construction of the Cascade volcanic range and an abrupt climate change from warm tropical to cool temperate. Lakes and ponds initially gave way to woodlands, drained by well-developed stream systems, and eventually grassland savannas in the late Oligocene and Miocene, 40 to 20 million years ago. Ongoing eruptions, resulting in heavy ash falls, mud flows of volcanic debris, and superheated gasses, killed and buried plants and animals on a grand scale. Destruction and mass mortality in the vicinity of the volcanoes was spectacular and total. Herds of plains-dwellers such as sheep-like oreodons, camels, rhinoceroses, and horses - dependent on the plants for food - may have been overwhelmed by the rain of volcanic debris that would have killed off much of the vegetation, ruined the water supply, and made the air unbreathable.

The Clarno Formation at Clarno Ferry is layers of mud flows and lava along with multicolored fossil soils [photo courtesy Condon Museum].

269

The dawning of the Pliocene five million years ago saw continued outpourings from the High Cascades and moderating climate. This brief interval lasted only a few million years until temperatures dropped and sheets of ice repeatedly advanced and retreated during the Pleistocene. Glaciers blocked stream and river drainages, that released huge floods, backing up 400-foot deep lakes in the Willamette Valley. Between floods, herds of strange-looking elephants, bison, and clawed sloths along with carnivores such as large cats and wolves populated the state. Shallow lakes in south and eastern Oregon provided a habitat for flocks of migratory birds as well as fish, and other animals, many of which became extinct around 11,000 years ago. Following continued elevation of the Coast Range and retreat of glaciers, the state acquired its present day appearance.

ANIMALS OF THE EOCENE EPOCH

Eocene fossil mammal remains are rarely preserved in Oregon, and most are in deposits of the Clarno and lowermost John Day formations in Wheeler County. Located a few miles from the abandoned village of Clarno, mud flows, volcanic tuffs, and stream debris of the Clarno Formation entomb not only fruits, wood, leaves, and seeds of the famed Nut Beds, but vertebrate remains of the equally widely known Hancock Mammal Quarry as well. In contrast to the younger 39.2-million year old Mammal Quarry, the 44-million year old Nut Beds have ample representation of plant life but limited animal fossils.

Hyrachyus, **a small fleet running rhinoceros, is remarkably horse-like in appearance [B. Horsfall in Scott, 1913].**

Restricted to a small area on the west side of Hancock Canyon, the Nut Beds have yielded a meagre collection of 80 fossil vertebrate specimens, and, of these, six species are larger animals. The first-known mammal fossil from the Nut Beds was a tooth of the upland running rhinoceros, *Hyrachyus*, discovered near Clarno bridge next to a fossilized walnut. Spotted in 1942 by Lorene Bones, whose husband amassed a fabulous collection of plant remains here, the tooth was given to Alonzo W. Hancock, a collector from Portland. Hancock had already spent more than 20 years in search of eastern Oregon vertebrate fossils and immediately realized the value of the find. The tooth was sent to the Museum at the University of Oregon for identification and then presented to the University of California, Berkeley, where it was described by Ruben Stirton. Slender and strikingly pony-like in appearance, the agile *Hyrachyus* was about the size of a Great Dane.

In subsequent years Hancock found several unidentifiable bone fragments, but in 1952 a jaw, several teeth, and vertebra, shown to Arnold Shotwell, director of the Condon Museum at Eugene, proved to be a small brontothere named *Metarhinus*. Shotwell suggested that he clean the matrix from the bones and urged Hancock to "turn the specimen over to the Museum" because of its value for research.

A *Patriofelis* [cat] from the Clarno Formation [from B. Horsfall in Scott, 1913].

Even though these finds were unusual, there were few published reports, and it wasn't until 1996 that a University of California student, C. Bruce Hanson, described the fauna. At the same time Hanson closely examined tooth patterns [dentition] of animals from the Clarno Nut Beds and Mammal Quarry previously collected and housed in museums in Oregon, California, Washington, and elsewhere. In his recent study of vertebrates from the Nut Beds, Han-

271

son listed such creatures as *Hadrianus* [a land turtle], *Hyrachyus* [rhinoceros], *Orohippus* [4-toed horse], *Patriofelis* [cat], *Telmatherium* [brontothere] and crocodiles. The presence of crocodilians and large land tortoises in the Clarno is quite significant in that it indicates a frost free subtropical to temperate climate.

A brontothere *Telmatherium* from the Clarno Nut Beds [from B. Horsfall, in Scott, 1913].

A Clarno Formation horse *Orohippus* [from B. Horsfall, in Scott, 1913].

About 1/2 mile northeast of the Nut Beds, the Hancock Mammal Quarry in the upper part of the Clarno Formation has yielded a trove of animal remains dominated by the spectacular elephant-sized brontotheres, which became extinct very early in the Oligocene. Confined to a narrow area 16 by 120 feet, these mammal beds were explored by Lon Hancock beginning in the Spring of 1954. Hancock, who had been directed to the site by a friend and agate enthusiast, Albert McGuiness, recovered close to 200 bones that April. These were identified by Arnold Shotwell at Eugene as those of large aquatic rhinoceroses [*Amynodon* and *Metamynodon*], and an unitathere. An immense herbivore, common in the Eocene, the unitathere had paired bony protruberances on the head and greatly elongate canine teeth. As he continued field work over the summer, Hancock and student volunteers from the Oregon Museum of Science and Industry summer camp turned up a spectacular 3,000 fragments of bone and teeth of other late Eocene animals.

Alonzo "Lon" Hancock with a rhinoceros skull from the Clarno Formation [photo courtesy Condon Museum].

Born in Harrison, Arkansas, in 1884, Alonzo "Lon" Hancock's career with the U.S. Postal Service in Portland didn't hamper his interest in paleontology and geology. As far back as 1940 when Lon and his wife Berrie worked in eastern Oregon, they were accompanied by young students - camping, lecturing, and educating them on geologic history. Many of these summer students went on to become professional paleontologists. After retirement, Lon and Berrie organized and operated a permanent camp here until Hancock's death in 1961. In 1946, fifteen years earlier, Hancock, who had amassed over 10,000 fossils, donated his collection to Oregon Museum of Science and Industry. These were subsequently transferred from his home to a memorial room at the OMSI building in Portland.

Hancock's field site was formalized in 1951 as Camp Hancock in Wheeler County under the auspices of the Portland-based Oregon Museum of Science and Industry. Initially a few primitive tents, open-air mess hall, and classrooms, permanent buildings were constructed in the late 1960s under the director and former student John Armentrout. Since the first years when about a dozen boys remained at Camp Hancock for two weeks, the camp now hosts up to 1,300 students from the middle of March through October. Most of the fossil-rich exposures were on land once owned by the Emil Maurer family, and representatives of OMSI secured a lease for the land that covered much of the fossil beds. Because Emil and Katherine Maurer were friends of Hancock, they only charged $1.00 for the contract. OMSI has since purchased the 10 acres of the immediate campground, and the surrounding land is owned by the National Park Service. OMSI, in a cooperative effort with the Park Service and Bureau of Land Management, periodically sweeps across the fossil-rich vertebrate exposures, utilizing aerial photos to locate, excavate, clean, record, and store bones that come to light.

Hancock's 1954 discovery of numbers of fossil mammals in the Eocene Clarno Formation had an electrifying effect on paleontologists in North America and focused attention on eastern Oregon. George Gaylord Simpson of the American Museum, Donald Savage and Ruben Stirton from the University of California, Earl Packard, Dean of Sciences at Oregon State University, Arnold Shotwell from the University of Oregon, and the Portland Oregon Museum of Science and Industry all expressed interest in the Clarno material and were concerned about how "this discovery of major scientific importance" would be handled as Simpson put it in a letter of August 24, 1954. Simpson suggested that Shotwell, as a professional paleontologist, was the obvious person to oversee the excavation. Earl Packard, then at Palo Alto, California, called it "one of the most important vertebrate discoveries in the Oregon Tertiary since the early 80s" and felt that Shotwell or the American Museum should handle the excavation. Donald Savage volunteered to send someone up from Berkeley, and on September 13, Shotwell wrote to Hancock that "I am sure you and I can work together well. As far as I'm concerned that's the way it will be."

A formal contract was drawn up between OMSI and the Condon Museum at the University for the site to be excavated jointly under supervision of Hancock and Shotwell. All material from the quarry was to be housed ultimately in Eugene at the Museum. This cooperative agreement worked well, and in the summer of 1955 Shotwell enlisted Malcolm McKenna, Burton Coombs, and Donald Russell from the University of California, Berkeley, to assist.

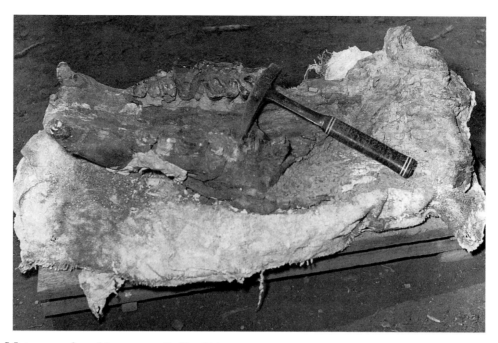

A *Metamynodon* rhinoceros skull still in plaster field jacket [photo courtesy Condon Museum].

From the middle of June until August 31, over 355 bones and skulls and 17 small teeth were washed out of the matrix. A daily journal kept by Coombs recorded for Monday, June 20, a typical day. "Walked up to the mammal bed from camp first thing this morning. Put a cast over the top and sides of the large femur. This plaster mix was good, but that on the skull cast yesterday wasn't [dry]... so scraped the undried plaster from the skull cast down to the burlap and will recast when dry." There was concern that visitors might damage some of the specimens, and Coombs recorded of a visitor on Monday, July 4, "Will have to keep an eye on him until he leaves..."

A truck was often used to handle heavier loads, and the journal reads for Sunday, June 19. "Decided to take the truck up to the mammal bed ... but ... on the way up the engine died and would not start. Finally found the trouble to be a broken exhaust line (copper tubing) from the heater .. We patched this with a handkerchief and string." And on Tuesday, August 30: "Hauled 2 loads of casts back from the mammal bed this morning. Had to build a road down into it to get a big 400 lb. cast into it. Worked hard all morning and rested and went swimming all afternoon."

Much of the Clarno mammal material stored from the 1950s is still unworked and unpublished. The partially crushed skull of *Hemipsalodon grandis* was identified by Malcolm McKenna, curator at the American Museum of Natural History, who turned the information over to James Mellett, at the Department of Geology, New York University. Mellett noted in an 1969 paper that the 16-inch long skull was that of an old individual about the size of a bear. *Hemipsalodon* was the largest member of the Hyaedontidae family of extinct carnivorous mammals.

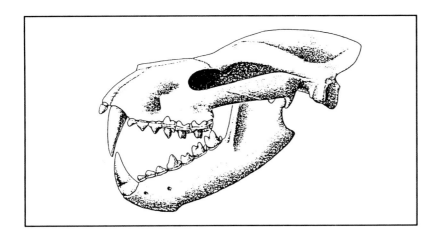

A heavy duty predator-scavenger *Hemipsalodon grandis* [after Mellett, 1969].

A 1988 graduate thesis by Jennifer Pratt from the University of Oregon examines the paleoenvironment of the Quarry. Supervised by Professor Greg Retallack, Pratt's study looked at the fossil plants, animals, soils [paleosols], and deposition, concluding that a clay paleosol layer preserved the mammals, fish, and aligators. The animal remains accumulated on an inside meander of a stream during times of flood. Since the bones were scattered but showed little signs of wear, Pratt suggested that the animal carcasses were carried in the water while still covered by flesh. She lists both animals and plants from the Hancock Quarry, noting that plants such as vines, dogwoods, and nuts grew as part of a forest covering.

A primitive tapir *Protapirus* from the Eocene Hancock Quarry [from B. Horsfall, in Scott, 1913].

A clawed oreodon *Agriochoerus* [from B. Horsfall, in Scott, 1913].

The small browsing, three-toed horse *Haplohippus* is typical of the Clarno Formation [from B. Horsfall, in Scott, 1913].

For his 1996 study of the fauna of the Hancock Quarry, C. Bruce Hanson examined over 2,000 items. He was able to identify 14 vertebrate species, 11 of which were mammals, along with an alligator and an aquatic turtle of the Chelydridae family - the only recorded North American specimen from the interval 40 to 30 million years ago. He documented other remarkable finds such as the skull and jaws of the supercarnivore, *Hemipsalodon grandis,* the tooth of a member of the Nimravidae [cat] family - the earliest North American record of this carnivore - the horses *Haplohippus* and *Epihippus,* the rhinoceroses *Procadurcodon* and *Teletaceras,* a tapir *Protapirus*, a brontothere *Protitanops*, a pig-like *Heptacodon* - the only record west of the Rocky Mountains, a *Diplobunops* - an oreodon that had claw-like feet - as well as two teeth of unidentified juvenile rodents.

There were significant migrations of mammals between North America, Europe, and Asia during certain intervals of the Cenozoic, and similarities between the fauna of the Mammal Quarry and that of east Asia point to a high rate of interchange across continents 40 million years ago. Four of the ten large mammals from the Oregon Eocene are also found in Japan, Russia, and North Korea.

ANIMALS OF THE OLIGOCENE EPOCH

Tropical conditions of the Eocene Clarno and early John Day formations gave way to the more temperate climates of the middle and late John Day time beginning 34 million years ago. Of all the rock formations in the state, none approaches the Oligocene John Day for quantity of fossil remains and quality of preservation. Located west of the Deschutes River and east of Fossil in Wheeler County, John Day strata range from 700 to 1,500 feet in thickness and is a complex succession of volcanic tuffs, fossil soils, lake and stream deposits, and intermittent layers of lava.

Discovery of the fossil beds in the John Day valley is credited to Thomas Condon, who had an unlikely career as pioneer geologist and minister of the Congregational Church at The Dalles from the middle 1800s. Condon recognized the scientific significance of the John Day as a rich fossil repository of both plant and animal remains. Born in southern Ireland in 1822, Thomas was 11 years of age when the Condon family moved to New York. After graduating from the theological seminary at Auburn, Thomas Condon married Cornelia Holt in 1852, and in the fall of that year they sailed for Oregon under the auspices of the Congregational Church. It was because he took up a position in the "wild" frontier town of The Dalles and the proximity of the John Day fossil region that Condon was able to pursue his long-time interest in geology. One of his first scientific papers in 1871 was on the John Day valley. Soon Condon's collection of fossils, enthusiasm, and geologic knowledge attracted distinguished visitors to his home, and his reputation in the science spread outside of the state. In 1872 he was made the inaugural State Geologist, a position he resigned in 1876 when he accepted an appointment as geology and natural history professor at the fledgling University of Oregon in Eugene. For over 40 years the Condons travelled throughout the state, building a collection that forms the basis for the present day Condon Museum at the University. Condon retired from teaching at age 82 and died shortly thereafter in 1907. He is perhaps best remembered for bringing an awareness of Oregon's fossil wealth to students at the University as well as to paleontologists worldwide and for his book *The Two Islands*, which was the first comprehensive geologic treatment of the state.

Dr. Thomas Condon standing by the Condon oak, which remains today next to Villard Hall on the University of Oregon campus [photo courtesy Condon Museum].

While at The Dalles, Condon journeyed as far south as the Harney valley in 1865 or 1866 with a cavalry company under Captain John Drake, when he collected fossil bones, teeth, and leaves on the John Day River and at Bridge Creek. The leaves were sent to John Newberry of Columbia University in New York, and the bones and teeth to the Smithsonian Museum in Washington, D.C. The Smithsonian redirected them to Joseph Leidy, a professor of anatomy at the University of Pennsylvania. Because of his reputation and knowledge of vertebrates, Leidy was called upon for much of the early mammal paleontology work in North America. Unlike other researchers, Leidy's turn around time for specimens was remarkably prompt and decisive. Writing to the Smithsonian, Leidy said he had received two boxes on an October morning in 1870, had "overhauled them this afternoon," identified and named the specimens, and presented them that evening at the Philadelphia Academy of Sciences. He described two new forms of rhinoceros, a *Leptomeryx* [modern pecora], a tapir-like *Lophiodon*, an *Elotherium* [pig-like animal], several sheep-like *Oreodon*, and a small *Anchitherium* [horse] that he named after Condon, *Anchitherium condoni*.

John Day Formation in the Painted Hills. Characteristic color banding is due to multiple fossil soils [photo by Ed Bushby; courtesy Condon Museum].

Since these specimens had been sent round-about to Leidy via the Smithsonian Institution, a flurry of letters began between Condon and Spencer Baird and Joseph Henry of that Museum. During the 1870s they wrote that Leidy found the fossils "extremely interesting. Please gather all you can," volunteeering to pay Condon's expenses and send him scientific books, circulars, or other reading matter. They hoped that Condon would "lend ... for a suitable time, the unique specimens of fossil animals in your possession."

HISTORY OF JOHN DAY FOSSIL COLLECTIONS

The search for the remains of fossil mammals - once eastern paleontologists and museums picked up the scent of unique and ample finds in central Oregon - was the stimulus for expeditions that extracted boxloads of material sent back east. Curiously the bulk of this material languished in storage for many years, and much of it was never examined.

By November of 1870 Othniel C. Marsh, professor at Yale University, was aware of the new fossil finds. "I have heard for several years past ... of the very interesting collection of fossil vertebrate fossils you have made ..." requesting a "good and full collection ... of your region". Marsh's letters in 1870 and 1871 display his anxiety that he had not seen the fossils sooner - before Leidy and Cope - and immediately directed Condon's attention to the horse fossils, noting the small size.

Condon did send Marsh a small package of fossils from John Day. Marsh, who was "very much pleased", promised to acknowledge Condon's contributions for the discoveries. This he did in 1871 when he published and named the peccary, *Platygonus condoni*, "for Rev. Thomas Condon, who discovered the specimen ... in ... Oregon." Marsh's appetite was merely whetted, however, by the package, and he decided to visit Oregon himself in the fall of 1871. Arranging to meet Condon at Canyon City, the party consisted of a local rancher, Sam Snook, who often helped out, the guide and commercial fossil collector, Leander Davis, horses, wagons, supplies, and the 15 or so young college men from Yale, who accompanied Marsh. They had been working in the "wild west" for about five months already, and the group was anxious to return home. On top of that, Marsh had a bad cold, and it was well into October. To Condon's dismay, they rushed through eastern Oregon, with no side trips to the remarkably productive site at Turtle Cove. After examining Condon's collection at The Dalles, the group left for Portland and home. In an 1874 paper Marsh listed the horses *Anchippus, Miohippus, Protohippus* from the trip and *Anchitherium* donated to the Peabody Museum by the Reverend Condon. This list was expanded in 1875 with *Diceratherium* [rhinoceros], *Eporeodon* [sheeplike oreodon], and two peccaries *Thinohyus* and *Dicotyles*.

It was in 1871 that Condon began to exchange letters with Edward Cope of the Philadelphia Academy of Sciences. Cope also requested specimens, promised to send scientific journals, and wanted to purchase Condon's fossils. As with others, Condon promised to send duplicates but refused to sell "you any first class specimens."

Othniel C. Marsh [back center] and members of an expedition in 1872. While the display of firearms may seem theatrical, General Custer was defeated at Little Big Horn just a few years after the photograph was taken [photo courtesy Yale University, Archives].

In 1870, a time when the midwest was virtually unknown territory and the far west was even more remote, it was remarkable for Marsh and Cope, considered to be the leading American vertebrate paleontologists of their day, to participate themselves in explorations with the intent of collecting fossil animal remains. Cope and Marsh took over from Joseph Leidy, who had to work with mere fragments of bones gathered and sent to him, in many cases, without precise locations or stratigraphic data. By taking to the field themselves, Cope and Marsh were able to inspect specimens *in situ*. A fierce competition ensued between these masters of paleontology to see who could amass the largest and most complete collections for their museums. Both employed professional agents in the race to triumph, a life-long rivalry that tainted much of their scientific contributions.

Cope and Marsh were energetic men, possessed of rare insight and intellect, and sufficient finances to enable them to pursue their scientific interests. Although he was from a family of modest means, Othniel Charles Marsh was subsidized by a well-to-do uncle until he graduated from Yale in 1862. After several years of study in Europe he took a position on the Yale faculty in 1866. Marsh never married and was able to devote his full attention to the "dominating ambition to obtain everything there was in it [in every field of acquisition], and leave not a single scrap behind" as noted by George Merrill, a contemporary geologist and curator at the Smithsonian. From 1870 to 1875 Marsh led expeditions of Yale students across the western territories, paying for many of these trips from his own funds until he was appointed as the official United States vertebrate paleontologist in 1882, working in conjunction with the U.S. Geological Survey. He rarely returned to the west after that but hired professional collectors to fill out his accumulations of fossils. Because of his precise instructions, these men provided Marsh with remarkably complete specimens. The material assembled by Marsh forms the nucleus of the vertebrate sections at the Smithsonian Museum and Yale University. In spite of an annual budget of $15,000, 35 collectors, 9 preparators, 8 scientific aides, and artists, however, Marsh himself was completely overwhelmed by the amount of fossils, and most were left for later paleontologists to examine and describe after he died in 1899.

Several researchers connected with the Yale Peabody Museum worked with this during the 1920s. Among these were Malcolm Rutherford Thorpe, who wrote on oreodons and carnivores, Richard Lull, who worked on camels, and George Eaton on cats. Eaton had an interesting, if not cautious, perspective to offer on Marsh's efforts. "while it would be ungracious to criticize the methods of collecting in vogue in the seventies of the last century, it appears that the superior value of a good skull over the other skeletal parts, which were then somewhat disparagingly termed "joints", was a little over-emphasized in Marsh's instructions to his collectors. A result of this is possibly to be seen in the predominance of cranial material, unaccompanied by other skeletal parts ... that would now greatly enhance the value of the collection." Eaton does go on to express "the admiration that is felt for the generous enthusiasm" which led Marsh to the John Day valley in search of fossils.

Marsh's competitor, Edward Drinker Cope was born of a wealthy Quaker family in 1840. Fascinated by the unexamined western regions, Cope spent eight months of the years from 1871 to 1879 with state geologic surveys making prodigeous discoveries, all of which he published on in rapid succession. An abrasive personality combined with scientific errors, that were inevitable when covering vast areas so quickly, led Cope to disputes with Marsh, who was, by that time, chief paleontologist for the U.S. Geological Survey.

[photo courtesy Archives, Smithsonian Institution].

Cope's loss of his family fortune on a mining scheme forced him to find work to support a wife and daughter. This he did at the University of Pennsylvania where he taught geology until his death in 1897. Cope is remembered for unravelling the complexities of Tertiary fossils throughout the west and for his numerous eclectic publications. Contributing close to 40 works on western fossils, Cope added more than any other single person to the knowledge of the state's prehistory. A mention of a few of the important papers provides a glimpse into his breadth. He furnished monographs on cats in 1880, dogs and cats in 1882 and 1883, rodents in 1883, camels in 1886, horses in 1879, 1880 and 1889, as well as several overviews. The most outstanding was his 1009 page behemoth *Vertebrata of Tertiary Formations of the West* that includes 100 plates for a pondrous five and one-half inch-thick volume.

Because he lived in Oregon, Condon's initial role was to provide information, localities, and material to the better known eastern paleontologists, which he generously did. Later, as he began to build up his own cabinet of specimens that he was using for teaching, Condon became more reluctant to send fossils. In 1870 Condon forwarded specimens to Marsh, marking those to be returned, and nine years later he loaned a number of prize bird bones from Fossil Lake to Cope, some of which had no duplicates. Both men were negligent in returning their loans. In 1890 Condon wrote about the status of his bird fossils, but it wasn't until 1926, long after Condon's and Cope's deaths, that the fossils were recovered. Marsh's loans weren't returned until 1906, years after his death and shortly before Condon himself died. The specimens came back to Oregon only when the new head of the Yale Museum, Charles E. Schuchert, responded to Condon's letters.

Problems with the perception of Thomas Condon by the eastern science community began almost immediately. Even after he had become a professor at the University of Oregon, Condon's knowledge and assistance were frequently minimized. In 1978 an Oregon State University student, Ellen Drake, put together an interesting article on Condon's contribution to the science and Marsh's failure to acknowledge that contribution. Because of key fossil specimens that Condon sent from the John Day area, Marsh was able to demonstrate how horses evolved from the Eocene *Orohippus* to the modern *Equus*. In an 1874 paper Marsh described *Miohippus*, an unknown genus, but whether deliberate or not he did not credit Condon with the discovery. For his work, Marsh received congratulations from none other than Charles Darwin himself.

Drake reaches the somewhat ambiguous conclusion that Condon had an established reputation as a scientist, but, on the other hand, he should have sent his specimens east, "in the spirit of science". She felt that Marsh should have acknowledged Condon's role in his discoveries, but noted frequently this is how a lone scientist is treated by The Establishment. In 1889, paleobotanist William B. Scott wrote to Condon - "Now from what I have heard of the treatment you have received at the hands of some eastern paleontologists, I infer that you would be unwilling to let any of your material leave your hands..."

Overlooking the Columbia River near The Dalles, this 1901 expedition may have been part of John Merriam's group from the University of California [photo courtesy Condon Museum].

Curiously Condon never returned to eastern Oregon after leaving The Dalles in 1873, but he advised those who wanted to prospect there for fossils. Scientists continued to exploit the west, a region that was viewed as a source of valuable new finds as well as the chance to participate in a Great Adventure. According to the *Oregonian* newspaper of October, 1899, visitors learned to sleep on "Oregon soil" which "makes your bones a little sore" - learned "the language of the country" - and how to wash "clothes in the boiling pot."

Princeton University sent expeditions of professors and students to the badlands and regions of the west in 1877 and most years through 1889. Led by William Berryman Scott, they visited Colorado, Nebraska, the Dakotas, Wyoming, Montana, in addition to Oregon, "as a result of which the museum at Princeton contains one of the most important collections of American fossil mammals in existence."

In the middle of July, 1889, Scott and the Princeton students were in the John Day valley where they were assisted by the professional collector Leander Davis. According to Scott's autobiography, it was "self-trained scientific workers" like Davis, whose exact knowledge of the fossil beds made these expeditions so successful. The party left from Baker City by horseback at a cost of $30 each for a six day trip to the North Fork of the John Day River. Fossil remnants of rhinoceroses and the 3-toed horse recovered from this location were supplemented by the remains of turtles, camels, deer, oreodon, several carnivores, and rodents from Turtle Cove where a permanent camp was made. At the Cove the beautiful pine grove and abundance of grass and water entranced Scott, while Davis worried about the numerous rattlesnakes in and around camp. One that was killed measured three feet long with 12 rattles.

At the end of the field season, several tons of bones were taken carefully by wagon to Dayville and there packed for shipment to Princeton. Dayville was a community of six unpainted houses that included a barn, hencoop, and combination grocery-hotel, so this "mail" and the appearance of the easterners must not have been commonplace.

The six day ride back to Baker City, through thick clouds of alkali dust, was particularly trying, and according to one student's account, they arrived looking dilapidated and dirty. However, their fame must have preceded them, because, as the *Oregonian* newspaper of 1899 reports, the townspeople ran out calling "Here they come". After a wash and more fashionable clothes, "we emerged a party of eastern swells". Of the specimens shipped to Princeton, some of the best were cleaned and cataloged, but to an enquiry by Rudolph Erickson of the Portland-based Geological Society of Oregon Country, Marjorie Hindle, a Princeton Museum official, replied in November 15, 1949, that most of them were stored in the basement of Nassen Hall where they were carried off or destroyed by workmen installing a new central heating system.

A similar fate awaited a John Day collection in the museum at Munich, Germany. In a letter to Condon at The Dalles in December 17, 1900, Leander Davis reported that he successfully filled "4 good sized boxes of material for his University, and I got seven boxes of very good fossils for Prof. von Zittel of Munich University." Karl von Zittel, author of the highly-regarded *Textbook of Paleontology*, never came to Oregon but frequently contracted with Davis and Charles Sternberg to supply him with specimens. The museum and fossils at Munich were destroyed in bombing raids during World War II.

A curator at the American Museum of Natural History in New York, William Matthew was one of six people sent out almost continuously at the turn of the century for geologic and paleontologic purposes. Matthew's co-worker, Jacob L. "Jake" Wortman, was born to a pioneering family near the falls at Oregon City and had been Thomas Condon's first paleontology student at the University of Oregon in 1876. Before securing his position at the American Museum, Wortman had worked for paleontologist Edward Cope and professional collector Charles Sternberg. A gifted field geologist, Wortman led expeditions to the Rocky Mountains and beyond. After a hard day in the field, Wortman liked to return to camp, eat a good meal, roll a cigarette, and, while having a large cup of hot coffee, recount the day's discoveries or unsuccessful searches. In 1885, after being awarded a Masters degree from Oregon, he was appointed as an anatomist to the Army Medical Museum, and six years later as paleontology curator at the American Museum, a position he held for eight years. He then became curator at the Carnegie Institute, and following that held a similar position at Yale University. One of Wortman's chief contributions to the literature was a book on the anatomy of teeth. In conjunction with Matthew he published on carnivores and camels, and, at Marsh's request, he continued to oversee the collection at the Peabody Museum at Yale University. He retired to Brownsville, Texas, where he died in June, 1926.

Jacob L. Wortman, the first geology student at Eugene, who led an eclectic life as a guide, paleontologist, and museum curator [photo courtesy Oregon Dept. Geology and Mineral Industries].

Due to professional associations and physical proximity, geologists at the University of California, Berkeley, began to play a dominant role in central Oregon. From the University of California, John C. Merriam was one of the leading practitioners of paleontology on the West Coast who spoke of "my very deep interest in Oregon, and all it represents". Born in Hopkinton, Iowa in 1869, Merriam moved with his family to Berkeley. Here he studied botany and geology with the noted Joseph LeConte and in 1893 received a PhD in vertebrate paleontology in Munich, Germany, from the equally renowned Karl von Zittel. Afterward Merriam became an instructor at Berkeley and ultimately Chairman of the Department of Paleontology. He was one of the founders of the Save-the-Redwoods movement, and, moving to Washington, D.C., became president of the Carnegie Institute from 1920 to 1938. He lived his final years on the West Coast, finding it difficult to escape his paleontology pursuits. He continued to serve on numerous committees, journeying often to Eugene where he preferred staying at the Osburn Hotel rather than as the guest of Chairman Warren Smith. "It is, however, generally easiest for me to live at the hotel, as I can invite friends in to breakfast, lunch, and dinner ... with the maximum of convenience for the friends..." He became a familiar figure in the hotel dining room. Even though he was not of an approachable nature and considered serious rather than jovial - with an imperious manner that earned him the nickname "Jesus Christ" - he sponsored many students such as John Buwalda, Earl Packard, Charles Weaver, W.S.W. Kew, Jorgen Nomland, Chester Stock, and Bruce Clark, among others, and influenced the course of paleontology on the West Coast for future years.

John C. Merriam [left] and Lloye Miller in the John area in 1899 extracting fossils from the massive greenish ash of the middle John Day Formation [photo courtesy Condon Museum].

As a result of his numerous trips and personal interest in the state, Merriam's contribution to Oregon geologic knowledge is significant. A frequent visitor to the John Day beds, he led a small party consisting of Loye Miller [photographer and ornithologist], Frank Calkins [mineralogist], George Hatch [fisherman], and Leander Davis down the Deschutes River to The Dalles at the end of May, 1899. Miller's journal of the expedition wasn't published until 1972. In this he tells of their difficulties during the rough trip to the Bridge Creek beds and of the problems that arose during the 25 day campout. The jaw of an *Oreodon*, two teeth of *Anchitherium* [horse], and the skulls of a pig-like animal *Entelodon* were extracted before the party moved to Turtle Cove. Over 300 pounds were added to the wagon loads already waiting at Mitchell, and under this heavy weight the wagons broke down frequently on the slow trip back to The Dalles.

In 1917 Merriam proposed to Warren Smith and Earl Packard at the University of Oregon that they combine forces and take up a detailed study of the John Day region. Since Packard had already been working "down in the Jurassic and earlier formations", he was to continue while Smith, Merriam, Chester Stock, and John Buwalda were to look at the Tertiary. J.B. Winstanley, one of Condon's students, hoped "to connect up" with them, provided, as Smith wrote in March, 1917, "you will furnish the machine [car] [so] we can make some interesting side trips". The University had appropriated $450, and Smith and Packard volunteered their time. The U.S. Geological Survey was even solicited for funds and contributed $500. However, this mapping effort was sidetracked by World War I and not resumed until the end of that conflict.

A University of California collecting party [left to right: unknown, Lloye Miller, John Merriam, and Leander Davis; photo courtesy Condon Museum]

Merriam's most important contribution, however, resulting from his dynamic personality, was plans for utilizing the fossil resources of the John Day basin. He felt that "The John Day picture seems to be a great heritage which we must understand, interpret, and use as in some measure as a guide for the future." During the 1940s he proposed to develop a display for the Condon Museum that would have "ultimately very great importance for research and education in the state". In addition he suggested a book with chapters on specific aspects of the region written by various paleontologists and an organization called The Associates, a committee to oversee a John Day park. In conjunction with the Highway Department, "a series of these semi-popular books on the outstanding geological features of our state..." were to be issued. A year or so before he died, Merriam wrote of an impending trip to Eugene when he wanted to bring "together materials for the book covering things of special interest in the John Day Region ... I am therefore inclined to think that it is desirable to take a relatively small number of items for descriptions and to do the study of these things with the greatest possible care." Notable outcomes were Warren Smith's *"Scenic Values in the John Day"* and Chester Stock's *"Oregon's Wonderland of the Past - the John Day"*. Merriam was working on these plans at the time of his death in Oakland, California, on October 30, 1945.

Office of

Charles H. Sternberg, A. M.

617 Vermont Street

Lawrence, Kansas

Feb 4th 1930

Prof Warren D Smith

University of Oregon

Eugene

My dear Sir:-

      I am sending under another cover halftone prints of my great fish skeleton Portheus molossus ,13 feet long ⊤ offer you for $1000 00 and the skeleton od Equus scotti for same price The two for $1800 .

I have a lot of chalk material unprepared that would give instructive work for y your students

Back part if skull and 20 continuous vert with ribs and front paddles of

a Tylosaurus $50 00

Platecarpus ten feet and more of columnwith ribs many caudals   25 00

Portheus skull .   25 00

I can fill an order as before if ⊥ am allowed to select for 25 oo will send bones of camel Teeth and bones of two sps of horse and elephant bone from the Staked Plains of Texas and the chalk of Kansas and Dinosaur beds of Alberta

       Faithfully yours

       Charles H Sternberg

A letter from the professional collector Charles Sternberg to Warren Smith at Eugene showing the sale prices for his fossils [courtesy Condon Museum].

Attrition to the John Day fossil beds by local residents, most of whom collected to different degrees, also began during the 1800s. As noted in the *Oregonian* of November, 1946, "Nearly everyone in the vicinity is a fossil hunter of sorts", and at the turn of the century the role of commercial fossil collectors can not be overstated. Of these Leander Davis and Charles Sternberg were the most active, supplying Thomas Condon at The Dalles and a host of eastern scientists and museums. Through the efforts of these collectors, a steady flow of fossils made its way elsewhere, frequently without the necessity of the scientist taking to the field. The most dynamic of these individuals nationwide was Charles Sternberg, whose career took him through most of the western fossil-rich beds from Texas to the Dakotas and west to Oregon on expeditions for the eastern institutions. Edward Cope, who employed Sternberg for many years, felt "It is evident that an enthusiastic devotion to science has actuated these explorers of our western wilderness, financial considerations having been but a secondary enducement. All may agree that finances were a secondary consideration".

In Oregon, Sternberg hired local residents as William Day and Jake Wortman to assist him and relied on farm and ranch families for room and board. This arrangement was beneficial to both parties since ranchers, miners, and sheepherders, who picked up fossils from slopes and in streambeds over the course of their daily lives, found a source of revenue leading paleontologists to sites, staking out big specimens, or providing room, board, and pack animals for enthusiastic outsiders.

Despite the remoteness of the field area, for camping on the William Mascall Ranch in July, 1916, a cast iron cookstove was a necessity. Paleontologist Clarence Moody with a group from the University of California [photo courtesy Archives, Page Museum, Los Angeles].

290

The Days and Mascalls were two such families. A small number of Cretaceous shells from eastern Oregon collected by the Days made their way to the Condon Museum at Eugene, and William Day was hired by such scientists as John Merriam, Othniel C. Marsh, and Sternberg. In his classic tale *Life of a Fossil Hunter*, Sternberg describes William Day as knowing "every inch of the fossil beds and all the best camping grounds, his services were invaluable." Sternberg also pays tribute to the pioneer William Mascall family, who provided not only a bed and home cooked meals, but a store room for fossils as well. The Mascall ranch was near the John Day River just west of Dayville, and the the family would ferry packs and men across the river to begin the climb up to the fossil beds. As early as 1878 Sternberg found to his astonishment that "all the ground in the fossil beds which was easy to get at had been gone over. Here and there we would run across a pile of broken bones and a hole from which a skull had been taken." In answer to Sternberg's query as to why the bones had been left behind, Day replied that "We were only looking for heads, though we sometimes saved knucks and jints." Despite the difficulties of fending off Indians in the John Day valley, chipping fossils located on high perpendicular cliffs, and packing out heavy boxes of specimens, Sternberg's narrative shows he thoroughly enjoyed his adventurous experiences. The fossil beds near Dayville were named by John Merriam to honor the William Mascall, who died in 1943 at the age of 81.

Homesteader and collector Thomas Jefferson Weatherford in front of his cabin, which was located just south of the road to Picture Gorge [photo courtesy E. Baldwin].

Thomas Jefferson Weatherford, an old time cowboy, trapper, and stage driver, began to amass a sizeable vertebrate collection in the late 1800s. This he stored in boxes in a root cellar of his unpainted two-room cabin. Weatherford welcomed visitors, including Earl Packard and his students from the University of Oregon. When he and Packard and disagreed about the identification of some bones, Weatherford's poor opinion of college professors was confirmed. Even though the precise localities for his specimens were not always known, Weatherford hoped to sell his collection to the government, but it wasn't until after his death that his sons received $10,000 from the the Grant County Chamber of Commerce for it. Ultimately the fossils became part of the collection at the John Day National Monument.

Private collectors are also responsible for bringing new discoveries to light. Many valuable specimens, found by casual hunters, are generously donated to the scientific community for study, but others feel their "find" is intrinsically valuable in and of itself and attempt to sell to the highest bidder.

William Mascall standing atop the fossiliferous rock formation named for him [photo courtesy L. Mascall].

In order to protect the fossils from being harvested from central Oregon and sent to museums from coast to coast and in Europe, 14,402 acres were set aside as the federal John Day Fossil Beds National Monument on October 26, 1974. The Monument is made up of three separate tracts - the Clarno area west of the town of Fossil, the Painted Hills northwest of Mitchell, and Sheep Rock northwest of Dayville in Grant and Wheeler counties. Ted Fremd, who graduated from the University of Alberta in 1979, is responsible for overseeing science efforts in the Park. Currently Fremd is engaged in the ambitious task of refining the biostratigraphy and paleoenvironments of the John Day Formation and maintains a growing database of faunas from various localities.

The idea to provide protection and supervise the fossil resources of the John Day valley was proposed as early as December, 1933, when Thomas Large of Spokane, who founded the Northwest Scientific Association and published the journal *Northwest Science*, wrote to four of the state's most preeminent geologists, Warren Smith, Earl Packard, Edwin Hodge, and Ira Allison. "I wish to know what your opinions are regarding the need for some authority over the fossil beds of the John Day Region. When in there on a brief visit last summer, Mr. A.M. Zavely told me of serious difficulties he had encountered in getting out fossils due to tourists ... who for souvenirs did not hesitate to break up and carry off parts.. I felt pretty strongly that some form of Federal administration should be established ... A few days later ... having seen some bonehead administration and administrators ... I became doubtful." Large went on to express the opinion that any regulations should not effect qualified local geologists and placed the matter in the hands of the Oregon professionals.

Earl Packard, then Dean of Science at Oregon State University, seemed to have misunderstood the gist of Large's letter, because he responded several weeks later that "I am heartily in accord that it would be very desirable to call attention to the general public of localities of which ... ancient life in the northwest might be found." Packard wrote in December, 1933, that it was fine to be concerned with specimens which might be destroyed by amateurs before they could reach scientists, but it would also be nice if there were "appropriate places where the general public could easily see them ... if ... a local group, headed by Mr. William Maskell [sic], for instance, [could set up specimens] along the highway. I am quite sure that many tourists would be attracted to such an exhibit. One of Mr. Maskell's sons in a small way is attempting to do that sort of thing in the service station located in the Picture Gorge..."

Almost 15 years later on November 10, 1946, the *Oregonian* noted that while major fossil-bearing areas in federal and state lands are protected by the Antiquities Act of 1906, few collectors observe these regulations. Prior to this, eminent regional scientists such as John Merriam, Chester Stock, John Buwalda, and Warren Smith had banded together as the John Day Associates to oversee reserving fossil-rich areas for state parkland. The *Oregonian* commented that for the Associates and local residents the "National Park" designation was "received frigidly on the ground that the West already has many thousands of acres withheld from reasonable use in such parks..."

The association was ultimately responsible for much of the John Day park acquisition. Whereas they had hoped the state would purchase a solid block of land from Dayville to Picture Gorge, a major hindrance was encountered when private owners, whose lands had fossil locations, refused to sell. One such rancher was James Cant, with 886 acres of choice beds, who couldn't decide between helping establish the park or maintaining his ranch intact. State Park superintendent, Sam Boardman, intended to put markers at mileposts to point out the geologic story to tourists who might otherwise "drive through the entire fossil bed district without realizing..." Wooden boards were already in place at specific sites where, for example, John Merriam had found the tooth of *Ursa major*, described as "the granddaddy of all bears." Not overly scientific, but maybe enticing.

Today collecting on federal lands is severely restricted or at best heavily regulated, while state land is loosely overseen by a variety of interests.

At the University of California, some members of The Associates [left to right, back row: Earl Packard, W.S.W. Kew, and J.D. Nomland; front row: John Buwalda, John Merriam, Chester Stock, and Bruce Clark. Photo courtesy David K. Smith, Museum of Paleontology, University of California, Berkeley].

THE JOHN DAY FORMATION

The first comprehensive treatment of John Day stratigraphy came in Merriam's 1901 report in which he labelled his collections "as accurately as possible in the field" in order to "obtain more information regarding the vertical distribution of species." Because of his field work in Grant and Wheeler counties, Merriam was able to break the formation into three members based on color: the lower reddish beds, the middle greenish beds, and the uppermost cream to white beds. For the most part the lower (reddish) John Day is barren of vertebrate remains, but the middle (greenish) and upper (cream) layers are rich in well-preserved fossil material.

Since many of the early localities and stratigraphic markers were not recorded or lost because local place names could no longer be found, Richard Fisher and John Rensberger from the University of Washington undertook to redefine the stratigraphy in areas where classic sites existed. By basing their 1972 stratigraphic analysis on the occurrence of distinctive rodents such as pocket gophers, beaver, and a bizarre horned gopher *Mylagaulodon,* they were able to identify four individual intervals or members in the formation.

Beginning with the oldest, the deeply-oxidized red claystone Big Basin Member has locally common Eocene and Oligocene plant remains but very little in the way of vertebrates. Above the Big Basin, the late Oligocene to early Miocene Turtle Cove Member is dominantly greenish tuffs [volcanic ash] with an extremely rich vertebrate fauna, followed by late Oligocene to early Miocene buff to gray tuffs of the Kimberly Member, also rich in mammals. The uppermost early Miocene member is fossil-rich tuffs and conglomerates of the Haystack Valley sequence. Of these, the Turtle Cove is by far the most fossiliferous. While the formal names of members are commonly used, Merriam's color breakdown has been dropped because at several localities the distinction between individual layers is not clear.

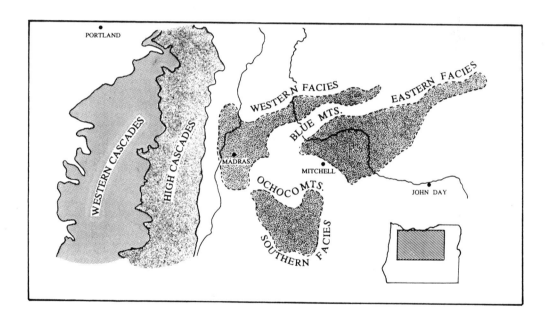

Geographic divisions of the John Day Formation are separated from each other by the Blue and Ochoco mountains [after Robinson, Brem, and McKee, 1984]

In 1984, the John Day Formation was further divided geographically into eastern, western, and southern regions or facies by Paul Robinson of the University of California, Riverside. Vertebrates are more common in the eastern and southern regions, but a few years prior to this Robinson discovered rare vertebrates in the western area near Warm Springs in Jefferson County. Dated as early Miocene, this fauna is the youngest of any from the John Day Formation and contains the horses *Archaeohippus* and *Merychippus,* a deer [*Bouromeryx*], a rabbit [*Hypolagus*], *Cynorca* [peccary], *Mesogaulus* [horned rodent], and the oreodons *Merycochoerus* and *Ticholeptus.* Most of the fossils were found as float or loose bone fragments in the soil above the rock layer. Robinson and Michael Woodburne from the same institution concluded that deposition persisted near Warm Springs west of the major John Day basin for a short period after it had ceased elsewhere.

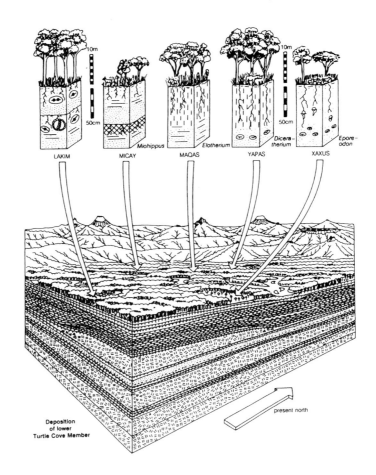

In his study of John Day fossil soils, Greg Retallack has been able to identify a wide variety of land-scapes and vege-tation that make up the formation [courtesy E. Bestland and G. Retallack, 1994].

Even though there are minor gaps in the Cenozoic record of plants and animals from the John Day valley, the area still offers one of the most complete sequences of Tertiary fossils anywhere. An extraordinary diversity of fossil animal remains have come from the John Day Formation. Among the 100 genera are several cats, many varieties of dogs, weasels, otters, rabbits, and rodents such as squirrels, rats, mice, and the larger beavers. Hoofed mammals, which are extinct or only vaguely resemble their present-day relatives, include tapirs, horses, pigs, brontothere, rhinoceroses, camels, and oreodons.

Opossums
Marsupials [opossums] are routinely found in late Cretaceous strata of North America, but only one such fossil has been reported in Oregon. In 1920 a field party from the

University of California under supervision of Chester Stock and Eustace Furlong, visiting the southern facies of the John Day beds near Logan Butte in Crook County, obtained the fragmentary skull and lower jaw of a new species of opossum, *Peratherium merriami*. Dated as Oligocene, *Peratherium* was similar in size to the modern Virginia opossum *Didelphis*.

A primitive John Day opossum

Shrews and Moles

One remarkable anomaly in John Day faunas is the limited incidence of insectivores. Insectivores, or insect-eaters, are known from rocks as old as Cretaceous, and elsewhere in the world they have a persistant though not overly spectacular fossil record throughout the Tertiary. Near Courtrock in Grant County, a young lad Anthony Morgan found the front of a skull and left jaw of a new shrew-like species of insectivore. The boy's father, who had collected fossils in the John Day valley for years, recognized the specimen as unusual and gave it to the University of California, where it was described by Ruben Stirton and John Rensberger as *Micropternodus morgani*. This animal has no modern equivalent, and even its relationship to other groups is uncertain.

Bats and Lemurs

Two exceptionally rare animals from the John Day are remnants of a bat [Chiroptera] and a lemur-like dermopterid. One of the very few fossil bats in Oregon is represented by a jaw and shoulder bones recovered from the shales behind the schoolhouse at Fossil in Wheeler County. In 1959 Roland Brown, paleobotanist at the U.S. Geological Survey, was looking for plants, abundant in the shales here, when he came across the bat remains. Because the fragments were in such poor condition, the bat could not be identified, and, indeed, the fossil record of Chiroptera before the Pleistocene is sparce.

The other exceptional find is a fragment of the upper teeth of *Ekgmowechashala*, an animal as obscure as its peculiar name. In the Sioux language, "Ekgmo" means cat, "wechasha" means man, and "la" means little or little cat man. Originally classified as a lemur-like primate, it has now been taken out of the primates and placed in the Dermoptera, which has living equivalents such as flying lemurs in Asia, Indonesia, and the Philippines. Existing on an herbivorous diet, modern members of these animals are nearly helpless on the ground, but are quite adept in the trees flying by means of a gliding membrane between the limbs. The Oregon fossil was found in 1961 by John Rensberger, doing field work as a student at the University of California, Berkeley, in the pale green Turtle Cove tuffs near Picture

Gorge. Rensberger's dilligent search for additional remains has spanned several decades, but he has not turned up anything else. This was the only Dermopterid known from the Pacific Northwest until 1998 when more specimens of the distinctive teeth were found near Sheep Rock. The specimens are housed at the Burke Museum at the University of Washington and at the John Day National Monument.

Only two specimens of the lemur-like *Ekgmowechashala* have turned up in Oregon.

Carnivores

The list of carnivores or flesh eating mammals from the John Day region is small and, of these, the dogs *Cormocyon, Mesocyon,* and *Temnocyon,* the cats *Dinaelurus* [*Archaelurus*] and *Nimravus,* and the bears *Allocyon* and *Enhydrocyon* are the most frequent.

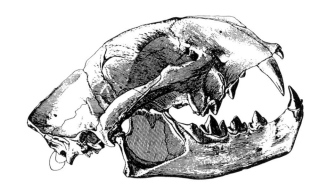

Nimravus and *Dinictis,* rapacious cats from the John Day [from B. Horsfall, in Scott, 1913; skull from Eaton, 1922].

298

Other cats from in the John Day include sleek lightweight predators such as *Eusmilus* [*Hoplophoneus*] and *Dinictis* [*Pogonodon*], which were somewhat larger than a lynx. Early day *Nimravus* were referred to by Edward Cope as false sabre-tooth cats since they lack the sharp extremely elongate canine teeth common to those of later periods. *Nimravus* and *Dinaelurus* are remarkably similar, and in 1906 John Merriam expressed the opinion that they might be the same genus. For his PhD degree in 1959 from Princeton University, Loren Toohey produced an interesting analysis of the cat genus *Nimravus*. Examining feline specimens from many institutions throughout the United States, Toohey observed that *Nimravus* was the most common in the John Day.

Cormocyon is regarded as a primitive dog [from B. Horsfall, in Scott, 1913].

The dog family [Canidae] has been undergoing revision by Xiaoming Wang, who made it the focus of his 1991 PhD from the University of Kansas. A subsequent paper by Wang and Richard Tedford, both at the the American Museum in New York, reviews in detail how errors arose in definining the early canids. By comparing *Cormocyon* and *Nothocyon* Wang and Tedford point out differences between the two. They regard *Cormocyon,* about the size of a fox and almost weasel-like in the proportions of its long tail and body, as a primitive dog; however, *Nothocyon* is seen as a raccoon-dog. Raccoons, pandas, and related animals of the Procyonidae family evolved from dogs during middle Tertiary time and both families share similar characteristics.

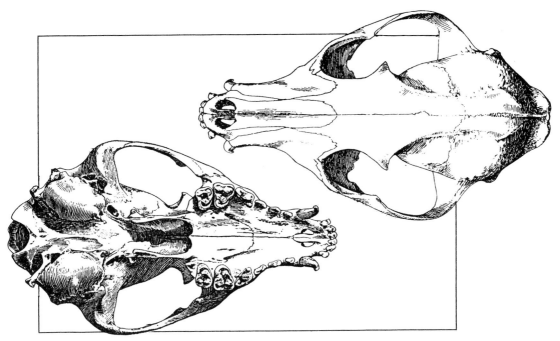

A beautifully preserved skull of a John Day dog *Cormocyon* [from Matthew, 1899].

Pigs

The John Day basin has a particularly nice inventory of pigs, peccaries, and the now extinct, giant "pig-like" entelodonts. Nearly the size of a horse, entelodonts have a distinctive plate-like bony shelf that projects just below the eyes. The pronounced high ridge or sagittal crest atop the skull attests to the powerful jaws of these animals. In 1905 William Sinclair named a new species, *Entelodon* [*Elotherium*] *calkinsi* for

Powerfully built as a predator-scavenger, *Entelodon* is customarily a member of middle Tertiary faunas [from B. Horsfall, in Scott, 1913].

Frank Calkins, the mineralogist who accompanied John Merriam on his 1899 trip to the fossil beds. "All hands repaired to the cliff to work on the *Entelodon*" was how Loye Miller put it in his Journal. The recovered cranium measured a stunning 36 inches in length and resides today at the University of California, Museum of Paleontology.

Oreodons

Hoofed mammals for which the John Day is perhaps best-known are the oreodons. These animals are even-toed ungulates [artiodactyls], and their particularly numerous remains suggest large herds of the beasts roamed eastern Oregon. Ranging in size from a dog up to a small horse, these curious sheep-like animals displayed a wedge-shaped skull, similar to that of pigs and peccaries, which prompted their early designation as "ruminant hogs". However the tooth structure between the two is vastly different. Oreodons were browsers whose molar cusps in crown view form pairs of crescents [selenodont teeth], whereas pigs - with an omnivorous diet - possess low cusp rounded molars, or bunodont teeth.

The 1968 volume by Bernard Schultz of the University of Nebraska and Charles H. Falkenbach of the American Museum is the most definitive work on oreodons yet published. At almost 500 pages, the text and accompanying beautiful line drawings examine specimens of three subfamilies, Merycoidodontinae, Eporeodontiniae, and Leptaucheniinae, and five genera [*Agriochoerus, Eucrotaphus, Merycochoerus, Oreodontoides, Promerycochoerus*] found in museums throughout the United States.

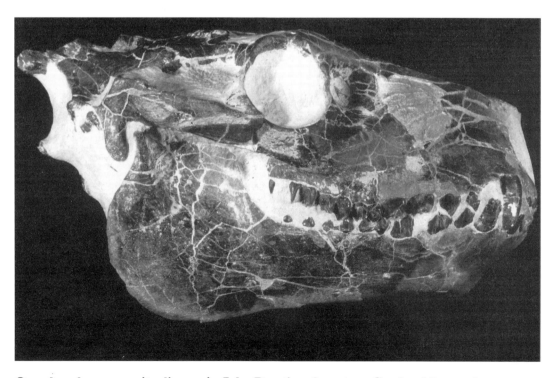

Oreodons became quite diverse in John Day time [courtesy Condon Museum].

Camels

In North America camels are restricted to the Tertiary period, and as plains dwellers their fossil record is extensive and relatively complete. The delicate small hoofs of the Tertiary creatures contrast to the flat pads of the modern-day animals, pointing to a late adaptation to arid or desert environments. Richard Lull, a vertebrate paleontologist whose varied specialties were fossil footprints and limited groups of dinosaurs, examined camels in the Marsh collection at Yale. He recognized three genera from the John Day Formation - *Paratylopus, Gentilicamelus* [*Poebrotherium*] and *Procamelus. Poebrotherium*, a slender animal about the size of a domestic sheep, is the oldest of the three.

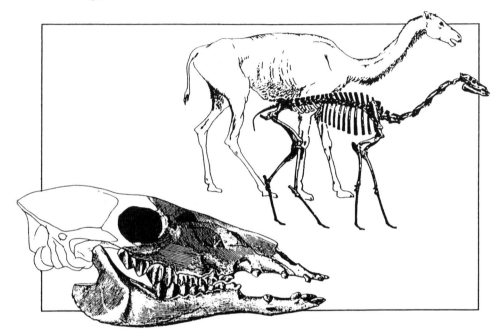

Miocene camels of eastern Oregon. *Paratylopus* displays the typical elongate skull [Lull, 1921].

Hypertragulus,
**related to a "mouse"
deer or "dawn" deer,
has characteristic
elongate canine teeth
[Orr, Orr, and Baldwin, 1992].**

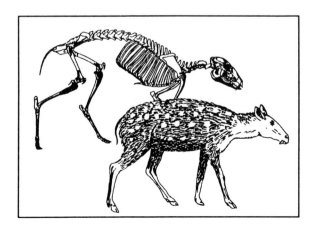

Deer

Primitive deer and the deer-like pecora are present as members of the Leptomerycidae and Hypertragulidae families, but, although the most common artiodactyl remains in John Day sediments and very abundant at Turtle Cove, they are not as diverse as other even-toed hoofed mammals [artiodactyls]. Several of these animals are as small as a domestic dog but appear to have been as fleet as they were diminutive. The large deer-like *Protoceras* developed antlers or bony outgrowths in bizarre patterns on the skull, and some sported dagger-like canines closely resembling those of the modern day pecora [hypertragulids].

With multiple paired horns and elongate canine teeth, the deer-like *Protoceras* was similar in size to modern blacktail deer [from B. Horsfall, in Scott, 1913].

Horses

As a domestic animal long exploited for agricultural power and transport, horses have a special place in human history. Because of the resultant fascination and love of horses, they have been studied in detail not afforded to other large animals. When Spanish explorers arrived in North America, they found no horses, but, once introduced by Europeans, these animals spread widely across the continent. Horses along with camels and elephants, which had been abundant in North America since the Eocene, became extinct here as late as 11,000 years ago near the end of the Pleistocene. Because horse remains are among the most plentiful fossils in the North American Tertiary, they provide a continuous evolutionary picture, and those from the John Day valley are particularly outstanding in quality and quantity. In central Oregon the Oligocene horses *Mesohippus* and *Miohippus* were sheep-sized, three-toed animals whose low crowned cheek teeth were better suited for browsing than grazing. *Miohippus* may have given rise to all later species of horses.

303

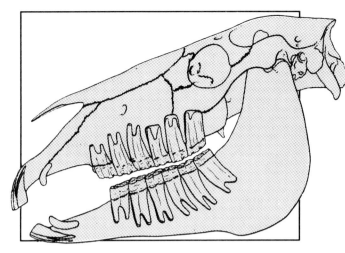

Adapted to grazing, the horse developed high crowned [hypsodont] teeth making the skull and jaw markedly deep and elongate.

Reverend Thomas Condon already had a fairly representative number of horses when he was visited by Othniel Marsh of Yale in 1870. One set of specimens, the tiny foot bones of a 3-toed horse, fascinated Marsh, and he tried to buy them. Condon refused to sell the bones, which Marsh proceeded to lay out in order and sew onto a card, naming it *Hipparion*. *Hipparion* was later recognized as the dominant equine genus during the Miocene. Marsh, honored for his work on horse genealogy, presented two separate papers in 1874, describing the evolution of Tertiary horses in North America.

In a 1940 research paper for his PhD thesis from the University of California, Ruben Stirton revised the phylogeny of the North American horse family Equidae. For his now classic approach, Stirton considered not only the evolution but global geographic distribution of horses. His subsequent interests were in the fields of Tertiary stratigraphy, fossils, and recent mammals. After serving for two years as a mammalogist for the Donald R. Dickey expeditions in El Salvador, Stirton accepted a position with the Museum of Paleontology at Berkeley in 1928, where he remained throughout his career. One of Stirton's greatest contributions was the book *Time, Life, and Man* that treated paleontology and stratigraphy and which greatly promoted the importance of Oregon's fossil horses.

By the 1980s research on horses reached the synthesis stage, and accumulated data on the fossil record is such that it is now possible to draw conclusions on entire lineages. Monographs on the evolution of horses are now based on thousands of specimens in museums collected during the prior 100 years. The 1989 book *The Evolution of Perissodactyls*, edited by Donald Prothero and Robert Schoch, includes *"The Evolution of Oligocene Horses"* and *"Phylogeny of the Family Equidae"*, among other chapters.

Tapirs

Tapirs are comparatively rare in the Eocene and early Oligocene of North America, and their abrupt appearance here may reflect a migration from Europe. The skeletal structure of these odd animals has a striking resemblance to rhinoceroses, and indeed tapirs, rhinoceroses, and horses are closely related. The small but stocky John Day *Protapirus* was just about half the size of the living South American tapir *Tapir americanus*.

Muscular and imposing in height, chalicotheres were persistent but never abundant during the Tertiary [from B. Horsfall, in Scott, 1913].

Chalicotheres

Large clawed browsing mammals, Chalicotheriidae were never numerous, and their remains consequently are even more exceptional. These curious beasts first appeared during the Eocene epoch and persisted into the Pleistocene when they fell to extinction. It is easy to see why early workers failed to link the great claws to the dentition and skull of these animals, and Edward Cope placed them in the family with horses in 1887. North American chalicotheres have been reevaluated by Margery C. Coombs of the University of Massachusetts, Department of Zoology, who has established a reputation for her research on this family since the middle 1970s. In several of her papers she compared the chalicothere genus, *Moropus*, from the John Day in the Smithsonian and in Marsh's Yale material and concluded that these are among the earliest in North America.

One bizarre Miocene adaptation was a chalicothere with a distinctive domed skull. Found in the Astoria Formation north of Newport in Lincoln County by Douglas Emlong, several of these odd-shaped skulls were described in 1979 by California paleontologist Jens Munthe and Margery Coombs. Munthe and Coombs speculated on the adaptive significance of the domes. Among their considerations, the dome may have been used as an aquatic snorkel, as an attachment for jaw muscles, for water retention [like a camel's hump], for filtering or humidifying the air, and as an increased brain capacity in one area of smell, hearing, or other senses. They conclude the probable function of the dome was either for butting during mating, as a sexual display, or as an acoustical signaling device.

Domed skull of the Chalicothere from the Astoria Formation led to speculations about the significance of this distinctive feature [after Munthe and Coombs, 1979].

Rhinoceroses

Rhinoceroses have consistantly been one of the most diverse and widespread perisso-dactyls [odd-toed hoofed mammals], adapting to an herbiverous life-style and far outnumber-ing horses, tapirs, chalicotheres, and brontotheres. Rhinoceroses once lived in great numbers in North America and are represented in the John Day Formation by several creatures such as *Caenopus, Diceratherium*, and *Metamynodon*. The first was a large hornless animal ap-proximately the size of a modern white rhino. *Diceratherium* was somewhat smaller with paired horns placed side-by-side on the tip of the snout, and *Metamynodon* was a large aquatic rhinoceros. Edward Cope's papers on perissodactyls treat in detail the evolution of rhinocer-oses, however it wasn't until over 100 years later that they again became the subject of con-certed study. At that time a large amount of fossil material in museums and in private hands awaited examination. By putting together descriptions and identifications, Don Prothero and Robert Schoch compiled *The Evolution of Perissodactyls* in 1989. In this volume individual chapters address the evolution, classification, and history of the family Rhinocerotidae.

Remarkably adaptive to a variety of habitats from forest to plains to rivers, rhinoceroses compiled a splendid fossil record that included the horned *Diceratherium* [from B. Horsfall, in Scott, 1913].

The skull of the aquatic rhinoceros *Metamynodon* displays attachments for the powerful jaw muscles to operate the anvil-like grinding molars [from B. Horsfall, in Scott, 1913; skull from Cope, 1887].

Rodents

Rabbits and rodents probably shared a common ancestor in the distant past, but the two groups separated sometime in the early Cenozoic into Lagomorpha and Rodentia. In the Oregon fossil record, only three genera of rabbits are known - *Hypolagus, Lepus,* and *Palaeolagus*. This is on par with a modest diversity of 12 Tertiary genera worldwide. Rodents, on the other hand, virtually exploded into 400 genera, and fossil beaver, gophers, and squirrels are common locally. One of the more cosmopolitan rodent families, the Sciuridae, includes squirrels, chipmunks, prairie dogs, and marmots. In his lengthy 1963 document, Craig Black of the Carnegie Museum looked at a number of museum collections to trace relationships between members of the Sciuridae. Some 14 species of fossil squirrels alone were recorded from the John Day and later formations.

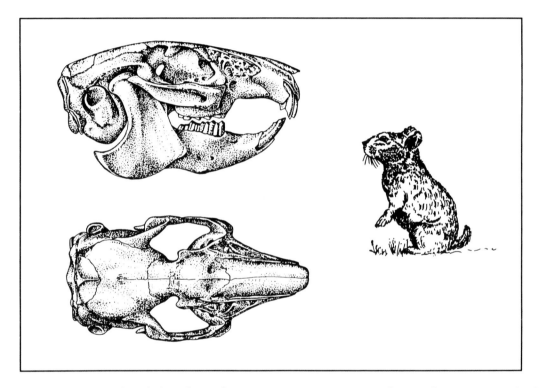

Rabbits are readily distinguished from rodents by the screen-like perforated bones in the skull in front of the eyes, by their extra set of incisor teeth, and by the design on the molars.

Now at the Burke Museum, University of Washington, John M. Rensberger's interest in the John Day began with his 1967 PhD from Berkeley in entoptychine gophers and expanded after that to other Oligocene and Miocene rodents. Because of their generous populations in comparison to those of larger mammals, rodents are of considerable practical value in biostratigraphy. By comparing rodent teeth, Rensberger was able to construct a stratigraphic chronology for mountain beavers [Aplodontidae] and pocket gophers [Geomyidae] for John

Day strata. He found that the moderately abundant Pleurolicine rodents occur stratigraphically below Entoptychine gophers - both from the pocket gopher family. His studies during the 1970s also revealed that individual species of Entoptychine gophers succeeded one another from youngest to oldest in a vertical sequence. Often it is apparent that one species replaced another, but it is rare that evidence as good as Rensberger's is found to show actual displacement.

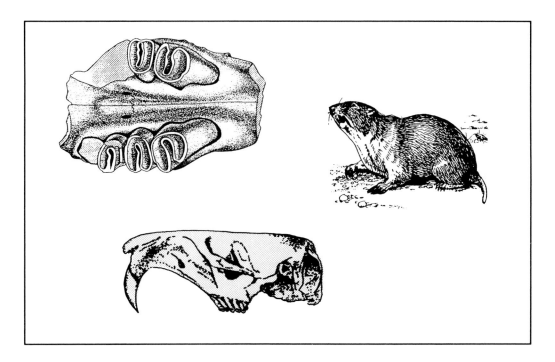

Details of gopher teeth [*Entoptychus*] and pocket gopher skull [*Geomys*]. Cheek teeth of common gophers are particularly nice for dating parts of the John Day Formation [after Rensberger, 1971].

Many new and exciting middle Miocene faunas were discovered in eastern Oregon during the 1950s and 1960s [photo courtesy Condon Museum].

ANIMALS OF THE MIOCENE EPOCH

Lakes, ponds, and sluggish sediment choked streams of the Miocene epoch, 25 to 5 million years ago, were a consequence of periodic volcanic episodes in the eastern part of the state. Even as volcanic ash and lava disrupted the streams, they preserved a record of plants and animals that might have otherwise been lost. Of all the Cenozoic volcanism, the 50,000 cubic miles of accumulated flows of Columbia River basalts were the most devastating. Building a lava plateau across northeast and central Oregon as well as into Washington and Idaho, the basalts provided an uneven surface that blocked streams and ponded water, thereby accumulating sediments where animal remains were buried and preserved. Fine volcanic ash from local vents on the southeast Owyhee Uplands contributed to the same optimum conditions for fossil preservation.

310

Since the beginning of the Miocene epoch, the environment of eastern Oregon has changed dramatically from thick forests to savanna grasslands to high desert. Equally impressive changes here are evident in the animal fauna as whole habitats were demolished and new ones created. Paleontologists have been able to document these changes by carefully recording and studying the evolution and adaptation of prehistoric animals and plants during these intervals.

The most extensive and productive fossil-rich sedimentary basins lie beneath the John Day valley, along the Deschutes River to The Dalles, adjacent to the Columbia River near Arlington and McKay Reservoir, on the Owyhee plateau at Juntura, and at nearby smaller isolated depressions across Harney and Malheur counties.

THE JOHN DAY BASIN

Layers of Columbia River basalts that covered the John Day basin were followed by falling ash from erupting Cascades and local volcanic cones. Volcanic debris of the Mascall Formation, covered by muds, ash, and gravels of the Rattlesnake, was spread by extensive stream systems across flood plains of central Oregon. Fine ash of the Mascall Formation records deposition by wind and water into a broad shallow basin over what is now Picture Gorge in Grant County. During this period in the middle Miocene, smaller ponds across the the basin expanded during rainy intervals to flood the depression. Theodore Downs noted that suffocating volcanic clouds - dust storms and volcanic gasses - might have overcome the animals and destroyed the vegetation. Continually falling particles produced rapid burial of the bloated carcasses that would have been carried into lakes where they settled into muddy layers on the bottom. Peculiar accumulations of bones in discrete pockets, characteristic of the Mascall, are thought to be evidence of ancient geologic catastrophies such as dust storms or natural poisoning of the water.

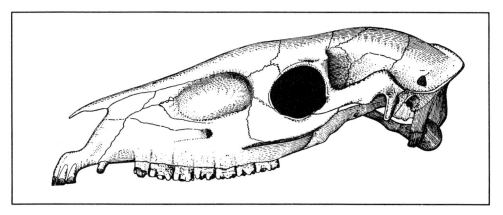

With relatively short [low-crowned] jaw teeth, the pony-sized three-toed *Merychippus* horse from the Mascall was adapted to browsing on brush and trees

311

The concentration of bones in this formation is not as high as in the older John Day strata, perhaps because of dispersal by rivers and streams. Plant remains, such as leaves, wood, and seeds, scattered throughout the Mascall, suggest dense upland forests, grasslands, and wetlands in and around the basin.

Mascall vertebrate faunas are documented by predators, hoofed mammals, birds, rodents, fish, and turtles. The sheep-like oreodons, so prevalent in the older John Day Formation, were not as numerous. Plains-dwelling camels and horses were more frequent here, especially the graceful pony-sized *Merychippus* horse, which still had three toes. Superbly preserved skulls of *Merychippus* display grinding teeth adapted for browsing on tough shrubs. *Dromomeryx*, a primitive deer-like pecora, had curved blunt horns and is represented by numerous skeletal parts. A partial jaw of the horned gopher *Mylagaulus*, reported by Downs, displays the characteristic complex pattern on the crown of the molar teeth. Mylagaulid teeth from Paulina Creek in Crook County were located in Marsh's collection at Yale University, but the first noted specimen was sent to Professor Karl von Zittel in Munich by the professional fossil hunter Leander Davis. In 1984 Bruce MacFadden produced almost 200 pages in the edition on *Systematics and Phylogeny of Hipparion, Neohipparion, Nannippus, and Cormohipparion* ... covering several horses from the Oregon Mascall.

John Merriam of Berkeley made a brief faunal list of Mascall strata in his overview of the stratigraphy of the John Day valley in 1901, then provided a more thorough compilation in conjuntion with his co-worker William Sinclair in 1907. He observed that skeletal remains were dispersed throughout the sediments and that teeth and isolated bones made up most of the fauna.

The deer-like *Dromomeryx* sported fluted, foreward-projecting horns [from B. Horsfall, in Scott, 1913].

The fossil beds just west of Dayville were named by Merriam to honor the family of William R. Mascall, pioneer rancher from Petaluma, California, who homesteaded near Picture Gorge. Mascall settled here in 1864, and his ranch was visited by many in search of fossils. When foreclosure threatened Mascall in 1938, Warren Smith at the University of Oregon wrote to enlist the assistance of Merriam, paleobotanist Ralph Chaney, and paleontologist Earl Packard. He also wrote to the presiding Judge "to help the old man in his present trouble. In case Mr. Mascall cannot find gold on his place, I hope you can grant stay of proceedings long enough to enable his friends to work out some plan by which the old gentleman will not be dispossessed." Judge Claude McColloch granted a one year stay, however, in February, 1939, a State Department of Geology employee noted that Mascall's property was for sale "as a placer". In July Smith arranged for a local dredging company to work some of the ground near the river, but they had not done so in August. Although Mascall was still holding onto the land and hoping for a gold strike, he again sent enquires to Smith for an assessment. "I would like to have a real prospect job done, for I am sure there is gold." Eventually, to stave off foreclosure, William's son Lawrence and his wife Lillian Cant Mascall bought the ranch in 1938 with money Lillian made driving a gasoline truck from Fossil to Dayville. Lillian still lives on the original property.

In 1951 Theodore Downs produced the initial detailed study of the Mascall fauna for his PhD dissertation from the University of California under guidance of Ruben Stirton. In a later paper he not only reviewed Mascall specimens stored in various North American museums but also did his own collecting in eastern Oregon, taking advantage of the hospitality of the Mascalls and other local ranch families. After completing his doctorate, Downs pursued a career at the Los Angeles County Museum where he was curator of vertebrate paleontology until his death in 1997. His illustrative *Fossil Vertebrates of Southern California* presents the geologic history of this region in a non-technical style.

Theodore Downs [photo courtesy Archives, Page Museum, Los Angeles].

Near Baker several primitive Miocene elephants were turned up by local ranchers. In 1924 parts of a distinctive mastodon, identified as *Gomphotherium*, were found by Albert Werner 15 miles east of Baker in volcanic ash and tuffs thought to be Mascall. The relatively complete mandible was eventually obtained by Stirton, who turned it over to Downs. Some 25 years later Downs contacted the Werner brothers who led him to the tuff beds where the specimen had been entombed. Downs described the elephantine creature in 1952, speculating that it had been carried swiftly by floods and deposited before much decomposition could take place. The most striking feature of the mastodon is the forward projecting elongate incisor teeth. The extension of the entire lower jaw is pronounced, and the family Gomphotheriidae is called the "long jawed mastodons." The jaw and teeth may have been used for plowing up plants and roots from the forest floor.

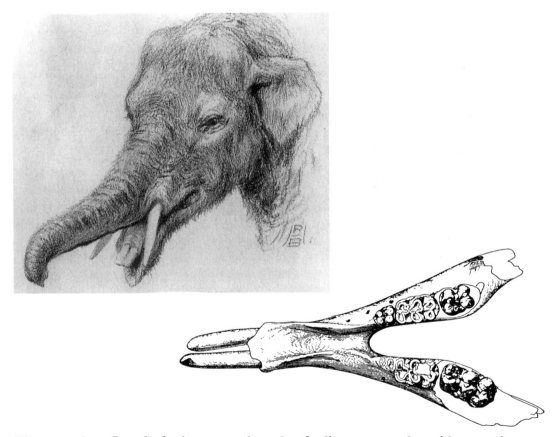

The mastodon, *Gomphotherium*, was adapted to feeding on roots dug with a massive lower jaw [from B. Horsfall, in Scott, 1913].

A second *Gomphotherium* from John Day sediments near Unity in Baker County was brought to the attention of John Merriam who described the teeth of of what was probably a mastodon. Yet a third Miocene elephant, this one from the Mascall, was uncovered at Ironside in Malheur County by Lon Hancock, who had amassed a superb private fossil collection after years spent in eastern Oregon. In 1941 Hancock and Chester Arnold, paleobotanist from the University of California, were searching for fossil leaves in Miocene lake sediments when Hancock broke open a piece of sandstone to reveal a tusk. Many hours of chiselling freed an enormous 450 pound upper jaw and skull of a *Miomastodon*. Mislabelled for years as the similar *Tetrabelodon*, the significance of the jaw wasn't realized until George Gaylord Simpson, a distinguished paleontologist from the American Museum in New York, examined the specimen which was kept in Hancock's home. Simpson recognized the mandible as that of *Miomastodon merriami*. In a letter of February 5, 1953, Simpson wrote to Hancock that "It is much the best specimen of that genus or species that has ever been collected. It is therefore of outstanding scientific importance..." Because of Simpson's reputation, the story was picked up by *Time* magazine where a photograph of Hancock and his find appeared in the April, 1953, issue.

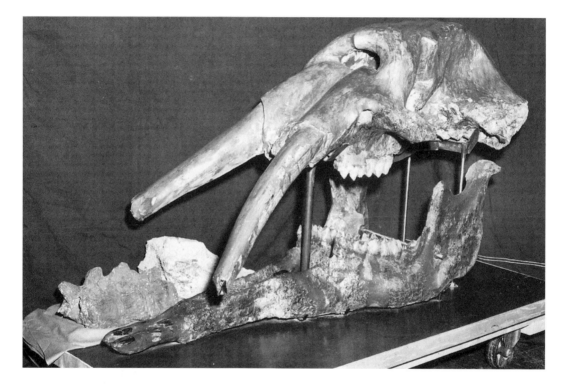

Reconstructed *Miomastodon* skull and jaw. The lower jaw was discovered a dozen years after the skull [photo courtesy Condon Museum].

Fortified by Simpson's identification and desire to locate the missing lower jaw, Hancock and a friend, Lloyd Ruff, of the Army Corps of Engineers, set out to search for it in early April when snow was still on the ground. Astonishingly, after breaking up the hard sandstone with a sledge hammer, the lower jaw, teeth, and short tusks were exposed about 15 feet from where the skull had been discovered 12 years earlier. In the excavation process the jaw was broken, and the entire skull and jaw were transported to the Museum at Eugene to be pieced back together over several year's time. The massive lower mandible was pinned to a plywood base and put on display there. Hancock wanted the specimen in his home museum in Portland, although, as Shotwell pointed out, it was very heavy and far too wide to go through the door of his house. Undaunted, Hancock cut a large hole in the outer wall of his display room and unloaded the bulky specimen from Shotwell's truck that was backed up to the building. Today the *Miomastodon* is stored at the Oregon Museum of Science and Industry in Portland.

Episodes of tilting, folding, and erosion at the end of Mascall time separate that formation from the overlying gravels, tuffs, and silts of the Rattlesnake Formation, dated at 6.4 million years before the present. In the John Day region, the Rattlesnake beds have even fewer fossils than the moderately fossiliferous Mascall below and considerably less than the wealth of vertebrate remains found in the John Day Formation, the oldest of the three. Much of the Rattlesnake fauna is modern in aspect, but the presence of such exotic animals as elephants and sloths give it an unmistakable late Tertiary complexion. Dog and cat predators, a bear, a particularly large camel, a pronghorn antelope, numerous horses, a rhinoceros, and a very large peccary, collected by Leander Davis for Marsh in 1894, make up the fauna.

Malcolm Thorpe, Curator at the Peabody Museum and Professor at Yale University, examined Marsh's collection in 1922 and noted the similarity of a dog-like carnivore *Simocyon* [*Araeocyon*] to those from Europe suggesting that this animal might have been an intercontinental migrant. Another specimen in the Marsh collection, a *Condylura*, star-nosed mole, from the Rattlesnake is the earliest known occurrence of this genus in western North America. A humerus [front limb bone] of the mole, collected by Davis and sent to Marsh in 1880, was examined and identified

almost 100 years later by Howard Hutchison at the Berkeley Museum of Paleontology. Three molar teeth and jaw fragments of another distinctive animal from this formation, a grizzly-sized bear *Indarctos*, much like *Indarctos oregonensis*, were collected by John Merriam, Chester Stock, and Clarence Moody during the summer field season in 1916 near the Mascall ranch. A decade later, while searching at the same spot, Merriam located the remainder of the jaw, today housed at Berkeley.

Fossil animals and plants from Rattlesnake strata reflect a climate that was significantly drier than that of the earlier intervals. Continuing expansion of grasslands accompanied the steady loss of the older forested Mascall period. This environmental shift is most profoundly demonstrated by the evolution of horses, which show a progressive increase in body size, a reduction in the number of toes, and an adaptation of molar teeth from browsing to grazing. One of the more important browsing animals, the rhinoceroses, became extinct in North America during the Pliocene, shortly after Rattlesnake time. Arnold Shotwell of the

Condon Museum at Eugene was able to demonstrate a sharp increase in the grazing horse *Pliohippus* during the late Miocene [Hemphillian] that coincided nicely with a diminished occurrence of the browsing *Hipparion* in the northern Great Basin. These two distinctive horses attest to the profound transition of the fauna as the environment altered.

John Merriam and his student Chester Stock published more on the Rattlesnake fauna than other paleontologists. Taking a PhD from the University of California in 1917, Stock took over classes from Merriam, who left in 1921. Chester Stock was born in San Francisco of German parentage in 1892 and died in Pasadena in 1950. He entered the University of California in 1910 where he was so enthused by Merriam's lectures that he majored in geology. Following graduation, most of his career was as a professor at California Institute of Technology and on the staff of the Los Angeles County Museum. Stock's early studies focused on Pleistocene mammals, but he branched out into the Eocene and Miocene of the Great Basin, Pacific Coast, and northern Mexico. His friendly and cheerful outlook, genuine enthusiasm for vertebrate paleontology, and efforts to popularize the science won him many friends and students. Many of Stock's students such as Robert Wilson, C. Lewis Gazin, John R. Schultz, and David Scharf went on to outstanding careers in paleontology. One of his efforts to publicize Oregon's fossils is his article *"Oregon's Wonderland of the Past - the John Day."*

Chester Stock measuring dire wolf skulls from the LaBrea tar pits [photo courtesy Archives, Page Museum, Los Angeles].

At the University of California, Stock was part of a field party that devoted five weeks in the summer of 1916 to secure larger collections from the Rattlesnake and Mascall formations in Grant County. The results were published by Merriam, Stock, and another student Clarence Moody in 1916, 1917, and 1925. This was the beginning of several consecutive summers spent exploring for vertebrates in eastern Oregon and Idaho.

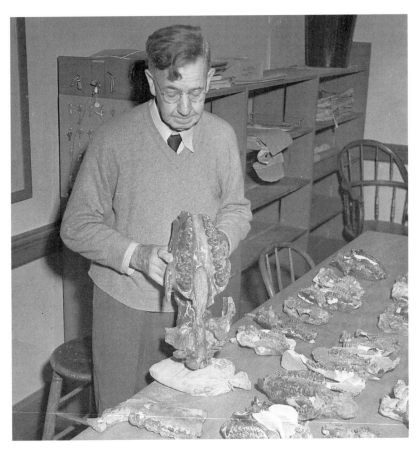

Eustace Furlong inspecting a rhinoceros skull [photo courtesy Condon Museum].

In the collection, preparation, and cataloging of material from newly discovered sites, Stock was aided by Eustace Furlong, who followed him from Berkeley to the California Institute of Technology. A skilled outdoorsman, fisherman, and a meticulous field worker, Furlong contributed significantly to unravelling the Tertiary history of the Great Basin and Mexico by leading and supervising parties of graduate students and by his subsequent careful curation of specimens. At the invitation of the University of Oregon, Furlong went to Eugene in 1945 to prepare and study oreodons from Thomas Condon's collection. While there he was struck by an automobile and severely injured. Furlong never fully recovered and returning to Davis, California, he died in January, 1950, the same year as Stock. Several years later, when Arnold Shotwell began his career at the Museum in Eugene, the oreodons, still untouched, were laid out in the preparation laboratory with Furlong's notations.

The most contemporary study of Rattlesnake faunas was by James Martin, curator of Vertebrate Paleontology at the South Dakota School of Mines and Technology. Martin evaluated specimens secured for the Museum of Geology by his assistant W. Steve Nelson. Martin himself visited the area describing four new species in 1983: leg bones of a frog [*Rana*], poorly preserved bones of a bat of the family Vespertilionidae, similar to a *Myotis*, teeth and bones of a camel [*Hemiauchenia*]. An aquatic turtle [*Clemmys*], a rhinoceros [*Teleoceras*], and the frog point to a streambed setting.

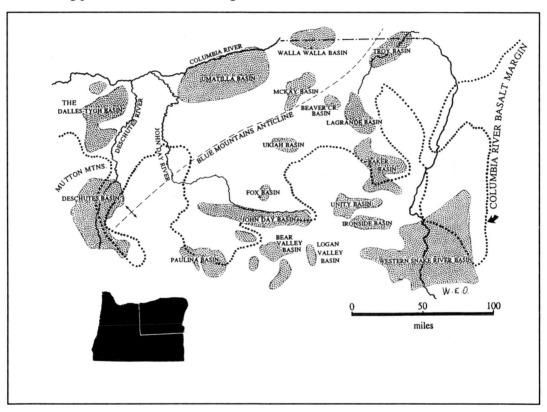

Miocene basins that developed in eastern Oregon when stream systems blocked by ash and lava formed natural traps for fossil bone, leaves, and wood [from Orr and Orr, 1996].

THE DALLES BASIN

Of the late Miocene basins along the Deschutes River drainage, only the most northerly at The Dalles has a handful of vertebrate remains. In volcanic debris redeposited by streams in eastward spreading fans, fragments of camel leg bones were found in an old stone quarry in The Dalles Formation by Thomas Condon around 1868, but no additional fossils turned up here for close to 60 years. In 1927 Merriam's students John Buwalda and Bernard Moore found a horse tooth and fragment of elephant bone, and in 1959 paleobotanist Ralph

Chaney records the partial jaw of a dog [*Aelurodon*] and scant camel bones near a well-known Miocene plant local on Chenoweth Creek.

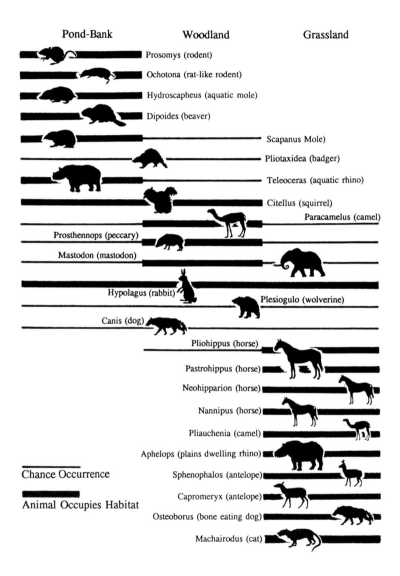

Miocene mammalian faunas in the Great Basin vary from pond to woodland to grass habitats [after Shotwell, 1958].

Across northeast Oregon small isolated depressions in the vicinity of McKay Reservoir, Arlington and Umatilla, and near Troy in Wallowa County tell a different story. Here fossils are plentiful in sediments carried by ancient rivers to be deposited atop the Columbia basalt plateau. Of these locations, McKay basin has the richest and most varied fauna. Strong winds, eroding the fossil-rich sands, produce long depressions or blowouts in which bones accumulate at the bottom. Arnold Shotwell recorded in his journal for July, 1954, that "the wind blowing like mad. Almost impossible to keep dry plaster in my mixing bowl." In addition to crayfish, frogs and turtles, bats, birds, rabbits, carnivores, horses, camels, elephants, and plentiful rodents make up the McKay fauna. These vertebrate remains were first discovered in 1949 by Ray Spangle of Portland and excavated for the next four years by field parties directed by Shotwell.

Some of the most significant additions to unravelling the mammal paleontology of the eastern Oregon Miocene were made by J. Arnold Shotwell [photo courtesy Archives, University of Oregon].

Late Miocene mammal material here was so abundant that Shotwell was able to use the region as the basis for broad paleoenvironmental deductions. In his classic 1956 and 1958 studies, Shotwell distinguished three major paleoenvironments, a pond-bank, woodland, and grassland. The dominant local habitat was a stream setting at McKay, bordered at a distance by grassy prairies and forests at Ordnance and Arlington. He was also able to distinguish animals that had been carried into the basin [allochthonous] from those which had died *in situ* [autochthonous] by the statistical frequency of the separate bones of the skeleton. In-place or local faunas are typically represented by a large array of skeletal elements, whereas transported material is often fragmented, worn, and not as numerous. Overall, most of the smaller bones were well-preserved and showed little abrasion. The excellent condition of the fossils at the federally-owned McKay Reservoir and the relative ease with which they can be separated from the soft matrix of white ash contributed significantly to the success and accuracy of Shotwell's work.

Certain elements of McKay Reservoir faunas are remarkably like those in the same interval from north China suggesting migrations from that continent to North America during the late Miocene. The carnivores, or flesheaters, display the highest degree of similarity, whereas there is little in common between the rodents and hoofed mammals of both continents.

J. Arnold Shotwell worked in the Museum of Natural History in Eugene as curator from 1947 to 1953 and as director from then until his retirement in 1971. Born in North Bend in October, 1923, Shotwell attended schools in Oregon but completed his PhD in paleontology from the University of California, Berkeley, in 1953. Specializing in the paleoecology of mammals and the effects of extinction, climate, and migration on populations, Shotwell and his wife Ginny spent their summers in eastern Oregon where they located and opened many new sites of Miocene vertebrates. The bulk of the splendid faunas at the Condon Museum are the result of his well thought-out and executed research on Tertiary mammals. At present the Shotwells live in Bay Center, Washington.

At the South Dakota School of Mines, James Martin's work in northeast Oregon followed that of Shotwell. Martin's 1979 PhD from the University of Washington on Miocene rodents of Ordnance, Arlington, and McKay Reservoir and their relationship to other North American rodents provided the basis for later papers. A 1981 study of coprolites or fossil dung from this same region by Martin casts a new light on the accumulations of rodents and other small animals. He addressed the sometimes puzzling occurrence of small mammal bones in discrete pockets, here-to-fore thought to have been deposited by stream systems.

A thorough worker, James Martin's current research is with Miocene faunas from the eastern part of the state [photo courtesy J. Martin].

Martin, among others, has interpreted these concentrations as the fecal droppings of carnivorous mammals or birds. Most were probably from mammals because the bones were broken, which is not typical of bird pellets. Squirrels [Sciuridae] and pocket gophers [Geomyidae] from Ordnance, the former Army depot south of Hermiston, fish, snakes, squirrels, and pocket gophers from Arlington, and squirrels and rabbits from McKay Reservoir were the most common groups. In addition, Martin found one beaver at Ordnance and a large coprolite at McKay, which contained parts of a young dog [Canidae]. Bones of the rats *Oregonomys*, *Parapliosaccomys*, and *Perognathus* were abundant in coprolites from Arlington and Ordnance. Martin has suggested the paleoecological intrepretations by Shotwell might be reevaluated to consider the effects of contamination by animal fecal debris.

The analysis of coprolites was pioneered by Chester Stock, whose student Jerome Laudermilk made a complete examination of the dung balls of the Pleistocene ground sloth *Nothrotherium* from Gypsum Cave, Nevada. Laudermilk was able to identify plants and deduce paleoenvironments by a thorough examination of the vegetable fibers that made up the mass.

Similar in size and proportions to a hippopotamus, the aquatic rhinoceros *Teleoceras* usually was present with other pond bank animals in late Tertiary settings [from B. Horsfall, in Scott, 1913].

BASINS OF THE OWYHEE PLATEAU

Geographically included in the northern Great Basin, the Owyhee plateau is part of an extensive contiguous area in southeast Oregon and adjacent Nevada marked by a number of small and larger depositional basins atop lava flows. Within these depressions fossil remains are evidence that animals flourished around regional lakes during the Miocene. This area of Oregon was virtually unexplored in the early 1900s, and scientists, primarily led by Chester Stock, California Institute of Technology, itemized new faunas as they were uncovered. Later efforts, by Arnold Shotwell from Eugene were able to focus on the comparative evolution and paleoenvironments of whole communities.

Miocene sediment accumulations on the Owhyee plateau include the Juntura basin in Harney and Malheur counties, the basins near Lake Owyhee in Malheur County, and those scattered at Rome and Beatys Butte near the southern border of the state.

During the mid 1950s Arnold Shotwell and his field crew from Eugene relocated well southeast of McKay Reservoir to the town of Juntura in Malheur County. For his research program Shotwell's intent was to study changes in vertebrate communities over long intervals of time, and to do this complete sequences or chronologies of vertebrates from several areas had to be established. This was accomplished by compiling thorough lists of local faunas. He realized variations in the lists were inevitable when geographic separation, different ages, or multiple environments occurred, but by factoring out the first two, he was able to determine paleoenvironments and show how a community evolved. His technique was refined in the 1950s and published in 1958.

Shotwell's efforts to set up a reliable vertebrate chronology were rewarded in the Juntura basin where he found complete Miocene sequences of fossils in the Juntura and Drewsey formations. The northern Juntura basin of southeast Oregon is bisected east to west by U.S. Highway 20 and north-south by the Malheur-Harney county line. The southern limits of the basin are overlapped and obscured by younger lavas, volcanic tuffs, mudflows, and sandstones of the Juntura and Drewsey formations. As Shotwell's team progressed through the basin, they were overwhelmed by the amount of new material. It is remarkable that both faunas from eastern Oregon at the Clarno Mammal Quarry and Juntura basin were uncovered and worked simultaneously, and, even though he was to oversee both operations, Shotwell had little time to give to the Clarno finds.

In the Juntura basin, the older Juntura Formation contains the temperate Stinking Water leaf flora and no animal remains, while the younger Juntura layers have diatoms and a wealth of vertebrates. The uppermost intervals, designated as the Drewsey Formation, also yield a wide variety of vertebrate fossils.

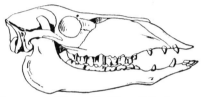

About the size of a llama, *Procamelus* was a light-footed browser [from B. Horsfall, in Scott, 1913].

Within the Juntura Formation, late Miocene fossils can be found at Black Butte in Malheur County. Those from Black Butte, a peak south of the town of Juntura, and from several surrounding hills were initially described by Donald Russell in a 1956 Masters thesis from the University of California Berkeley. Russell's material from the early years of working with Shotwell was refined by Shotwell in his classic paper on the Juntura basin in 1963. Dated at 11.3 million years before the present, the Black Butte fauna is assigned to the early late Miocene because of the presence of *Eucastor malheurensis* [beaver] and the absence of the horse *Hypohippus*. Also found at Black Butte are shrews [insectivores] and smaller rodents as mice. Larger mammals, which were less common, include carnivores as the hyaena-like *Aelurodon* and bone-eating dog *Osteoborus*, herbivores such as elephants *Mammut* and the shovel-tusker mastodon *Platybelodon,* camels [*Procamelus* and *Megatylopus*], and a horse [*Hipparion*]. Years later Shotwell would relate that when he first saw the sizeable fragments of *Platybelodon* lying on the surface during a reconnaissance trip in 1954, he was astounded. Tracing the pieces up slope he found a mandible and tusks and proceeded immediately to excavate the site.

Also in the Juntura basin, sediments of the Drewsey Formation lie immediately above Juntura strata. Deposited during the late Miocene in several areas close to Drinkwater Pass, Otis Basin, and Bartlett Mountain in Harney and Malheur counties, tuffs of the Drewsey yield scattered remains of vertebrates. These were initially prospected by Chester Stock and Eustace Furlong from California Institute of Technology during the 1920s and 1930s.

Arnold Shotwell and his field crew in the Juntura basin [photo by B.J. Freemesser; courtesy Condon Museum]

Arnold Shotwell and his team were investigating the Drewsey Formation during the middle 1950s, and their detailed account of the fauna was issued in 1963. On a spring break trip in March, 1954, while working up a draw about three miles west of the town of Drewsey, they found the mandible and tusk of an *Amebelodon* elephant. They couldn't purchase plaster locally, so a paste was made of flour, which Shotwell hoped would harden in the rain. "Flour cast didn't seem strong enough to hold" so plaster was bought in Burns and a cast successfully hardened. The Spring trip the following year produced only snow, but a side trip to Bartlett Mountain during July yielded characteristic large molars of a *Pliohippus* as well as teeth of the beaver *Dipoides* and horned gophers *Mylagaulus*.

Looking myopic in the bright light, a horned gopher exits its hole [from B. Horsfall, in Scott, 1913].

Slightly younger than the Drewsey Formation, stream, marsh, and lake sediments of the Chalk Butte Formation were deposited in and around ancient Lake Idaho that stretched across east central Oregon to present day Twin Falls, Idaho. Chalk Butte sediments accumulated as stream drainage systems of the western Snake River plain were periodically blocked by lava flows. Waters of several successive lakes rose then drained during the middle Miocene through the Pliocene. A small pocket of fossils from south and west of Vale near Little Valley and Juniper Creek were scrutinized by Shotwell, who concluded in 1970 that the obvious wear and fragmentary condition of the bones reflected post mortem transportation and redeposititon by water. Only a beaver *Dipoides*, a rabbit *Hypolagus*, a dog *Canis,* a camel *Megatylopus*, and the rodent *Diprionomys* were common in these sediments that are better known for their fossil fish.

South and east of the Juntura basin on the Owyhee plateau, Skull Springs, Sucker Creek, Quartz basin, and Red basin in Malheur County and Beatys Butte in Harney County are all smaller middle Miocene depositional sites marked by varying amounts of fossil vertebrates. All were part of the same landscape 15 million years ago where preservation of animal remains was linked to accumulations of volcanic debris. Several of these vertebrate faunas from southeast Oregon were recorded by students of Chester Stock - C. Lewis Gazin on Skull Springs, David W. Scharf on Sucker Creek, and Robert Wallace on Beatys Butte. Stock and Eustace Furlong had directed field reconnaissance from California Institute of Technology to this area between 1924 and the middle 1940s when Gazin, Scharf, and Wallace themselves visited the area and examined the vertebrates.

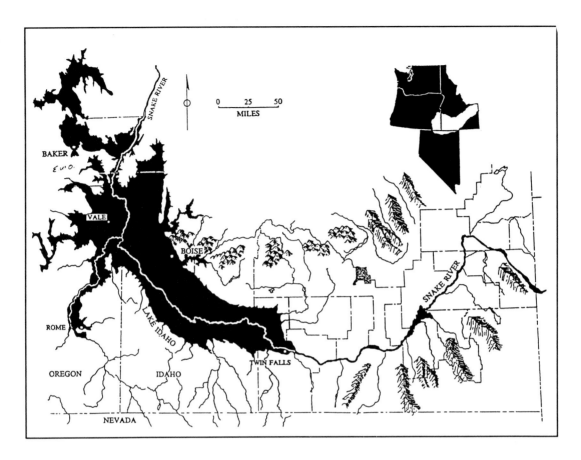

During the Miocene, lava dammed Lake Idaho [shaded], which stretched from eastern Oregon into southcentral Idaho, making it about the size of the present Lake Ontario. Deposits of this large lake preserved aquatic and nearshore fossils in its sediments [from Orr and Orr, 1996].

Of the three locals, Skull Springs yielded the most material. A surface collection from the Butte Creek Volcanic sandstone layer here produced vertebrates encased in nodules that had been worn to expose teeth and bones. The lack of camels, antelopes, and rabbits and presence of squirrels and rodents, especially the mountain beaver from the Alpodontidae family led Gazin to conclude that the environment 15 million years ago, in what is now a desert climate, was a semihumid forest.

Large for a gopher, aplodontids or mountain beaver are remarkably primitive.

Volcanic ash of the Sucker Creek Formation, derived from a nearby caldera complex, is more famous for its beautifully preserved fossil plants such as oak, pine, willow, and maple, than its fragmentary vertebrates. Browsing horses [*Hypohippus* and *Parahippus*], a chalicothere [*Moropus*], camels [*Dromomeryx*], rhinoceroses, peccary [*Prosthennops*], and a dog-like carnivore make up the fauna. First collected in 1924 and 1927, the result was a published report in 1935 by David Scharf, in which he presented a list of larger mammals and proposed a paleo-environmental setting of forested hills and basins filled by lakes.

Kevin Downing's 1992 PhD from the University of Arizona is the first study of small mammal populations from the Sucker Creek. After washing more than a thousand pounds of matrix, Downing found almost 30 separate species including several that were new at Devils Gate south and east of Owyhee Dam in Malheur County and at a second locality immediately across the border at Stagestop, Idaho. Recovering 2,700 skeletal elements, which were primarily teeth and limb bones, he identified shrews and moles [Insectivora], bats [Chiroptera], rabbits [Lagomorpha], and rodents [Rodentia]. A bat, flying squirrels [*Petauristodon*], and rodent [*Leptodontomys*] were recorded for the first time. Many of the bone fragments were encased in concretions. One of Downing's most important findings is that vegetative successions from woodlands to grasslands, brought about by volcanic disturbances, are not reflected by parallel changes in the composition of small mammals. Citing observations after the 1980 eruption of Mt. St. Helens, he notes that rodents occupy more environmentally diverse habitats and can therefore recover more quickly from such overwhelming disasters than plants.

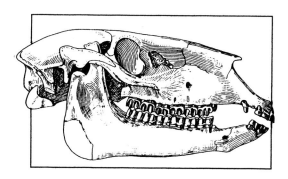

A nearly complete skull of *Parahippus,* a browsing Miocene horse [from Cope, 1883].

329

At Beatys Butte, bones of vertebrates occur in water deposited tuffs near the base of an old volcanic cone, where the even layering and stratification convey burial in calm water. Larger bone fragments regularly show gnaw marks made by rodents' teeth, and traces of rodent burrows, now filled with ash, can be detected in the beds. In 1938 the presence of these remains was brought to Stock's attention by Warren Smith at the University of Oregon and collected during several subsequent summers. From the faunal composition, Robert Wallace reconstructed a paleo-landscape of open woodlands adjacent to grassy plains.

Factors contributing to faunal changes from Quartz and Red basins were part of a study by Arnold Shotwell and a crew of 30 persons during the summers of 1960 and 1961. By perusing aerial photos and locating areas that looked promising, the party reconnoitered during the spring when Shotwell successfully uncovered several pockets of mammal fossils. These spring trips were frequently hampered by heavy snowfalls, up to 14 inches, and, on one occasion, delays because of fire in the Museum field truck.

During the first field season at Quartz basin in Malheur County, Shotwell's group set up camp near natural springs and vacant buildings on the old Ralph Page ranch. This was close to a remarkably rich source of vertebrates located in sandstones and conglomerates of the Deer Butte Formation, and it took the crew only 20 minutes to find all of the key or index species that delineate the specific Miocene stage of 13 to 16 million years ago. Over the summer, material was bagged and taken to the stock pond on the ranch where it was washed and screened. On Monday, July 1, they "moved screens away from the pond so Page's cattle could get in", and it wasn't until July 16 that Page removed his cows so work could continue. More than three tons of the vertebrate-rich strata was worked using 80 screens. Hauled to the museum laboratory at Eugene, the bone was laborously separated by hand from the remaining matrix.

By the next summer, working with an experienced crew, Shotwell moved up Dry Creek to the old town of Littlefield about 25 miles northwest of Quartz Basin. Here Red Basin proved a good site for vertebrates from the Butte Creek Volcanic Sandstone, a middle Miocene layer, examined years earlier by Stock and Furlong.

Shotwell's field crews used innumerable screens to soak fossil-rich rocks in water. As the volcanic sediment crumbles, bone fragments and teeth were saved by the fine wire mesh. [photo courtesy University of Oregon, Archives].

Shotwell's 1968 report on the sites at Quartz and Red basins recorded a large and diverse assortment of insectivores, rodents, carnivores, and hoofed mammals, but he noted contrasting groups of animals from the two areas. Large mammals were more abundant at Red Basin, while smaller animals characterize the Quartz Basin region. A total of seventy species were reported from both areas, but differences between the two faunas prompted Shotwell to conclude that they were nearly identical in age but represented markedly different paleo-environments.

In spite of the massive leg bone in his hands, Howard Hutchison is known for his work on Tertiary shrews and moles [photo courtesy Archives, University of California, Berkeley].

Working on eastern Oregon material obtained by Shotwell over several years, Howard Hutchison earned a Masters degree from the University of Oregon in 1964 on late Tertiary insectivores of the Great Basin. Five species of shrews [Soricidae family], including three new genera from Shotwell's Miocene deposits, were listed by Hutchison who noted that the published fossil record of North American late Tertiary shrews was virtually non-existant before 1950. Completing a 1976 PhD in paleontology at the University of California, Berkeley, from Ruben Stirton, Hutchison stayed on at the Museum there. In addition to his curatorial work, he enjoyed field work and trained many students. Hutchison's eclectic interests covered Cretaceous and Tertiary turtles, vertebrates from Burma, and alligators from Texas, along with his focus on the systematics, morphology, and ecology of recent and fossil Talpidae [moles]. In one of his more definitive papers on material from the Oregon Miocene, Hutchison observed five separate adaptive modes for fossil and modern moles ranging from ambulatory

331

[terrestrial], aquatic, semi aquatic, semi-fossorial [digging], and fossorial [burrowing]. In 1968 he records that this remarkable diversity decreases in the late Miocene and Pliocene when non-digging and moderately specialized moles become extinct during a climate change from semihumid to the desert scrubland of today. Hutchison retired in 1993 in order to have more time for research.

ANIMALS OF THE PLIOCENE EPOCH

There are very few vertebrates in Oregon that are unquestionably from the Pliocene epoch, and a revision of the Cenozoic time scale in 1974 has redesignated much of what was previously early Pliocene as late Miocene. This means that late Tertiary dates for a fossil allocated prior to 1974 might be incorrect. A single mole, *Scapanus,* from unnamed Pliocene sediments at Enrico Ranch near the southern Oregon border was recorded by Howard Hutchison in 1968. Because most late Tertiary moles are "fossorial" or burrowing animals, the limb bones are extremely distinctive. The upper front leg bone or humerus, in particular, is greatly enlarged and flattened as a support for the powerful digging muscles.

Possible Pliocene sediments of the Yonna Formation in the Klamath River basin contain freshwater diatoms and invertebrates as well as the skull of a peccary, *Prosthennops oregonensis.* Even though the stratigraphic position of the peccary, found in a quarry southeast of Klamath Falls, was not precisely established, Reuben C. Newcomb of the U.S. Geological Survey considered the matrix to be similar to tuffs of the Yonna, placing it in the Pliocene.

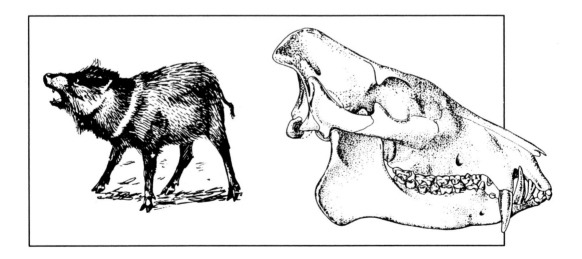

An unmistakable wedge-shaped skull of a Pliocene peccary from the Klamaths is similar to that of its modern relative.

Over 10 feet high at the shoulder, the Columbian mammoth was the most common elephant in the Northwest during the Ice Ages [from B. Horsfall, in Scott, 1913].

ANIMALS OF THE PLEISTOCENE EPOCH

The Pleistocene or Ice Ages of Oregon was a time of bleak and harsh cold weather at higher altitudes and heavy rainfall with vast wetlands at lower elevations. Although continental glaciers never reached as far south as Oregon, smaller sheets of ice on mountain crests flowed down into the lower valleys. The severe climate doesn't seem to have restricted the range of mammals that were scattered throughout the state. Most of the fossils, however, are concentrated in two areas - the Willamette Valley and the south-central region of the Great Basin - where swamps and lakes were optimum for fossil preservation. All were condusive to miring, entrapment, burial, and preservation of large and small animals.

As with other fossil finds, and perhaps even more so with Pleistocene vertebrates, the discovery of ancient animal remains is often the result of human activity. Many teeth and bones of elephants from Baker County appeared in gold-impregnated gravels of placer mining operations. Others, along the Columbia River, were discovered by engineers excavating for dam projects. But the highest frequencies of known Pleistocene vertebrate sites correlate with the most densely populated parts of the northern Willamette Valley. Digging for wells, septic systems, and foundations for buildings has turned up many fossils. In Lake County, due to the extreme concentration of surface remains in a small area - first seen by cattle ranchers - Fossil Lake became famous for its Pleistocene remains.

Oliver Hay's *The Pleistocene of North America and its Vertebrated Animals*, issued in two volumes in 1923 and 1927, has yet to be matched for its coverage of this time span. As a first step, Hay conducted a thorough literature search of reported vertebrates in journals and newspapers, then relied on correspondence to find the exact locality, strata, and, if possible, photographs. He also visited a number of museums to inspect specimens, where, to his regret, he often found incomplete data. The second volume, dealing with the west, has maps for each state [Oregon, Washington, Idaho, California, Nevada, Arizona, and Utah] that show the distribution of fossils.

Hay's career in paleontology began with undergraduate degrees in natural science from Illinois and a PhD from the University of Indiana in 1884. Born in Jefferson County, Indiana, he moved every few years throughout his lifetime, teaching at small colleges in Iowa, Illinois, and Indiana before taking a curatorial position at the Chicago Field Museum and then at the American Museum in New York. He was engaged in private consulting during 1907 to 1911, when he joined the staff at the Carnegie Institute, Washington, D.C., for his longest period as a research associate. He remained there until retirement in 1926. His splendid *Fossil Turtles of North America* is also a monumental compilations. Hay died in Washington, D.C., in 1930.

Oliver Hay [left], Charles Gilmore, and James Gidley [right], three eminent paleontologists at the turn of the century [photo courtesy Archives, American Museum].

Thomas Condon drew attention to Pleistocene deposits in the Willamette Valley when he wrote in 1902 that terraces of what he called "Willamette Sound" were proof of water depths at Salem of 165 feet and as high as 325 feet over Portland. According to his deductions, the Sound may have extended as far south as Eugene with a configuration not unlike that of present day Puget lowlands in Washington. As geologic knowledge of the Pacific Northwest increased, some of Condon's ideas have been confirmed. Ice sheets pushing into northern Washington and Montana blocked waterways to create enormous lakes that periodically released stupendous masses of water, sediment, and ice down the Columbia Gorge and into the Willamette Valley. Doubtless the sudden floods drowned many mammals, which were buried and preserved. Between the multiple flooding events the valley was carpeted by thick forests and low-lying swamps that supported dense animal populations. The most awesome of these were the ponderous mammoths, mastodons, and giant ground sloths. Bison, camels, horse, a rare tapir, deer, and beaver rounded out the picture.

Crown views of elephant teeth clearly distinguish the broad low cusps of the browsing mastodon [left] from those of the grazing mammoth [right] [photo courtesy Condon Museum].

Several varieties of elephants [Proboscideans] wandered far and wide across the northwest as is suggested by the numbers preserved in Ice Age bogs. Even though they became extinct during the late Pleistocene, the woolly mammoth, seen in European cave drawings, clearly coexisted at the same time as humans. In 1993 evidence has come to light that a peculiar hairy dwarf mammoth on Wrangel Island off the northeast Siberian coast survived several thousand years longer than previously thought.

Elephants - *Elephas boreus, Elephas columbi,* and *Elephas imperator* - populated Oregon, and, of these, *Elephas columbi* was by far the most numerous. Found in the Willamette Valley, at The Dalles, and in Lake, Baker, and Umatilla counties, this elephant was not exceptionally large - 11 feet at shoulder height. Well-developed grinding molars attest to a diet of grasses. Since it was a stopping-place for early pioneers on their way to the Willamette Valley, The Dalles in Wasco County has a considerable number of documented finds. The first probable elephant bones were reported to be "gigantic" by George Gibbs in 1855. Gibbs, appointed by President Filmore to the Port of Astoria, tells that the Indians saw similar-sized bones near Walla Walla. A tooth and shoulder blade of *Elephas boreus* from here were examined by Ira Williams, an engineer with the state Bureau of Mines and Geology, and by J. Harlan Bretz, who spent much time along the Columbia in his efforts to decipher destructive Ice Age floods.

In the Willamette Valley remains of *Elephas columbi* have been documented from Newberg, McMinnville, Dayton, St. Paul, Silverton, Harrisburg, and Eugene, to name just a few sites. As a beginning professor at Oregon, Packard wrote to Warren Smith at Eugene that he had purchased a "wonderful lower jaw, one side of a mastodon, a femur, rib, and a tooth and large tusk of a mammoth" for $50 from D.A. Wardle of McMinnville.

Fairly complete fossil remains from a bog near Silverton in Marion County generated much interest, but their fate was similar to many such finds. A large deposit of bones, a partial skull, and tusks were found in 1946 when Paul Pinson was digging for water to irrigate his cucumber crop in Evans Valley. Warren Smith visited the local where he expressed the hope that the bog would be excavated plot-by-plot. Unfortunately, when seen several weeks later by Oregon State University paleontologist Earl Packard, the fossil material, that had been stored untreated in a barn, was already drying and crumbling to fragments. Samples of peat were taken with a coring device by Henry Hansen, also from Oregon State, and an analysis of the locality was published by Packard and Hansen three years later.

Occasionally fossil bones are encountered on the ground. In a publicized case near Tualatin, the skeleton of a mastodon was half imbedded in the mud of a tomato field less than 200 yards from where the Fred Meyer parking lot is now located. The bones, projecting above ground, were in poor shape, but below the skeleton survived except for the skull. Following discovery by local resident Charlie Roberts, they were excavated by his acquaintance John George and a group from Portland State University over a month-long period. A retired dentist, George kept the tusk and teeth, but the remainder of the bones packed in wooden crates were variously stored at PSU, the Portland zoo, and even in a commercial storage unit. When brought back together thirty years later, the animal was reassembled in 1992 by Robert Linder, a University of Oregon student. Since the mastodon had been lying on its left side, Linder placed it in bas-relief along with a silhouette of the flesh. Today the articulated beast may be seen adjoining the wall of the Tualatin city library. Linder also assembled a somewhat smaller mastodon for the Portland zoo. This is an entire skeleton and can be seen in the elephant house.

The fossil remains of hoofed mammals with an even number of toes [artiodactyls] such as bison, camels, and deer have been exposed in river gravels in the Willamette Valley, on the surface of old lake beds in Lake County, and in the Wallowa Mountains. Credit for discovery of the first fossil bison goes to Ewing Young, a trapper and pioneer who arrived at Ft. Vancouver on the Columbia in 1834. Young found a metatarsal bone along with elephant teeth and parts of a ground sloth in 1839 on the bank of the "Walhaumet" River downstream from Eugene. Construction typically revealed vertebrate fragments as, in 1923, when channel dredgers uncovered remains of a bison above the falls at Oregon City. John Horner, a professor of history at Oregon Agricultural College [now Oregon State University], who founded the Horner Museum there, sent photographs of the skull and horns of a superb *Bison occidentalis* to Hay. Another photograph sent by Horner was of a partial skull uncovered on Lick Creek in Wallowa County. Horner wrote in February, 1924, that when a charge of TNT, blasting for road construction by the U.S. Forest Service, was "put under a fir tree 2.5 feet in diameter [it] blew the tree out of the ground and left a hole 5 feet deep, at the bottom of which was found the skull..."

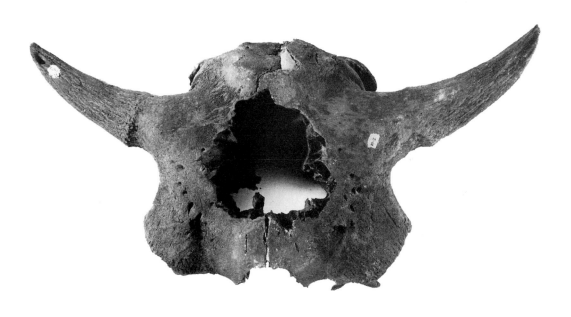

Ice Age bison may have been hunted out by early human inhabitants [photo courtesy Condon Museum].

The Horner Museum officially opened as the College Museum on February 20, 1925, and consisted of study collections put together by several campus departments. Horner was the impetus for the Museum, gathering material from the separate departments into one room on the ground floor of the Library building. The exhibits included natural history items, embroideries, historical weapons, and other artifacts. When "Jackie" Horner died in 1933, OSU President Peavy recommended to the Board of Higher Education that the College Museum be renamed to honor him. Financial difficulty forced the closure of the Museum in 1995, and most of the collection was moved to the University Archives.

THE COMPANY WILL APPRECIATE SUGGESTIONS FROM ITS PATRONS CONCERNING ITS SERVICE   1201-S

WESTERN UNION (42)

CLASS OF SERVICE	SYMBOLS
This is a full-rate Telegram or Cablegram unless its deferred character is indicated by a suitable symbol above or preceding the address.	DL = Day Letter
	NM = Night Message
	NL = Night Letter
	LC = Deferred Cable
	NLT = Cable Night Letter
	Ship Radiogram

R. B. WHITE PRESIDENT   NEWCOMB CARLTON CHAIRMAN OF THE BOARD   ...LEVER FIRST VICE-PRESIDENT

The filing time shown in the date line on telegrams and day letters is STANDARD TIME at point of origin. Time of receipt is STANDARD TIME at point of destination.

Received at   1938 APR 29 AM 11 44

PRE 47 54 DL=MEDFORD ORG 29 1051A

PROFESSOR WARREN D SMITH=

UNIVERSITY OF OREGON GN=

HUGE HEAD OF PREHISTORIC ANIMAL DISCOVERED HERE YESTERDAY
35 FEET BELOW GROUND. DUE TO EXPOSURE LIKELY TO DISINTEGRATE
VERY SOON. BELIEVE FIND OF SUFFICIENT IMPORTANCE TO JUSTIFY
YOUR INVESTIGATING ANIMAL AND IF POSSIBLE TO PRESERVE SAME.
PLEASE ADVISE IF YOU CAN EXAMINE IT. CONSIDERABLE INTEREST
HERE AND HUNDREDS HAVE SEEN IT DURING PAST DAY=
    A H BANWELL MANAGER JACKSON COUNTY CHAMBER OF COMMERCE.

WESTERN UNION GIFT ORDERS ARE APPROPRIATE GIFTS FOR ALL OCCASIONS

35.

The excitement over the discovery of a "prehistoric" beast is evident in a telegram from Jackson County officials to Warren Smith at the University of Oregon [telegram courtesy Condon Museum].

A flurry of telegrams, letters, and postcards in the Spring of 1938 announced recovery of the "huge head of prehistoric animal" from near Medford in Jackson County. The fossil turned out to be a bison, inspected by John Allen of the Department of Geology and Mineral Industries, who mailed photographs to Warren Smith. Allen advised sending the specimen to

Vertress Vanderhoof at the University of California for a monograph he was completing on extinct western bison. Allen encased the specimen in plaster, crated it, and left it for shipment. Jackson County officials wanted to place it in a local museum, but until arrangements could be made, the specimen was to be sent to the Condon Museum. But, as often happens, the ultimate destiny of the bison isn't known.

Many of Hay's Oregon photographs, specimens, and locations were sent to him by Ellen Condon McCornack, who assisted at the University of Oregon Museum after the death of her father, Thomas Condon. Hay also relied on McCornack's *A Study of the Oregon Pleistocene*, 1914, in which she reported that exotic creatures such as camels roved the state from Umatilla to Portland. Forty-one feet below the surface at Portland, a worn camel tooth was recovered while excavating for the City Park reservoir number three. The majority of Pleistocene camel remains are from the Ice Age lakes of southcentral Oregon, where numerous bones were sent to eastern paleontologists Othniel Marsh and Edward Cope by local residents. These were identified as species of *Camelops* and the larger *Camelus*.

Immense Ice Age sloths, *Mylodon,* were trapped in bogs of the Willamette Valley [from B. Horsfall, in Scott, 1913; skeleton from Stock, 1920].

Odd-toed, hoofed mammals [perissodactyls] take in the horses, which, except for those at Fossil Lake, one skull from Umatilla, and two teeth from Jackson County, appear mainly in the Willamette Valley. Many of the Oregon horse teeth are recorded in McCornack's publication. The numerous horse fragments from Fossil Lake, collected by Edward Cope, were identified as *Equus major, Equus occidentalis,* and *Equus excelsus.*

Probably one of the most remarkable Pleistocene animals in the Northwest was ground sloths, clawed members of the Edentata, that used their elongated digits for digging. Sloth remains are frequently found alongside those of elephants, horses, and bison. The ox-sized *Megalonyx* and *Nothrotherium* along with *Mylodon,* which was twice as large, were obtained from river gravels in the Willamette Valley, in Klamath County, and from surface debris at Fossil Lake. The most colossal Pleistocene sloth, the 20-foot long *Megatherium,* is unreported in Oregon. Earl Packard's 1952 monograph on fossil Edentates describes several bones, housed at the Horner Museum, as *Mylodon harlani,* a species characteristic of western Oregon. Sloths survived into the late Pleistocene, and the large beasts almost certainly co-existed with humans before disappearing around 11,000 years ago.

A scattering of other Ice Age mammals are represented by single examples of a wolf from the Willamette Valley, a tapir from the coast, and a bear and bighorn sheep from Lake County. A bog in Marion County on Mill Creek near the Woodburn high school produced an unusually large wolf, named by Packard *Aenocyon dirus.* The discoverer, Art Lowe, gave Packard the massive jaw and heavy teeth, which were so worn that Packard concluded the individual was old when it died.

This local, that also yielded a sloth [*Mylodon harlani*] for Packard, has been the focus of excavations during the 1990s because fossil bones of bison were discovered during horizontal drilling to place a sewer pipe under Highway 217. The bog here is considered to be one of the best localities for Ice Age remains in the Pacific Northwest, and a more recent deep excavation for a sewer turned up bones of sloth, bison, elephant, wolf, and bear. The material, now on display at the Woodburn library, was identified by William Orr of the Condon Museum at Eugene, and a carbon 14 date on the rich accumulation of preserved wood came out as 12,500 years old. The goal of a full-scale dig using backhoes and other heavy equipment during the summers of 1996 and 1997, under the direction of Rob Bonnichsen of Oregon State University and supervised by Alison Stenger an archaeological consultant from Portland, was to find the bone bed layer and look for evidence of early human culture. Their efforts turned up animal hair for DNA studies and a spectacular trove of beetles, seeds, and plants in the peaty layers along with abundant rodent and deer bones.

Just two tapirs from the Pleistocene of the Pacific Coast have been reported - one from Tuolumne County, California, and the other from Cape Blanco, Oregon. The well-preserved Oregon jaw and teeth were collected from the Elk River beds by Bruce Martin in 1911 for the California Academy of Sciences. These were examined by John Merriam, who pronounced the animal to be similar to *Tapirus haysii.* Mollusc shells and microfossils associated with the tapir suggest a shallow cold water embayment off the ocean. Like its modern

340

counterpart, this tapir probably lived in the luxuriant forest, and, after it died, was washed offshore into the bay.

Excavations at Fossil Lake in Lake County reveal a fossil elephant leg bone with only one toe bone missing. The small white "dot" near the lower leg is a snail shell. The name of the happy gentleman is also missing [photo from Allison, 1966].

Major Pleistocene fossil concentrations in several wide dry lake beds of southcentral Oregon yield the bones of vertebrates of all sizes. During this period of increased rainfall, vast lakes and wetlands filled depressions across the Great Basin. Of those in southern Oregon, two of the largest were Lake Chewaucan at 461 square miles and Lake Coleman, now Warner lakes, at 483 square miles. Remnants of Lake Chewaucan are the present Summer Lake, Lake Abert, and the Chewaucan Marshes. Fort Rock Lake, now the dry Silver and Fossil lakes, was up to 200 feet deep.

At the height of the Ice ages these bodies of water attracted animals from the surrounding countryside. The greatest variety and abundance of Pleistocene mammal remains in the state are concentrated on the surface at Fossil Lake in Lake County. Scattered among the beach sands and gravels are bones and teeth of all manner of animals such as elephants, horses, camels, sloths, peccaries, antelopes, rabbits and beaver, as well as other rodents. Carnivores as wolf, coyote, fox, bear, and puma are also present along with skeletal parts of birds and fish. Fossil bones are preserved by permineralization [mineral infilling of pore spaces],

341

creating a jet black polished appearance. So thoroughly are the bones petrified that fragments ring like a bell when tapped.

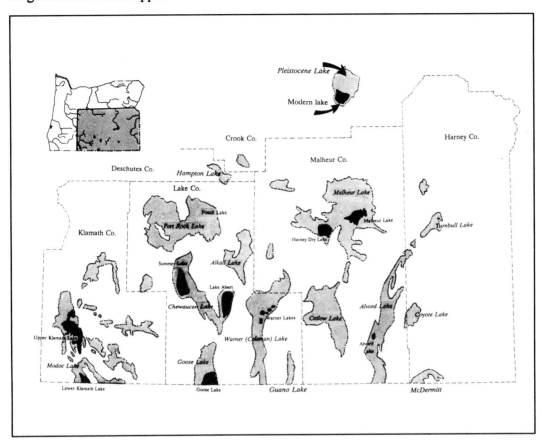

Small playas and lakes that dot southeast Oregon today are all that remain of much larger water bodies of the Ice Ages [from Orr, Orr, and Baldwin, 1992].

Because fossils are so abundant at these old lake beds, they have been the focus of many interested parties since their discovery in the middle 1800s. Bones from the paleolakes were picked up by cattlemen and brought to the attention of Governor John Whiteaker, who had business interests in a ranch at Summer Lake. On a trip to eastern Oregon in 1876 with a party of ranchers, Whiteaker jokingly called the small depressions "fossil lakes, east and west", a name that has stuck. The following summer Whiteaker provided a guide in the person of his son along with horses and gear for Thomas Condon to collect here. The son, Charles Whiteaker, was an enthusiastic student in Condon's geology classes at the University in Eugene. Condon's journal records the trip. On August 1, the party reached George Duncan's ranch at Silver Lake where travellers traditionally received "a hospitable welcome, good food and bed, and intense sympathy with the object of our visit." The next stop was Lee Button's ranch between Silver and Fossil lakes, where they left their wagon and proceeded on horseback. The catalog for the University of Oregon Museum reflects a diversity of fossil horses, camels, birds, and elephants from Condon's trip.

The professional collector, Charles Sternberg, working for Edward Cope, arrived just a few weeks after Condon's visit, and Cope himself appeared in 1879. Attached to the Philadelphia Academy of Sciences, Cope's account of his trip to Fossil Lake reflects his wry sense of humor and attention to detail. Leaving Fort Klamath, Cope was riding a horse named Jim, accompanied by an Indian guide, "old Chaloquin", and supplied with provisions by the army. The easy going Chaloquin was pleased that Cope already knew Klamath Indian names for fish they caught and taught Cope additional words for the animals they encountered. While he was staying at Duncan's house, waiting for his supply wagon to appear, Charles Whiteaker happened by, and Cope, with little inducement, went with him to Fossil Lake. The two men camped at what Cope called the "bone yard" for several days. The result was descriptions of vertebrate fossils by Cope in 1878 and 1889 and fish in 1879 and 1883.

**Beaver are commonly found as fossils in the ancient
wetlands around Fossil Lake [from Orr, Orr, and Baldwin, 1992].**

Annie Alexander, John Merriam's student from Berkeley, along with a field party, were the next professionals at Fossil Lake in 1901. This group was followed by Chester Stock and Eustace Furlong in 1923 and 1924 from the California Institute of Technology. These collections in California museums, as well as those of Cope at the American Museum of Natural History, were analyzed and published by one of Stock's students Herbert Elftman in 1931. It is noteworthy that Alexander, whose family was in the shipping business, endowed the paleontology museum at Berkeley, giving it a virtually independent status among other departments at the University.

Later work on the sandy playas of the southcentral part of the state was less strenuous but equally thorough. Beginning in the 1930s, Ira Allison from Oregon State University covered not only the faunas but the environment and geology as well.

343

One of Oregon's pioneer geologic researchers, Ira S. Allison's interest in geology and education kept him at Corvallis for 62 years. He served on the staff at the University after moving to the state in 1928 with his wife Sadie Gilchrist Allison. Allison was born near Chicago in 1895 and obtained his PhD in 1924 from the University of Minnesota. His primary research interest emphasized Pleistocene history, and one of his early outstanding contributions to Oregon geology was a paper on the significance of glacial erratic dropstones derived from sources in Montana and the Rocky Mountains. Dropstones substantiate the theory of remarkable Ice Age floods. Another of his accomplishments was a popular physical geology text *Geology, Science of a Changing Earth*, which he co-authored and revised through many editions beginning in 1932. In 1988 the University established a professorship in geomorphology, naming a series of talks the Allison Lectures in his honor. When he died in 1990 of an inoperable tumor, he left 14 grandchildren and 12 great grandchildren.

**A Pleistocene geologist
by training and interest,
Ira Allison pioneered work
on the old lake beds of central
Oregon [photo courtesy
Archives, Oregon State
University].**

Work at Fossil and Summer lakes was begun in 1939 by Allison at the request of John Merriam, who by that time was president emeritus and research associate at the Carnegie Institute, Washington, D.C. Because of a long-standing interest in Oregon fossils, he organized and financed a group of consultants that included the geologists Earl Packard, Chester Stock, Warren Smith, Ernst Antevs, and John Buwalda, the paleobotanist Daniel Axelrod, and the anthropologist Luther Cressman, as well as Allison.

In September of 1939 Smith spent five days camping with Allison northeast of Fort Rock. They examined all of the old lake basins in the vicinity, including the Fossil Lake local where Allison had exhumed an almost complete Pleistocene horse. Merriam wrote "I was very favorably impressed ... with the thoroughness of [Allison's] work and his scientific attitude in his approach to all of these problems..." However, because of other obligations, Allison's work was not completed and published on Fossil Lake until 1966 and on Summer Lake until

1982. These two publications cover geomorphology as well as reviewing prior compilations on the fossils.

An imaginary Pleistocene scene of fierce bears in front of their cave, apparently having consumed an entire mastodon [Pouchet, 1882].

Two unusual Pleistocene finds from Lake County are bear tracks preserved in a mudflow and the skull of a bighorn sheep in stream gravels. A huge bear *Arctotherium,* walking across wet mud flats during the Ice Ages, left a series of alternating footprints for a distance of 15 feet before they became to faint to see. At Drews Gap the prints were called to the attention of Oregon State professors Earl Packard and Ira Allison by their discoverer Mr. Shook, a resident of Klamath Falls. Allison and Packard measured and made casts of the prints, concluding they corresponded closely to those of a Pliocene or Pleistocene bear. Although the actual structure of the foot pads of *Arctotherium* isn't known, Packard and Allison compared their measurements to foot bones from the LaBrea tar pits in Los Angeles to reach their conclusions.

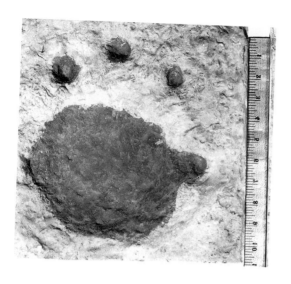

Although not as common as other animals, bear remains often turn up. The exceptionally rare preserved tracks of an extinct Pleistocene bear, measuring 10 inches in length, were found in Lake County [photo courtesy Oregon Department of Geology and Mineral Industries].

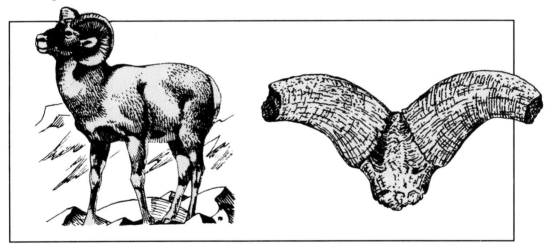

Once extinct in Steens Mountain, bighorn sheep have since been reintroduced. Their fossil remains from the Pleistocene are scarce because they lived in an upland environment where bones were scattered and destroyed [after Thoms and Smith, 1973].

Yet another uncommon fossil from near Adel in Lake County is the skull of a prehistoric bighorn sheep *Ovis catclawensis* turned up by a bulldozer operator Roy Collier. Once prevalent throughout the mountainous regions of the west, bighorn sheep were brought to extinction by hunting and destruction of their habitat in the late 1800s. A worked pebble, possibly a human tool, was recovered with the skull. In their article on the fossil, Richard Thoms of Portland State University and Harold Smith of the Oregon Game Commission pointed out that a modern equivalent of the Pleistocene bighorn sheep have been reintroduced to Hart Mountain and the Steens in the southeast part of the state. Collier retained the fossil specimen, but eventually it was donated to the Lake County Museum in Lakeview.

East of Lake County, Pleistocene environments of ancient Lake Idaho, created when the Snake River was blocked, have been traced in a 1995 paper by Charles Repenning and coauthors. By looking at faunal successions they were able to document the existence of several lakes in the Snake River basin and suggest a possible drainage route for the water to the Sacramento River through Nevada. They also consider dispersal patterns of rodents in the West, which began in the late Miocene and continued into the Pleistocene. As rodents migrated from the Arctic, they moved down both sides of the Rocky Mountains, across the Great Plains and southward into California. Basing his results on the appearance of certain small mammals at certain times, Repenning suggests the migrations and dispersal were controlled by climate changes. For example, *Mimomys* [bog lemming] appeared near the beginning of the Pliocene, *Mictomys* [muskrat] in the late Pliocene, and *Penacomys* [muskrat] at the first of the Pleistocene, all coincident with alterations in the paleo-climate.

Charles Repenning began his partnership with bones when he brought home dead animals on his bicycle, usually inside his shirt. "Rep", as he is known, was a pilot captured a during World War II and remained a prisoner until that conflict ended. Completing a PhD at Berkeley, he began a career with the U.S. Geological Survey. His opinions frequently incite controversy, especially those dealing with the placement of geologic time boundaries based on vertebrates, Retiring in 1992, he continues to work at his research.

In this photograph, Charles Repenning is standing in front of his car that has a POW license, a reminder of his war-time years [photo courtesy C. Repenning].

347

Catastrophic widespread extinctions in the fossil record have long attracted the attention of paleontologists, and one of the most profound of these took place with animals of the late Pleistocene. Near the end of this epoch most of the bigger animals disappeared from North and South America. Horses, camels, mammoth, mastodons, bison, and a variety of carnivores, which flourished throughout much of the later Tertiary and into the early Pleistocene, vanished here abruptly around 11,000 years ago. Attributing this large-scale demise to severe Ice Age conditions alone seems unreasonable as many of the species had survived several previous ice advances of greater severity only to disappear in North America near the end of the last ice withdrawal. The extinctions may correspond to the appearance of humans who migrated down from the Bering Strait about this time and began intensively hunting out the large creatures. It has been suggested that populations of the animals were at a low ebb because of the harsh climate and that humans may have merely destroyed those remaining. Warmer, more humid conditions at the end of the Pleistocene may even have driven mammals to the waterways where human cultures were located. More recent theories propose that these animals were killed off by disease carried by dogs, birds, rats, or other animals accompanying human arrival. The fact that these extinctions occurred as a wave that originated in North America and proceeded southward over several hundred years into South America is strong, though not conclusive, evidence that humans had a hand in their demise.

Local extinctions of large late Pleistocene mammals moved as a wave across the Americas from north to south at roughly 10 miles per year.

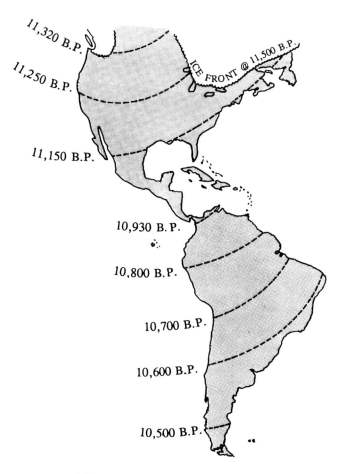

11,320 B.P.

11,250 B.P.

ICE FRONT @ 11,500 B.P.

11,150 B.P.

10,930 B.P.

10,800 B.P.

10,700 B.P.

10,600 B.P.

10,500 B.P.

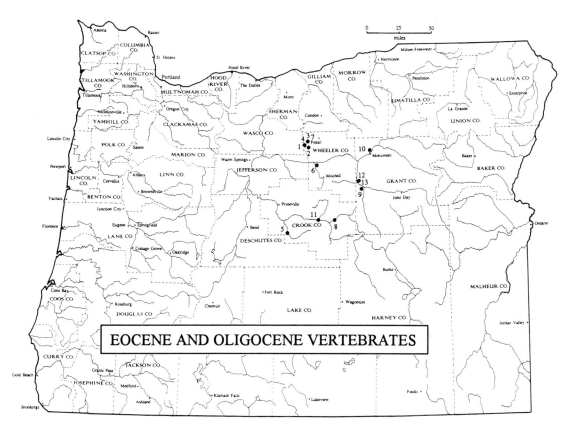

The following are selections of Oregon fossil vertebrate localities and authors who list faunas from them.

EOCENE

1. Clarno, Wheeler Co. Clarno Fm. Bestland and Retallack, 1994.
2. Clarno Nut Beds, Wheeler Co. Clarno Fm. Hanson, 1996.
3. Iron Mtn., Wheeler Co. Clarno Fm. Hancock, 1962.
4. Clarno Mammal Quarry, Wheeler Co. Hanson, 1996; Pratt, 1988.

OLIGOCENE

5. Bear Creek Valley, Crook Co. John Day Fm. Lowry, 1940.
6. Bridge Creek valley, Crook Co. John Day Fm. Merriam, 1901, Stock, 1946.
7. Clarno, Wheeler Co. John Day Fm. Bestland and Retallack, 1994.
8. Crooked River valley, Crook Co. John Day Fm. Downs, 1956; Leidy, 1873.
9. Dayville, Grant Co. John Day Fm. Matthew, 1899.
10. John Day River [North Fork], Grant Co. John Day Fm. Bestland and Retallack, 1994; Cope, 1883; Merriam, 1901; Stock, 1946.
11. Logan Butte, Crook Co. John Day Fm. Stock and Furlong, 1922.
12. Sheep Rock, Grant Co. John Day Fm. Fisher and Rensberger, 1972.
13. Turtle Cove, Grant Co. John Day Fm. Merriam and Sinclair, 1907; Retallack, Bestland, and Fremd, 1996.

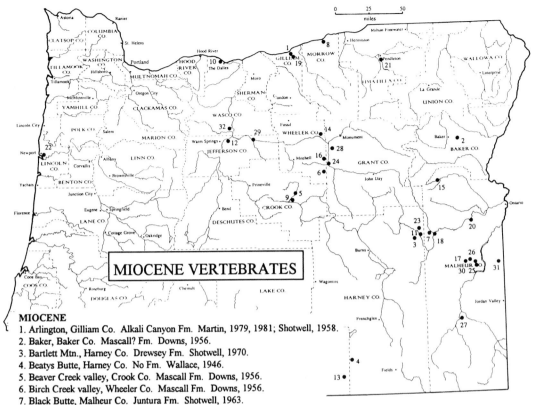

MIOCENE

1. Arlington, Gilliam Co. Alkali Canyon Fm. Martin, 1979, 1981; Shotwell, 1958.
2. Baker, Baker Co. Mascall? Fm. Downs, 1956.
3. Bartlett Mtn., Harney Co. Drewsey Fm. Shotwell, 1970.
4. Beatys Butte, Harney Co. No Fm. Wallace, 1946.
5. Beaver Creek valley, Crook Co. Mascall Fm. Downs, 1956.
6. Birch Creek valley, Wheeler Co. Mascall Fm. Downs, 1956.
7. Black Butte, Malheur Co. Juntura Fm. Shotwell, 1963.
8. Boardman, Morrow Co. No Fm. Shotwell, 1958.
9. Camp Creek, Crook Co. John Day Fm. Downs, 1956; Rensberger, 1971.
10. Chenoweth Creek, Wasco Co. Condon, 1902; Chaney, 1944.
11. Drinkwater Pass, Harney Co. Drewsey Fm. Hutchison, 1968; Shotwell, 1963.
12. Gateway, Jefferson Co. Mascall Fm. Downs, 1956.
13. Guano Lake, Lake Co. No Fm. Hutchison, 1968.
14. Haystack Creek, Wheeler Co. John Day Fm. Rensberger, 1973; Thorpe, 1922.
15. Ironside Mtn., Malheur Co. No Fm. Merriam, 1916.
16. John Day River valley, Wheeler Co. John Day Fm. Cope, 1883; Stock, 1946.
17. Juniper Creek valley, Malheur Co. Chalk Butte Fm. Shotwell, 1970.
18. Juntura Basin, Malheur Co. Juntura Fm. Shotwell, 1963.
19. Krebs Ranch, Gilliam Co. No Fm. Shotwell, 1963.
20. Little Valley, Malheur Co. Chalk Butte Fm. Shotwell, 1970.
21. McKay Reservoir, Umatilla Co. McKay Fm. Martin, 1979; 1981; Shotwell, 1956; 1958.
22. Newport, Lincoln Co. Astoria Fm. Munthe and Coombs, 1979.
23. Otis Basin, Harney Co. Drewsey Fm. Shotwell, 1970.
24. Picture Gorge, Grant Co. Rattlesnake Fm. Matthew, 1909; Merriam and Sinclair, 1907; Martin, 1983.
25. Quartz Basin, Malheur Co. Deer Butte Fm. Shotwell, 1968.
26. Red Basin, Malheur Co. Butte Creek Volcanic Sandstone. Shotwell, 1968.
27. Rome, Malheur Co. No Fm. Shotwell, 1970; Wilson, 1938.
28. Rudio Creek, Grant Co. John Day Fm. Rensberger, 1971.
29. Trout Creek valley, Jefferson Co. John Day Fm. Merriam and Sinclair, 1907.
30. Skull Springs, Malheur Co. Butte Creek Volcanic Sandstone. Gazin, 1932.
31. Succor Creek, Malheur Co. Sucker Creek Fm. Downing, 1992; Scharf, 1935.
32. Warm Springs, Wasco Co. John Day Fm. Woodburne and Robinson, 1977.

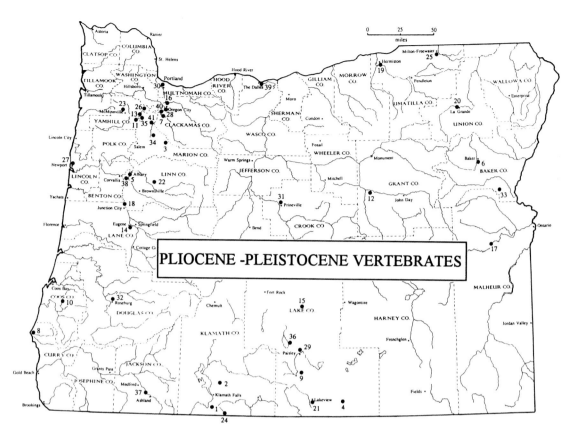

The following are selections Oregon fossil vertebrate localities and authors who list faunas from them.

PLIOCENE
1. Enrico Ranch, Klamath Co. No Fm. Hutchison, 1966.
2. Wilson's Quarry Pit, Klamath Co. Yonna Fm. Newcomb, 1958.

PLEISTOCENE
3. Abiqua Creek, Marion Co. McCornack, 1914.
4. Adel, Lake Co. Thoms and Smith, 1973.
5. Albany, Linn Co. Hay, 1927; McCornack, 1914.
6. Baker, Baker Co. Hay, 1927; McCornack, 1914.
7. Canby, Clackamas Co. McCornack, 1914.
8. Cape Blanco, Curry Co. Elk River Beds. Leffler, 1964;
9. Chewaucan Lake, Lake Co. Allison, 1982.
10. Coquille River, Coos Co. Hay, 1927; McCornack, 1914.
11. Dayton, Yamhill Co. Hay, 1927; McCornack, 1914.
12. Dayville, Grant Co. Hay, 1927.
13. Dundee, Yamhill Co. McCornack, 1914.

14. Eugene, Lane Co. Hay, 1927; McCornack, 1914.
15. Fossil Lake, Lake Co. Allison, 1966; Cope, 1889; Elftman, 1931.
16. Gladstone, Clackamas Co. McCornack, 1914.
17. Harper, Malheur Co. Shotwell, 1968.
18. Harrisburg, Linn Co. Hay, 1927; McCornack, 1914.
19. Hermiston, Umatilla Co. Hay, 1927.
20. LaGrande, Union Co. Hay, 1927;
21. Lakeview, Lake Co. Packard and Allison, 1980.
22. Lebanon, Linn Co. Hay, 1927; McCornack, 1914.
23. McMinnville, Yamhill Co. Hay, 1927.
24. Merrill, Klamath Co. Hay, 1927.
25. Milton-Freewater, Umatilla Co. Hay, 1927.
26. Newberg, Yamhill Co. Hay, 1927; McCornack, 1914.
27. Nye Creek, Lincoln Co. Hay, 1927.
28. Oregon City, Clackamas Co. Hay, 1927.
29. Paisley, Lake Co. Hay, 1927; McCornack, 1914.
30. Portland, Washington Co. Hay, 1927; McCornack, 1914.
31. Prineville, Crook Co. Hay, 1927; McCornack, 1914.
32. Roseburg, Douglas Co. Hay, 1927; McCornack, 1914.
33. Rye valley, Baker Co. Hay, 1927.
34. Silverton, Marion Co. Hansen and Packard, 1949.
35. St. Paul, Marion Co. Hay, 1927.
36. Summer Lake, Lake Co. Allison, 1966; Hay, 1927.
37. Talent, Jackson Co. Hay, 1927.
38. Tangent, Linn Co. McCornack, 1914.
39. The Dalles, Wasco Co. Hay, 1927; McCornack, 1914.
40. Wilsonville, Clackamas Co. McCornack, 1914.
41. Woodburn, Marion Co. Hay, 1927; Packard, 1952.

BIBLIOGRAPHY

PRIMARY SOURCES

Condon Museum, University of Oregon
        Bert Coombs Journal, Summer, 1955
        Joseph Diller Letters 1888-1907
        Lon Hancock Letters, 1935-1963
        John Merriam Letters and Notes
        Earl Packard Letters, 1920-1945
        Arnold Shotwell field notes, Summers, 1954-1960
        Warren Smith Letters, 1916-1945
        Chester Washburne letters and notes
        Condon Museum Catalog

Oregon Department of Geology and Mineral Industries
        Joseph Diller field notes, September, 1899; June to August, 1900
        Warren Smith field notes, Summer, 1927

Oregon State University, Archives
        Earl Packard Letters, 1933-1935

Oregon State Land Board
        Minutes, Meeting September 13, 1967

Inteviews
        Ewart Baldwin, 1996-1997
        Lillian Mascall, 1997
        Ellen Moore, 1996
        Arnold Shotwell, 1997

Newspapers
        The Oregonian 1880-1984

SECONDARY SOURCES

Abbott, W.H., 1970. Micropaleontology and paleoecology of Miocene non-marine diatoms from the Harper district, Malheur Co., Oregon. Masters, Northeast Louisiana University, 86p.

Addicott, W.O., 1964. A late Pleistocene invertebrate fauna from southwestern Oregon. Journal of Paleo., v.38, no.4, p.650-661.

---1972. Neogene molluscan paleontology along the West Coast of North America, 1840-1969. Trends and status. Journal of Paleo., v.46, no.5, pp.627-636.

---1980. Miocene stratigraphy and fossils, Cape Blanco, Oregon. Oregon Geology, v.42, no.5, pp.87-98.

---1981. Brief history of Cenozoic marine biostratigraphy of the Pacific Northwest. Geol. Society of America, Special Paper 184, pp.3-15.

---1983. Biostratigraphy of the marine Neogene sequence at Cape Blanco, southwestern Oregon. U.S. Geol. Survey, Prof. Paper 774-G., Shorter Contrib. to General Geology, pp.G1-G17.

Adegoke, O.S., 1967. A probable pogonophoran from the early Oligocene of Oregon. Journal of Paleo., v.41, no.5, pp.1090-1094.

Allen, J.E., and Baldwin, E.M., 1944. Geology and coal resources of the Coos Bay quadrangle, Oregon. Oregon Dept. Geol. and Mineral Industries, Bull.27, 153p.

Allison, I. S., 1966. Fossil Lake, Oregon - its geology and fossil faunas. Oregon State Univ. Monograph, no.9, 48p.

---1982. Geology of pluvial Lake Chewaucan, Lake County, Oregon. Oregon State University, Studies in Geology, no.11, 78p.

Anderson, F.M., 1958. Upper Cretaceous of the Pacific Coast. Geol. Society of America, Memoir no.71, 378p.

Andrews, H.N., 1980. The fossil hunters. Ithaca, Cornell Univ. Press, 421p.

Applegate, S.P., 1968. A large fossil sand shark of the genus *Odontaspis* from Oregon. Ore Bin, v.30, no.2, p.32-36.

Armentrout, J.M., 1967. The Tarheel and Empire Formations; geology and paleontology of the type sections, Coos Bay, Oregon. Univ. Oregon, Masters, 155p.

---ed., 1981. Pacific northwest Cenozoic biostratigraphy. Geol. Society of America, Special Paper 184, 172p.

---et al., 1983. Correlation of Cenozoic stratigraphic units of western Oregon and Washington. Oregon Dept. Geol. and Mineral Industries, Oil and Gas Investigation 7, 90p.

Arnold, C.A., 1937. Observations on the fossil flora of eastern and southeastern Oregon. Univ. Mich. Mus. Paleont., Contributions, pt.1, v.5, no.8, pp.79-102.

---1953. Fossil plants of early Pennsylvanian type from central Oregon. Paleontographica B., v.93, pp.61-68.

Arnold, R., and Hannibal, H., 1913. The marine Tertiary stratigraphy of the north Pacific Coast of America. American Philosophical Society, Proc., v.52, pp.555-605.

Ash, S.R., 1991. A new Jurassic flora from the Wallowa terrane in Hells Canyon, Oregon and Idaho. Oregon Geology, v.53, no.2, pp.27-33.

---1991. A new Jurassic *Phlebopteris* (Plantae, Filicales) from the Wallowa terrane in the Snake River Canyon, Oregon and Idaho. Journal of Paleo., v.65, no.2, pp.332-329.

---and Read, C.B., 1976. North American species of *Tempskya* and their stratigraphic significance. U.S. Geol. Survey, Prof. Paper 874.

Ashwill, Melvin, 1983. Seven fossil floras in the rain shadow of the Cascade Mountains, Oregon. Oregon Geology, v.45, no.10, pp.107-111.

---1987. Paleontology in Oregon: workers of the past. Oregon Geology, v.49, no.12, pp.147-153.

Axelrod, D.I., 1944. The Alvord Creek flora. Carnegie Inst. Wash., Publ.553, pp.225-306.

---1966. A method for determining the altitudes of Tertiary floras. Paleobotanist, v.14, no.1-3, pp.144-171.

---and Bailey, I.W., 1969. Paleotemperature analysis of the Tertiary plants. Paleo., Paleo., Paleo., v.6, pp.163-195.

Bailey, I.W., and Sinnott, E.W., 1916. The climatic distribution of certain types of angiosperm leaves. American Jour. Botany, v.3, pp.24-39.

Baldwin, E.M., 1950. Pleistocene history of the Newport, Oregon, region. Geol. Society of Oregon Country Newsletter., v.18, pp.29-30.

---1961. Geologic map of the lower Umpqua River area, Oregon. U.S.G.S., Oil and Gas Inv. Map OM-204.

---1964. Geology of the Dallas and Valsetz quadrangles, Oregon. Oregon Dept. Geol. and Mineral Industries, Bull.35, 52p.

---1973. Geology and mineral resources of Coos County, Oregon. Oregon Dept. Geol. and Mineral Industries, Bull.80, 82p.

---1974. Eocene stratigraphy of southwestern Oregon. Oregon Dept. of Geol. and Min. Indus., Bull. 83, 40p.

Bandy, O.L., 1950. Some later Cenozoic foraminifera from Cape Blanco, Oregon. Journal of Paleontology, v.24, no.3. pp.269-281.

Barnes, L.G., 1987. An early Miocene pinniped of the genus *Desmatophoca* [Mammalia: Otariidae] from Washington. Natural History Museum of Los Angeles County, Contributions in Science, no. 382, pp.1-20.

---1989. A new enaliarctine pinniped from the Astoria Formation, Oregon, and a classification of the Otariidae (Mammalia:Carnivora). Natural History Museum of Los Angeles, Contributions in Science, no.403, pp.1-26.

---1990. A new Miocene enaliarctine pinniped of the genus *Pteronarctos* (Mammalia: Otariidae) from the Astoria Formation, Oregon. Natural History Museum of Los Angeles, Contributions in Science, no.422, 20p.

---and Mitchell, E.D., 1975. Late Cenozoic northeast Pacific Phocidae. Conseil Permanent Internationale Explor. Mer, Rapports et Proces-verbaux des Reunions, v.169, pp.34-42.

---Domning, D.P., and Ray, C.E., 1985. Status of studies on fossil marine mammals. Marine Mammal Science, v.1, no.1, pp.15-53.

---et al., 1994. Classification and distribution of Oligocene Aetiocetidae [Mammalia; Cetacea; Mysticeti] from western North America and Japan. The Island Arc, v.3, pp.392-431.

Berglund, R.E., and Feldmann, R.M., 1989. A new crab, *Rogueus orri* n. gen. and sp. (Decapod: Brachyura) from the Lookingglass Formation (Ulatisian Stage: Lower Middle Eocene) of southwestern Oregon. Journal of Paleo., v.63, no.1, pp.69-73.

Berman, D.S., 1976. A new amphisbaenian (Reptilia: Amphisbaenia) from the Oligocene-Miocene John Day Formation, Oregon. Journal of Paleo., v.50, no.1, pp.165-174.

Berta, A., 1991. New *Enaliarctos** (Pinnipedimorpha) from the Oligocene and Miocene of Oregon and the role of "Enaliarctids" in pinniped phylogeny. Smithsonian Contributions to Paleobiology, no.69, 33p.

---1994. Pinniped phylogeny. *In*: Berta, A., and Demere, T.A., eds., Contributions in marine mammal paleontology honoring Frank C. Whitmore. San Diego Soc. Natural History, Proc., v.29, pp.33-56.

Bestland, E., and Retallack, G., 1994. Geology and paleoenvironments of the Painted Hills unit, John Day Fossil Beds National Monument, Oregon. Final Report NPS Contract CX-9000-1-10009, 211p.

Bird, K., 1967. Biostratigraphy of the Tyee Formation [Eocene] southwestern Oregon. University of Wisconsin, 209p.

Black, C., 1963. A review of the North American Tertiary Sciuridae. Harvard Univ., Museum of Comparative Zool., Bull., v.130, no.3, pp.113-248.

Blome, C.D., 1984. Upper Triassic radiolaria and radiolarian zonation from western North America. Bulletins of American Paleo., v.85, no.318, 88p.

---and Nestell, M.K., 1991. Evolution of a Permo-Triassic sedimentary melange, Grindstone terrane, east-central Oregon. Geol. Society of America, Bull., v.103, pp.1280-1296.

---and Nestell, M.K., 1992. Field guide to the geology and paleontology of pre-Tertiary volcanic arc and melange rocks, Grindstone, Izee, and Baker terranes, east-central Oregon. Oregon Geology, v.54, no.6, pp.123-141.

---and Reed, K.M., 1992. Permian and early(?) Triassic radiolarian faunas from the Grindstone terrane, central Oregon. Journal of Paleo., v.66, no.3, pp.351-383.

---et al., 1986. Geologic implications of radiolarian-bearing Paleozoic and Mesozoic rocks from the Blue Mountains province, eastern Oregon. *In*: Vallier, T.L., and Brooks, H.C., eds., Geology of the Blue Mountains region of Oregon, Idaho, and Washington. U.S. Geol. Survey, Prof. Paper 1435, pp.79-93.

Boardman, R.S., Cheetham, A., and Rowell, A.J., 1987. Fossil invertebrates. Palo Alto, Blackwell Scientific Publ., 713p.

Bones, T.J., 1979. Atlas of fossil fruits and seeds from north central Oregon. Oregon Museum of Science and Industry, Occasional Papers in Natural Science, no.1, 6p.

Bostwick, D.A., and Nestell, M.K., 1967. Permian Tethyan fusulinid faunas of the northwestern United States. *In:* Adams, C.G., ed. Aspects of Tethyan biogeography; a symposium. Systematics Assoc. Publ.7, pp.93-102.

Brattstrom, B.H., and Sturn, A., 1959. A new species of fossil turtle from the Pliocene of Oregon with notes on other fossil *Clemmys* from western North America. Southern Calif. Acad. Sciences, Bull.58, pp.65-71.

Brodkorb, P., 1958. Birds from the middle Pliocene of McKay, Oregon. Condor, v.60, pp.252-255.

---1961. Birds from the Pliocene of Juntura, Oregon. Florida Scientist, v.24, no.3, pp.169-184.

Brown, R. W., 1959. A bat and some plants from the upper Oligocene of Oregon. Journal of Paleontology, v.33, no.1, pp.135-139.

Buffetaut, E., 1979. Jurassic marine crocodilians (Mesosuchia: Telosauridae) from central Oregon: first record in North America. Journal of Paleontology, v.54, no.1, pp.211-215.

Cameron, K. A., and Pringle, P.T., 1991. Prehistoric buried forests of Mount Hood. Oregon Geology, v.53, no.2, pp.34-43.

Carroll, R.L., 1986. Vertebrate paleontology and evolution. New York, Freeman, 698p.

Cavender, T. M., 1968. Freshwater fish remains from the Clarno Formation Ochoco Mountains of north-central Oregon. Ore Bin, v.30, no.7, pp.125-141.

---1969. An Oligocene mudminnow (Family Umbridae) from Oregon with remarks on relationships within the Esocoidei. Mich. Univ., Mus. Zool., Occasional Paper 660, 33p.

---1986. Review of the fossil history of North American fishes. *In:* Hocutt, C.H., and Wiley, E.O., eds., Zoogeography of North American freshwater fishes, New York, Wiley, pp.699-724.

---and Miller, R.R., 1972. *Smilodonichthyes rastrosus*, a new Pliocene salmonid fish from Western United States. Univ. Oregon, Museum of Natural Hist., Bull.18, 44p.

Chaney, R.W., 1918. Ecological significance of the Eagle Creek flora of the Columbia River Gorge. Journal of Geology, v.26, pp.577- 592.

---1925. The Mascall flora; its distribution and climatic relation. Carnegie Inst. Wash., Contributions to Paleontology, no.349, pp.25-48.

---1927. Geology and paleontology of the Crooked River Basin with special reference to the Bridge Creek flora. Carnegie Inst. Wash., Publication 346, pt.4, pp.185-216.

---1938. The Deschutes flora of eastern Oregon. Carnegie Inst. Wash., Contributions to Paleontology, v.476, pp.185-216.

---1944. The Dalles flora. Carnegie Inst. Wash., Publication 553, pp.285-321.

---1956. The ancient forests of Oregon. Condon Lectures, Eugene, Oregon. 56p.

---and Axelrod, D.I., 1959. Miocene floras of the Columbia River Plateau. Carnegie Inst. Wash., Publication 617, 237p.

---and Sanborn, E.I., 1933. The Goshen flora of west central Oregon. Carnegie Inst. Wash., Publication 439, 103p.

Cockerell, T.D.A., 1927. Tertiary fossil insects from eastern Oregon. Carnegie Inst., Wash., Contributions to Paleo., no.346, pp.64-65.

Colbath, G. K., and Steele, M.J., 1982. The geology of economically significant lower Pliocene diatomites ... Lake County, Oregon. Oregon Geology, v.44, no.10, pp.111-118.

Colbath, S.L., 1985. Gastropod predation and depositional environments of two molluscan communities from the Miocene Astoria Formation at Beverly Beach State Park, Oregon. Journal of Paleontology, v.59, no.4, pp.849-869.

Condon, T., 1906. A new fossil pinniped (*Desmatophoca oregonensis*) from the Miocene of the Oregon coast. Univ. Oregon, Bull. suppl., v.3, pp.1-14.

---1902. The two Islands. J.K. Gill Co., Portland, Oregon, 211p.

Coombs, M.C., 1978. Reevaluation of early Miocene North American *Moropus* (Perissodactyla, Chalicotheriidae, Schizotheriinae). Carnegie Museum of Natural History, Bull.4, 62p.

Cooper, G.A., 1957. Permian brachiopods from central Oregon. Smithsonian Misc. Collections, v.134, no.12, 79p.

Cope, E.D., 1878. Descriptions of new vertebrata from the upper Tertiary formations of the West. American Philos. Soc., Proc.17, pp.219-231.

---1882. On the Nimravidae and Canidae of the Miocene period. U.S. Geol. and Geogr. Survey, Bull.6, pp.165-181.

---1883. Extinct dogs of North America. American Naturalist, v.17, pp.235-249.

---1883. On the fishes of the Recent and Pliocene lakes of the western part of the Great Basin and of the Idaho Pliocene lake. Acad. Natural Sciences, Philadelphia, Proc., pp.134-166.

---1883. Vertebrata of the Tertiary formations of the West. U.S. Geog. and Geol. Surv., Report, v.3, pp.762-1002.

---1886. Phylogeny of the Camelidae. American Naturalist, v.20, pp.611-624.

---1889. The Silver Lake of Oregon and its region. American Naturalist, v.23, pp.970-982.

Cushman, J.A., Stewart, R.C., and Stewart, K.C., 1947. Five papers on foraminifera from the Tertiary of western Oregon. Oregon Dept. Geology and Mineral Industries, Bull.36, pt.I-IV.

Dake, E.T., 1978. Horse genealogy: the Oregon connection. Geology, v.6, pp.587-591.

Dake, H.C., 1969. Oregon *Tempskya* locality. Gems and Minerals, no.384, pp.62-63.

Dall, W.H., 1909. Contributions to the Tertiary paleontology of the Pacific Coast. U.S. Geol. Surv., Prof. Paper 59, 216p.

Dana, J.D., 1875. The Geological story briefly told. New York, American Book Co., 263p.

David, L.R., 1956. Tertiary anacanthin fishes from California and the Pacific Northwest; their paleoecological significance. Journal of Paleontology, v.30, no.3, pp.568-607.

Dickinson, W.R., and Vigrass, L.W., 1965. Geology of the Suplee-Izee area, Crook, Grant, and Harney counties, Oregon. Oregon Dept. Geol. and Mineral Indus., Bull.58, 108p.

Diller, J.S., 1896. A geological reconnaissance in northwestern Oregon. U.S. Geol. Survey, 17th Ann. Rept., pt.1, pp.441-520.

---1898. Description of the Roseburg Quadrangle. U. S. Geol. Survey, Geol. Atlas, Roseburg Folio no.49.

---1901. Description of the Coos Bay Quadrangle, Oregon. U.S. Geol. Survey, Atlas, Coos Bay Folio 73.

---1907. The Mesozoic sediments of southwestern Oregon. American Jour. Science, 4th Ser., v.23, pp.401-421.

---1908. Strata containing the Jurassic flora of Oregon. Geol. Soc. Amer., Bull.19, pp.367-402.

Dodds, B.R., 1963. The relocation of geologic locales in Oregon. Ore Bin, v.25, no.7, pp.113-128.

Domning, D.P., and Ray, C.E., 1986. The earliest Sirenian (Mammalia: Dugongidae) from the eastern Pacific Ocean. Marine Mammal Science, v.2, no.4, pp.263-276.

---Ray, C.E., and McKenna, M.C., 1986. Two new Oligocene Desmostylians and a discussion of Tethytherian systematics. Smithsonian Contributions to Paleobiology, no.59, 56p.

Dott, R.H., 1966. Eocene deltaic sedimentation at Coos Bay, Oregon. Journal of Geology, v.74, no.4, pp.373-420.

---1971. Geology of the southwestern Oregon coast west of the 124th Meridian. Oregon Dept. Geology and Mineral Industries, Bull.69, 63p.

Downing, K.F., 1992. Biostratigraphy, taphonomy, and paleoecology of vertebrates from the Sucker Creek Formation [Miocene] of southeastern Oregon. PhD, Univ. of Arizona.

Downs, T., 1952. A new mastodont from the Miocene of Oregon. Univ. Calif., Publ. Geol. Sciences, v.29, no.1, pp.1-20.

---1956. The Mascall fauna from the Miocene of Oregon. Univ. Calif., Publ. Geol. Sciences, v.31, pp.199-354.

Durham, J.W., 1953. Miocene at Cape Blanco, Oregon [abstr.] Geol. Society of America, Bull., v.64, no.12, pp.1504-1505.

Dutro, T., 1985. Upper Mississippian brachiopods from Oregon and Washington-possible biogeographic affinities. Geol. Soc. America, Abstr. with Prog., v.17, no.6, pp.352-353.

Eaton, G.T., 1922. The John Day Felidae in the Marsh Collection. American Journal of Science, ser.5, v.4, pp.425-452.

Elftman, H.O., 1931. Pleistocene mammals of Fossil Lake, Oregon. American Museum Novitates, no.481, 21p.

Emlong, D.R., 1966. A new archaic cetacean from the Oligocene of northwest Oregon. Univ. of Oregon, Museum of Natural Hist., Bull.3, 51p.

Feldmann, R.M., 1974. *Haploparia riddlensis*, a new species of lobster (Decapoda: Nephropidae) from the Days Creek Formation (Hauterivian, lower Cretaceous) of Oregon. Journal of Paleontology, v.48, no.3, pp.586-593.

---1989. *Lyreidus alseanus* Rathbun from the Paleogene of Washington and Oregon, U.S.A. Annals of the Carnegie Museum, v.58, art.2, pp.61-70.

Fisher, R.V., and Rensberger, J.M., 1972. Physical stratigraphy of the John Day Formation, central Oregon. Univ. Calif. Publ. Geol. Sciences, v.101, p.1-45.

Flugel, E., Senowbari-Daryan, B., and Stanley, G.D., 1989. Late Triassic dasycladacean algae from northeastern Oregon: significance of first reported occurrence in western North America. Journal of Paleontology, v.63, no.3, pp.374-381.

Follo, M.F., 1994. Sedimentology and stratigraphy of the Martin Bridge limestone and Hurwal Formation (upper Triassic to lower Jurassic) from the Wallowa terrane, Oregon. U.S. Geol. Survey, Prof. Paper 1439, pp.1-27.

Fontaine, W.M., 1905. Notes on some fossil plants from the Shasta Group of California and Oregon. U.S. Geol. Surv., Monograph 48, pt.1, pp.221-273.

Frey, R.W., and Cowles, J.G., 1972. The trace fossil *Tisoa* in Washington and Oregon. Ore Bin, v.34, no.7, pp.113-119.

Fry, W.E., 1973. Giant fossil tortoise of genus *Geochelone* from the late Miocene-early Pliocene of northcentral Oregon. Northwest Science, v.17, no.4, pp.239-249.

Fugier, L., 1891. World before the deluge. New York, Cassell, 518p.

Gabb, W.M., 1864-1869. Palaeontology. 2 vols. Publ. Geological Survey of California.

Gazin, C.L., 1932. A Miocene mammalian fauna from southeastern Oregon. Carnegie Inst., Wash., Publication 418, pp.39-86.

Gilmore, C.W., 1928. A new pterosaurian reptile from the marine Cretaceous of Oregon. U.S. National Museum, Proc. no.2745, v.73, art.24.

Goedert, J.L., 1988. A new late Eocene species of Plotopteridae (Aves: Pelecaniformes) from north-western Oregon. Calif. Academy of Sciences, Proc., v.45, no.6, pp.97-102.

Gordon, Ian, 1985. The Paleocene Denning Spring flora of north-central Oregon. Oregon Geology, v.47, no.10, pp.115-118.

Gottesfeld, A.S., Swanson, F.J., and Gottesfeld, L.M., 1981. A Pleistocene low-elevation subalpine forest in the Western Cascades, Oregon. Northwest Science, v.55, no.3, pp.157-166.

Grabau, A.W., and Shimer, H.W., 1910. North American index fossils. New York, A.G. Seiler, 2v.

Graham, A.K., 1963. Systematic revision of the Sucker Creek and Trout Creek Miocene floras of southeastern Oregon. American Journal of Botany, v.50, no.9, pp.921-936.

---1965. The Sucker Creek and Trout Creek Miocene floras of southeastern Oregon. Kent State Univ. Research Series 9 (Bull.53, no.12), 147p.

Gregory, I., 1968. The fossil woods near Holley in the Sweet Home petrified forest, Linn County, Oregon. Ore Bin, v.30, no.4, pp.57-76.

---1969. Fossilized palm wood in Oregon. Ore Bin, v.31, no.5, pp.93-110.

Hancock, A., 1962. The new mammal beds. Geol. Society Oregon County, Newsletter, v.28, no.6.

Hanna, G.D., 1920. Fossil mollusks from the John Day Basin in Oregon. Univ. of Oregon, Publ., v.1, no.6, 8p.

---1922. Fossil freshwater mollusks from Oregon contained in the Condon Museum of the University of Oregon. Univ. Oregon Publ., v.1, no.12, 22p.

---1963. Some Pleistocene and Pliocene freshwater mollusca from California and Oregon. Calif. Academy of Sciences, Occasional Paper no.43, 20p.

Hansen, H.P., 1947. Post glacial forest succession, climate, and chronology in the Pacific Northwest. American Philosophical Soc., Trans., v.37, pt.1, 130p.

---and Packard, E.L., 1949. Pollen analysis and the age of proboscidian bones near Silverton, Oregon. Ecology, v.30, no.4, pp.461-468.

Hanson, C.B., 1996. Bridgerian-Duchesnean Clarno Formation, north-central Oregon. In: Prothero, D.R., and Emry, R.J., The Terrestrial Eocene-Oligocene transition in North America. Cambridge Univ. Press, pp.206-239.

Hart, R., and Peterson, C., 1997. Episodically buried forests in the Oregon surf zone. Oregon Geology, v.59, no.6, pp.131-144.

Hay, O., 1903. Two new species of fossil turtles from Oregon. Univ. Calif., Publications in Geol. Sciences, v.3, no.10, pp.237-241.

---1908. The fossil turtles of North America. Carnegie Inst., Wash., Publication 75, 568p.

---1927. The Pleistocene of the western region of North America and its vertebrated animals. Carnegie Inst., Wash., Publication 322B, 346p.

Hergert, H.L., 1961. Plant fossils in the Clarno Formation, Oregon. Ore Bin, v.23, no.6, pp.55-62.

Hickman, C.J.S., 1969. The Oligocene marine molluscan fauna of the Eugene Formation in Oregon. Univ. of Oregon, Museum of Natural History, Bull., no.16, 112p.

---1975. Bathyl gastropods of the family Turridae in the early Oligocene Keasey Formation in Oregon ... Bulletins of American Paleo., v.70, no.292, 119p.

---1976. *Pleurotomaria* (Archaeogastropoda) in the Eocene of the northeastern Pacific; a review of the Cenozoic biogeography and ecology of the genus. Journal of Paleontology, v.50, no.6, pp.1090-1102.

---1980. Paleogene marine gastropods of the Keasey Formation in Oregon. Bulletins of American Paleo., v.78, no.310, 111p.

---1984. Composition, structure, ecology, and evolution of six Cenozoic deep-water mollusk communities. Journal of Paleontology, v.58, no.5, pp.1215-1234.

Hopkins, W.S., 1967. Palynology and its paleoecological applications in the Coos Bay area, Oregon. Ore Bin, v.29, no.9, pp.161-183.

Howard, H., 1946. A review of the Pleistocene birds of Fossil Lake, Oregon. Carnegie Inst., Wash., Publ.551, pp.141-195.

---1964. A new species of the "Pigmy Goose", *Anabernicula*, from the Oregon Pleistocene, with a discussion of the genus. American Museum of Natural Hist., Novitates, no.2200, 14p.

Howard, J.K., and Dott, R.H., 1961. Geology of Cape Sebastian State Park and its regional relationships. Ore Bin, v.23, no.8, pp.75-84.

Howe, H.V., 1922. Faunal and stratigraphic relationships of the Empire Formation, Coos Bay, Oregon. Calif. Univ., Dept. Geological Sciences, Bull., v.14, pp.85-114.

---1926. Astoria: mid-Tertic type of Pacific Coast. Pan American Geologist, v.45, pp.296-306.

Hoxie, L.R., 1965. The Sparta flora from Baker County, Oregon. Northwest Science, v.39, no.1, pp.26-35.

Hubbs, C.L., and Miller, R.R., 1948. The Great Basin with emphasis on glacial and postglacial times. Utah University, Bull.,v.38, no.20, pp.17-166.

Hutchison, J.H., 1966. Notes on some upper Miocene shrews from Oregon. Univ. of Oregon, Museum of Natural Hist., Bull.2, 23p.

---1968. Fossil Talpidae (Insectivora, Mammalia) from the later Tertiary of Oregon. Univ. of Oregon, Museum of Natural Hist., Bull.11, 117p.

---1984. Cf. *Condylura* (Mammalia: Talpidae) from the late Tertiary of Oregon. Journal of Vertebrate Paleo., v.4, no.4, pp.600-601.

Imlay, R.W., 1968. Lower Jurassic (Pliensbachian and Toarcian) ammonites from eastern Oregon and California. U.S. Geol. Survey, Prof. Paper 593-C, pp.1-51.

---1973. Middle Jurassic (Bajocian) ammonites from eastern Oregon. U.S. Geol. Survey, Prof. Paper 756, 100p.

---1980. Jurassic paleobiogeography of the conterminous United States in its continental setting. U.S. Geol. Survey, Prof. Paper 1062, 134p.

---1986. Jurassic ammonites and biostratigraphy of eastern Oregon and western Idaho. *In*: Vallier, T.L., and Brooks, H.C., eds., Geology of the Blue Mountains region of Oregon, Idaho, and Washington. U.S. Geol. Survey, Prof. Paper 1435, pp.53-57.

---et al., 1959. Relations of certain upper Jurassic and lower Cretaceous formations in southwestern Oregon. Amer. Assoc. Petroleum Geol., Bull.,v.43, pp.2770-2785.

Irwin, W.P., Wardlaw, B.R., and Kaplan, T.A., 1983. Conodonts of the Western Paleozoic and Triassic Belt, Klamath Mountains, California and Oregon. Journal of Paleo., v.57, no.5, pp.1030-1039.

Jehl, J.R., 1967. Pleistocene birds from Fossil Lake, Oregon. Condor, v.69, no.1, pp.24-27.

Johnson, J.G., and Klapper, G., 1978. Devonian brachiopods and conodonts from central Oregon. Journal of Paleontology, v.52, no.2, pp.295-299.

Jones, D.L., 1960. Lower Cretaceous (Albian) fossils from southwestern Oregon and their paleogeographic significance. Journal of Paleontology, v.34, no.1, pp.152-160.

---et al., 1977. Wrangellia - a displaced terrane in northwestern North America. Canadian Journal Earth Sciences, v.14, no.11, pp.2565-2577.

Jordan, D.S., and Hannibal, H., 1923. Fossil sharks and rays of the Pacific slope of North America. Southern Calif. Academy of Sciences, Bull., v.22, pp.27-68.

Kimmel, P.G., 1975. Fishes of the Miocene-Pliocene Deer Butte Formation, southeast Oregon. Univ. Mich., Mus. Paleo., Papers on Paleo., no.14, pp.69-87.

---1982. Stratigraphy, age, and tectonic setting of the Miocene-Pliocene lacustrine sediments of the western Snake River plain, Oregon and Idaho. *In*: Bonnichsen, B., and Breckenridge, R.M., eds., Cenozoic geology of Idaho. Idaho Bureau of Mines and Geology, Bull.26, pp.550-578.

Kleinhaus, L.C., Balcells-Baldwin, E.A., and Jones, R.E., 1984. A paleogeographic reinterpretation of some middle Cretaceous units, north-central Oregon: evidence for a submarine system.

In: Nilsen, T. H., ed., Geology of the upper Cretaceous Hornbrook Formation, Oregon and California. Soc. Econ. Paleont. and Mineralog., Pacific Section, v.42, pp.239-257.

Kleweno, W.P., and Jeffords, R.M., 1961. Devonian rocks in the Suplee area of central Oregon. Ore Bin, v.23, no.5, p.50.

Klucking, E.P., 1964. An Oligocene flora from the western Cascades. Univ. Calif., PhD., 372p.

Knowlton, F.H., 1902. Fossil flora of the John Day basin, Oregon. U.S. Geological Survey, Bull. 204, 127p.

---1910. Jurassic age of the "Jurassic flora of Oregon." American Journal of Science, 4th ser., v.30, pp.33-64.

Koch, J.G., 1966. Late Mesozoic stratigraphy and tectonic history, Port Orford-Gold Beach area, southwestern Oregon coast. American Assoc. Petroleum Geol., Bull.50, no.1, pp.25-71.

---and Camp., C.L., 1966. Late Jurassic ichthyosaur from Sisters Rocks coastal southwestern Oregon. Ore Bin, v.28, no.3, pp.65-68.

Kooser, M.A., and Orr, W.N., 1973. Two new decapod species from Oregon. Journal of Paleontology, v.47, no.6, pp.1044-1046.

Lakhanpal, R.N., 1958. The Rujada flora of west central Oreogn. Univ. California, Publ. in Geological Sciences, v.35, no.1, pp.1-66.

Leffler, S.R., 1964. Fossil mammals from the Elk River Formation, Cape Blanco, Oregon. Journal of Mammalogy, v.45, pp.53-61.

Leidy, J., 1870. Remarks on a collection of fossils from ... Thomas Condon. Acad. Natl. Sci., Philadelphia, Proc., v.22, pp.111-113.

Lesquereux, L., 1888. Recent determinations of fossil plants from Kentucky, Louisiana and Oregon. U.S. National Museum, Proc., v.11, pp.11-38.

Lewis, R.Q., 1950. The geology of the southern Coburg Hills including the Springfield-Goshen area. Univ. of Oregon, Masters, 78p.

Linder, R.A., Durham, J.W., and Orr, W.N., 1988. New late Oligocene echinoids from the central Western Cascades of Oregon. Journal of Paleontology, v.62, no.6, pp.945-958.

Lockley, M.G., 1990. How volcanism affects the biostratigraphic record. *In*: Lockley, M.G., and Rice, A., eds., Volcanism and fossil biotas. Geol. Soc. Amer., Special Paper 244, pp.1-12.

Lowther, J.S., 1967. A new Cretaceous flora from southwestern Oregon (Abstr.). Northwest Science, v.41, no.1, p.54.

Lull, R.S., 1921. New camels in the Marsh Collections. American Journal of Science, ser.5, v.1, no.5, pp.392-404.

Lupher, R.I., 1941. Jurassic stratigraphy of central Oregon. Geol. Society of America, Bull., v.52, pt.1, pp.219-269.

---and Packard, E.L., 1930. The Jurassic and Cretaceous rudistids of Oregon. Univ. of Oregon, Geology Series, v.1, no.3, pp.203-212.

Mamay, S.H., and Read, C.B., 1956. Additions to the flora of the Spotted Ridge Formation in central Oregon. U.S. Geol. Survey, Prof. Paper 274-I, pp.211-226.

Manchester, S.R., 1979. *Triplochitioxylon* (Sterculiaceae): a new genus of wood from the Eocene of Oregon and its bearing on xylem evolution in the extant genus *Triplochiton*. American Journal of Botany, v.66, no.6, pp.699-708.

---1980. *Chattawaya* (Sterculiaceae): a new genus of wood from the Eocene of Oregon and its implications for xylem evolution of the extant genus *Pterospermum*. American Journal of Botany, v.67, no.1, pp.59-67.

---1983. Fossil wood of the Engelhardieae (Juglandaceae) from the Eocene of North America: *Engelhardioxylon* gen. nov. Botanical Gaz., v.144, no.1, pp.157-163.

---1987. The fossil history of the Juglandaceae. Missouri Botanical Garden, Monographs in Systematic Botany, v.21, 137p.

---1988. Fruits and seeds of *Tapiscia* (Staphyleaceae) from the middle Eocene of Oregon, USA. Tertiary Research, v.9, no.1-4, pp.59-66.

---1994. Fruits and seeds of the middle Eocene Nut Beds flora, Clarno Formation, Oregon. Palaeontographic Americana, no.58, 205p.

Marsh, O.C., 1873. Notice of new Tertiary mammals. American Journal of Science, ser.3, v.5, pp.407-410; 485-488.

---1874. Notice of new equine mammals from the Tertiary formations. American Journal of Science, ser.3, v.7, pp.147-158.

---1895. Reptilia of the Baptanodon beds. American Journal of Science, v.50, no.3, pp.405-406.

Martin, J.E., 1979. Hemphillian rodents from northern Oregon... University of Washington, PhD., 265p.

---1981. Contents of coprolites from Hemphillian sediments in northern Oregon ... Proc. South Dakota Acad. Sciences, v.60, pp.105-115.

---1983. Additions to the early Hemphillian (Miocene) Rattlesnake fauna from central Oregon. Proc. South Dakota Acad. Sciences, v.62, pp.23-33.

Matthew, W.D., 1909. Faunal lists of the Tertiary mammalia of the west. U.S. Geological Survey, Bulletin, 361, pp.91-138.

---1899. A provisional classification of the fresh-water Tertiary of the West. American Museum Natural History, Bull.12, pp.19-75.

MacFadden, B.J., 1984. Systematics and phylogeny of *Hipparion, Neohipparion, Nannippus,* and *Cormohipparion* ... from the Miocene and Pliocene of the New World. Amer. Museum Natural History, Bull., 179, 1-196.

MacGintie, H.D., 1933. The Trout Creek flora of southeastern Oregon. Carnegie Inst., Wash., Publ.416, pp.21-68.

McCornack, E.C., 1914. A study of Oregon Pleistocene. Univ. of Oregon, Bull., n.s., v.12, no.1, 16p.

---1928. Thomas Condon, pioneer geologist of Oregon. Eugene, Univ. of Oregon Press, 355p.

McFadden, J.J., 1986. Fossil flora near Gray Butte, Jefferson County, Oregon. Oregon Geology, v.48, no.5, pp.51- 55,58.

McKee, T.M., ?1970. Preliminary report on the fossil fruits and seeds found in the mammal quarry of the lower Tertiary Clarno Formation, Oregon. Oregon Museum of Science and Industry, Student Res. Center, 17p.

McKenna, M.C., 1990. Plagiomenids (Mammalia: ?Dermoptera) from the Oligocene of Oregon, Montana, and South Dakota, and middle Eocene of northwestern Wyoming. Geol. Society of America, Special Paper 243, pp.211-234.

McKillip, C.J., 1992. Paleoenvironment and biostratigraphy of the Eugene Formation near Salem, Oregon. Masters, University of Oregon, 109p.

Mellett, J.S., 1969. A skull of *Hemipsalodon* (Mammalia, order Deltatheridia) from the Clarno Formation of Oregon. American Museum Novitates, no.2387, 19p.

Merriam, C.W., 1942. Carboniferous and Permian corals from central Oregon. Journal of Paleontology, v.16, pp.372-381.

---and Berthiaume, S.A., 1943. Late Paleozoic formations of central Oregon. Geol. Soc. Amer., Bull., v.54, pt.1, pp.145-171.

Merriam, J.C., 1901. Contribution to the geology of the John Day basin. Univ. Calif. Publ. Geol. Sci., v.9, pp.269-314.

---1906. Carnivora from the Tertiary formations of the John Day region. Univ. Calif. Publ. Geol. Sci., v.5, pp.1-64.

---1913. Tapir remains from the late Cenozoic beds of the Pacific Coast region. Univ. Calif. Publ. Geol. Sci., v.7, no.9, pp.169-175.

---1916. Mammalian remains from a late Tertiary formation at Ironside, Oregon. Univ. Calif. Publ. Geol. Sci., v.10, no.9, pp.129-135.

---and Gilmore, C.W., 1928. An ichthyosaurian reptile from marine Cretaceous of Oregon. Carnegie Inst., Wash., Contrib. to Paleo., no.393, pp.1-4.

---and Sinclair, W.J., 1907. Tertiary faunas of the John Day region. Univ. Calif. Publ. Geol. Sci., v.5, no.11, pp.171-205.

---and Stock, C., 1927. A hyaenarctid bear from the later Tertiary of the John Day basin, Oregon. Carnegie Inst., Washington , Publication 346, pp.39-44.

---Stock, C., and Moody, C.L., 1925. The Pliocene Rattlesnake Formation and fauna of eastern Oregon, with notes on the geology of the Rattlesnake and Mascall deposits. Carnegie Inst., Wash., Publication 347, pp.43-92.

Merrill, G.P., 1924. The first one hundred years of American geology. New Haven, Yale University Press, 773p.

Meyer, H., 1973. The Oligocene Lyons flora of northwestern Oregon. Ore Bin, v.35, no.3, pp.37-51.

---and Manchester, S.R., 1997. The Oligocene Bridge Creek Flora of the John Day Formation, Oregon. Berkeley, University of California Press, 195p.

Miles, G.A., 1981. Planktonic foraminifera of the lower Tertiary Roseburg, Lookingglass, and Flournoy formations [Umpqua Group], southwest Oregon. Geological Society of America, Special Paper 184, pp.85-103.

Miller, A.H., 1911. Additions to the avifauna of the Pleistocene deposits at Fossil Lake, Oregon. Univ. Calif. Publ. Geol. Sci., v.7, no.5, pp.61-115.

---1931. An auklet from the Eocene of Oregon. Univ. Calif. Publ. Geol. Sci., v.20, pp.23-26.

---1944. Some Pliocene birds from Oregon and Idaho. Condor, v.46, pp.25-32.

Miller, C.N., 1992. Structurally preserved cones of *Pinus* from the Neogene of Idaho and Oregon. International Jour. Plant Science, v.153, no.1, pp.147-154.

Miller, L., 1899. Journal of first trip of University of California to John Day beds of eastern Oregon. University of Oregon, Museum of Natural History, Bull.19, 21p.

Miller, P.R., and Orr, W.N., 1986. The Scotts Mills Formation: Mid-Tertiary geologic history and paleogeography of the central Western Cascade Range, Oregon. Oregon Geology, v.48, no.12, pp.139-151.

---and Orr, W.N., 1988. Mid-Tertiary transgressive rocky coast sedimentation: central Western Cascade Range, Oregon. Jour. Sedimentary Petrology, v.58, no.6, pp.959-968.

Miller, R.R., 1965. Quaternary freshwater fishes of North America. *In*: Quaternary of the United States. Princeton, N.J., Princeton Univ. Press, pp.569-581.

Mitchell, E., 1966. Faunal succession of extinct North Pacific marine mammals. Norsk Hvalfangst-Tidende, no.3, pp.47-60.

Mobley, B.J., 1956. Geology of the southwest quarter of the Bates Quadrangle, Oregon. Univ. of Oregon, Masters, 66p.

Moore, E.J., 1963. Miocene marine mollusks from the Astoria Formation in Oregon. U.S. Geol. Surv., Prof. Paper 419, 190p.

---1971. Fossil mollusks of coastal Oregon. Oregon State Univ., Monograph no.10, 64p.

---1976. Oligocene marine mollusks from the Pittsburg Bluff Formation in Oregon. U.S. Geol. Survey, Prof. Paper 922, pp.1-66.

---and Addicott, W.O., 1987. The Miocene Pillarian and Newportian (Molluscan) Stages of Washington and Oregon and their usefulness in correlations from Alaska to California. U.S. Geol. Survey, Bull.1664, Shorter Contributions to Paleontology and Stratigraphy, pp.A1-A13.

Moore, R.C., and Vokes, H.E., 1953. Lower Tertiary crinoids from northwestern Oregon. U.S. Geol. Survey, Prof. Paper 233-E, pp.113-148.

Morris, E.M., and Wardlaw, B.R., 1986. Conodont ages for limestones of eastern Oregon and their implication for pre-Tertiary melange terranes. *In*: Vallier, T.L., and Brooks, H.C., eds., Geology of the Blue Mountain region of Oregon, Idaho, and Washington. U.S. Geol. Survey, Prof. Paper 1435, pp.59-63.

Mumford, D.F., 1989. Geology of the Elsie-lower Nehalem River area ... northwestern Oregon. Masters, Oregon State University, 392p.

Munthe, J., and Coombs, M.C., 1979. Miocene dome-skulled chalicotheres (Mammalia, Perissodactyla) from the western United States: a preliminary discussion of a bizzare structure. Journal of Paleontology, v.53, no.1, pp.77-91.

Murchey, B.L., and Jones, D.L., 1994. The environmental and tectonic significance of two coeval Permian radiolarian-sponge associations in eastern Oregon. *In:* Vallier, T., and Brooks, H., eds., Geology of the Blue Mountains region of Oregon, Idaho, and Washington. U.S.G.S. Prof. Paper 1439, pp. 183-198.

Nauss, A.L., and Smith, P.L., 1988. *Lithiotis* (bivalvia) bioherms in the lower Jurassic of east-central Oregon, U.S.A. Paleo., Paleo., Paleo., v.65, pp.253-268.

Naylor, B.G., A new species of *Taricha* [Caudata: Salamandridae], from the Oligocene John Day Formation of Oregon. Canada Jour. Earth Science, v.16, pp.970-973.

Newberry, J.S., 1882. Brief descriptions of plants, chiefly Tertiary from western North America. U.S. National Museum, Proc.5, pp.502-514.

Newcomb, R.C., 1958. Yonna Formation of the Klamath River Basin, Oregon. Northwest Science, v.32, no.2, pp.41-48.

Newton, C.R., 1983. Paleozoogeographic affinities of Norian bivalves from the Wrangellian, Peninsular, and Alexander terranes, western North America. *In:* Stevens, C.H., ed., Pre-Jurassic rocks in western North American suspect terranes. Soc. Econ. Paleont. and Mineralogists, Pacific Sect., pp.37-48.

---1986. Late Triassic bivalves of the Martin Bridge Limestone, Hells Canyon, Oregon: taphonomy, paleoecology, paleozoogeography. *In*: Vallier,T.L., and Brooks, H.C., eds., Geology of the Blue Mountains region of Oregon, Idaho, and Washington. U.S. Geol. Survey, Prof. Paper 1435, pp.7-17.

---1987. Biogeographic complexity in Triassic bivalves of the Wallowa terrane, northwestern United States: Oceanic islands, not continents, provide the best analogues. Geology, v.15, pp.1126-1129.

---et al., 1987. Systematics and paleoecology of Norian (late Triassic) bivalves from a tropical island arc: Wallowa terrane, Oregon. Journal of Paleontology, v.61, no.4, Suppl.4, 83p.

Niem, A.R., et al., 1994. Sedimentary, volcanic, and tectonic framework of forearc basins and the Mist gas field, northwest Oregon. *In:* Swanson, D.A., and Haugerud, R.A., eds., Geologic field trips in the Pacific Northwest. Geol. Soc. America, Ann. Mtg., pp.IF1-IF42.

Nicholson, N.A., 1897. The ancient life - history of the earth. New York, Appleton, 406p.

Nilsen, T., ed., 1984. Geology of the upper Cretaceous Hornbrook Formation, Oregon and California. Pacific Section, Society of Economic Paleontologists and Mineralogists, 257p.

Oliver, E., 1934. A Miocene flora from the Blue Mountains, Oregon. Carnegie Inst., Wash., Publication 455, pt.1, pp.1-27.

Orr, E.L., and Orr, W.N., 1984. Bibliography of Oregon paleontology, 1792-1983. Oregon Dept. Geol. and Mineral Indus., Special Paper 17, 82p.

---and Orr, W.N., 1996. Geology of the Pacific Northwest. New York, McGraw-Hill, 409p.

---Orr, W.N., and Baldwin, E., 1992. Geology of Oregon. Dubuque, Kendall-Hunt Publ., 254p.

Orr, W.N., 1986. A Norian (late Triassic) ichthyosaur from the Martin Bridge Limestone, Wallowa Mountains, Oregon. *In*: Vallier, T.L., and Brooks, H.C., Geology of the Blue Mountains Region of Oregon, Idaho, and Washington. U.S. Geol. Survey, Prof. Paper 1435, pp.41-47.

---and Katsura, K.T., 1985. Oregon's oldest vertebrates (Ichthyosauria [Reptilia]). Oregon Geology, v.47, no.7, pp.75-77.

---and Kooser, M.A., 1971. Oregon Eocene decapod Crustacea. Ore Bin, v.33, pp.119-129.

---and Miller, P.R., 1983. Fossil cetacea (whales) in the Oregon Western Cascades. Oregon Geology, v.45, no.9, pp.95- 98.

---and Miller, P.R., 1984. The trace fossil *Cylindrichnus* in the Oregon Oligocene. Oregon Geology, v.46, no.5, pp.51- 52.

---and Orr, E.L., 1981. Handbook of Oregon plant and animal fossils. Eugene, 285p.

---Ehlen, J., and Zaitzeff, J.B., 1971. A late Tertiary diatom flora from Oregon. Calif. Acad. Sciences, Proc., 4th Ser., pp.489-500.

Packard, E.L.,1923. An aberrant oyster from the Oregon Eocene. Oregon Univ. Publ., v.2, no.4, pp.1-6.

---1940. A new turtle from the marine Miocene of Oregon. Oregon State Univ., Studies in Geology, no.2, 31p.

---1947. Fossil baleen from the Pliocene of Cape Blanco, Oregon. Oregon State Univ., Studies in Geology, v.5, pp.1-12.

---1947. A fossil sea lion from Cape Blanco, Oregon. Oregon State Univ., Studies in Geology, v.6, pp.13-22.

---1947. A pinniped humerus from the Astoria Miocene of Oregon. Oregon State Univ., Studies in Geology, v.7, pp.23-32.

---1952. Fossil edentates of Oregon. Oregon State Univ., Studies in Geology, v.8, 15p.

---and Allison, I.S., 1980. Fossil bear tracks in Lake County, Oregon. Oregon Geology, v.42, no.4, pp.71-72.

---and Jones, D.L., 1965. Cretaceous pelecypods of the genus *Pinna* from the Pacific Coast region of North America. Journal of Paleontology, v.39, no.5, pp.901-905.

---and Kellogg, A.R., 1934. A new cetothere from the Miocene Astoria Formation of Newport, Oregon. Carnegie Inst., Wash., Publication 477, pp.1-62.

Peck, D.L., Imlay, R.W., and Popenoe, W.P., 1956. Upper Cretaceous rocks of parts of southwestern Oregon and northern California. Bull., Amer. Association of Petroleum Geologists, v.40, no.8, pp.1968-1984.

---et al., 1964. Geology of the central and northern parts of the Western Cascade Range in Oregon. U.S. Geological Survey, Prof. Paper 449, 56p.

Pessagno, E.A., and Blome, C.D., 1986. Faunal affinities and tectonogenesis of Mesozoic rocks in the Blue Mountains province of eastern Oregon and western Idaho. *In*: Vallier, T.L., and Brooks, H.C., eds. Geology of the Blue Mountains region of Oregon, Idaho, and Washington. U.S. Geol. Survey, Prof. Paper 1435, pp.65-78.

---and Blome, C.D. Implications of new Jurassic stratigraphic, geochronometrics, and paleolatitudinal data from the western Klamath terrane (Smith River and Rogue Valley subterranes). Geology, v.18, no.7, pp.665-668.

Peterson, J.V., 1964. Plant fossils of the Clarno Formation. Earth Sci., v.17, no.1, pp.11-15.

Popenoe, W.P., Imlay, R.W., and Murphy, M., 1960. Correlation of the Cretaceous formations of the Pacific Coast (United States and northwestern Mexico). Geol. Society of America, Bull., v.71, pp.1491-1540.

Pouchet, F.A., 1882. The universe; or, the wonders of creation. Portland, Maine, Hallett Publ., 761p.

Pratt, J.A., 1988. Paleoenvironment of the Eocene/Oligocene Hancock Mammal Quarry, upper Clarno Formtion, Oregon. Masters, Univ. of Oregon, 104p.

Prothero, D.R., and Schoch, R.M., eds., 1989. The evolution of Perissodactyls. New York, Oxford Univ. Press, 537p.

Ramp, L., 1969. Dothan (?) fossils discovered. Ore Bin, v.31, no.12, pp.245-246.

Rathbun, M.J., 1926. The fossil stalk-eyed Crustacea of the Pacific slope of North America. U.S. National Museum Bull.138, 155p.

Rau, W., 1977. Pacific Northwest Tertiary benthonic foraminiferal biostratigraphic framework; an overview. Geol. Society America, Special Paper 184, pp.67-84.

Ray, C.E., 1976. Fossil marine mammals of Oregon. Systematic Zool., v.25, no.4, pp.420-436.

Read, C.B., and Brown, R.W., 1937. American Cretaceous ferns of the genus *Tempskya*. U.S. Geol. Survey, Prof. Paper 186-F, pp.127-128.

---and Merriam, C.W., 1940. A Pennsylvanian flora from central Oregon. American Journal of Science, v.138, no.2, pp.107-111.

Rensberger, J.M., 1971. Entophychine pocket gophers (Mammalia, Geomyoidea) of the early Miocene John Day Formation, Oregon. University of Calif. Publ. Geol. Sci., v.90, 209p.

---1973. Pleurolicine rodents (Geomyoidea) of the John Day Formation, Oregon, and their relationships to taxa from the early and middle Miocene, South Dakota. Univ. Calif. Publ. Geol. Sci., v.102, 95p.

---1979. Hemphillian rodents from northern Oregon and their relationships to other rodent faunas in North America. PhD., Univ. of Washington.

---1983. Successions of Meniscomyine and Allomyine rodents (Aplodontidae) in the Oligo-Miocene John Day Formation, Oregon. University of California Publications in Geological Sciences, v.124, 157p.

Repenning, C.A., 1967. Subfamilies and genera of the Soricidae. U.S. Geol. Survey, Prof. Paper 565, 74p.

---and Tedford, R., 1977. Otaroid seals of the Neogene. U.S. Geol. Survey, Prof. Paper 992, pp.1-93.

---Weasma, T.R., and Scott, G.R., 1995. The early Pleistocene [latest Blancan-earliest Irvingtonian] Froman Ferry fauna... U.S. Geological Survey, Bull.2105, 86p.

Retallack, G.J., 1981. Preliminary observations on fossil soils in the Clarno Formation (Eocene to early Oligocene) near Clarno, Oregon. Oregon Geology, v.43, no.11, pp.147-150.

---1991. A field guide to mid-Tertiary paleosols and paleoclimatic changes in the high desert of central Oregon-Part 1. Oregon Geology, v.53, no.3, pp.51-59.

---1991. A field guide to mid-Tertiary paleosols and paleoclimatic changes in the high desert of central Oregon-Part 2. Oregon Geology, v.53, no.4, pp.75-80.

---Bestland, E.A., and Fremd, T.J., 1996. Reconstructions of Eocene Oligocene plants and animals of central Oregon. Oregon Geology, v.58, no.3, pp.51-69.

Richardson, H.E., 1950. The geology of the Sweet Home petrified forest. Univ. of Oregon, Masters. 44p.

Robinson, P.T., Brem, G.F., and McKee, E.H., 1984. John Day Formation of Oregon: a distal record of early Cascade volcanism. Geology, v.12, pp.229-232.

Rooth, G.H., 1974. Biostratigraphy and paleoecology of the Coaledo and Bastendorff formations, southwestern Oregon. Oregon State Univ., PhD, 207p.

---1987. Miocene *Gyrolithes* (Lebensspurn) from the Astoria Formation, Lincoln County, Oregon. Oregon Geology, v.49, no.4, pp.47-48.

Rose, K.D., and Rensberger, J.M., 1983. Upper dentition of *Ekgmoweschashala* (Omomyid primate) from the John Day Formation, Oligo-Miocene of Oregon. Folia primatol., v.41, p.102-111.

Roth, B., 1979. Late Cenozoic marine invertebrates from northwest California and southwest Oregon. University of California, Berkeley, PhD., 2 vols.

Sanborn, E.I., 1937. The Comstock flora of west central Oregon. Carnegie Inst., Wash., Publication 465, pp.1-28.

---1947. The Scio flora of western Oregon. Oregon State Univ., Studies in Geology, v.4, pp.1-47.

Savage, N.M., and Amundson, C.T., 1979. Middle Devonian (Givetian) conodonts from central Oregon. Journal of Paleontology, v.53, pp.1395-1400.

Scharf, D.W., 1935. A Miocene mammalian fauna from Succor Creek, southeastern Oregon. Carnegie Inst., Wash., Publ.453, pp.97-118.

Schenck, H.G., 1928. Stratigraphic relations of western Oregon Oligocene formations. Univ. Calif. Publ. Geol. Sci., v.18, 50p.

---1931. The stratigraphy and paleontology of the Triassic of the Suplee region of central Oregon. Univ. of Oregon, Masters.

---1936. Nuculid bivalves of the genus *Acila*. Geological Society of Amer., Special Paper 4, 149p.

Schoch, R.M., 1989. A review of the Tapiroids. *In*: Prothero, D.R., and Schoch, R.M., eds., *The Evolution of Perissodactyls*, New York, Oxford Univ. Press, pp.298- 320.

Schultz, C., and Falkenbach, C.H., 1968. The phylogeny of the oreodonts. American Museum of National Hist., Bull., v.139, 498p.

Scott, R.A., 1913. Fossil fruits and seeds from the Eocene Clarno Formation of Oregon. Palaeontographica B., v.96, pp.66- 97.

Scott, W.B., 1937. A history of land mammals in the Western Hemisphere. New York, Mcmillan, 693p.

Senowbari-Daryan, B., and Stanley, G.D., 1988. Triassic sponges (Sphinctozoa) from Hells Canyon, Oregon. Journal of Paleontology, v.62, no.3, pp.419-423.

Shotwell, J.A., 1951. A fossil sea-lion from Fossil Point, Oregon. Geol. Society of America, Bull., v.2, p.97 (abstr.).

---1956. Hemphillian mammalian assemblage from northeastern Oregon. Geol. Society America, Bull.67, pp.717-738.

---1958. Inter-community relationships in Hemphillian (Mid- Pliocene) mammals. Ecology, v.39, no.2, pp.271-282.

---1963. The Juntura Basin: Studies in earth history and paleoecology. American Philos. Society, Trans., v.53, 77p.

---1968. Miocene mammals of southeastern Oregon. Univ. of Oregon, Museum of Natural History, Bull.14, 67p.

---1970. Pliocene mammals of southeast Oregon and adjacent Idaho. Univ. of Oregon, Museum of Natural History, Bull.17, 103p.

Shroba, C.S., 1992. Paleoecology and taphonomy of middle Tertiary and Recent sediments from Oregon and Washington, and biogeographic affinities of the Wallowa terrane, eastern Oregon. PhD., Univ. of Oregon, 181p.

Shufeldt, R.W., 1891. On a collection of fossil birds from the Equus beds of Oregon. American Naturalist, v.25, pp.259-262.

---1912. Prehistoric birds of Oregon. Overland Monthly, v.60, pp.536-642.

---1915. Fossil birds in the Marsh Collection of Yale University. Conn. Acad. Arts and Sciences, Trans., v.19, pp.1-110.

Sinclair, W.J., 1901. Discovery of a new fossil tapir in Oregon. Journal of Geology, v.9, pp.702-707.

---1905. New or imperfectly known rodents and ungulates from the John Day series. Univ. Calif. Publ. Geol. Sci., v.4, no.6, pp.125-143.

Smith, G.R., 1981. Late Cenozoic freshwater fishes of North America. Ann. Review Ecol. Systematics, 12, pp.163-193.

---et al., 1982. Fish biostratigraphy of late Miocene to Pleistocene sediments of the Western Snake River plain. *In*: Bonnichsen, B., and Breckenridge, R.M., eds., Cenozoic geology of Idaho. Idaho Bureau of Mines and Geology, Bull.26, pp.519-541.

Smith, H., 1932. The fossil flora of Rockville, Oregon. Univ. of Oregon, Masters.

Smith, J.P., 1912. Occurrence of coral reefs in the Triassic of North America. American Journal of Science, 4th ser., v.33, pp.92-96.

Smith, P.L., 1980. Correlation of the members of the Jurassic Snowshoe Formation in the Izee Basin of east-central Oregon. Canadian Jour. Earth Science, v.17, no.12, pp.1603-1608.

---et al., 1988. An ammonite zonation for the lower Jurassic of Canada and the United States: the Pliensbachian. Canadian Jour. Earth Science, v.25, pp.1503-1523.

Smith, W., and Allen, J.E., 1941. Geology and physiology of the northern Wallowa Mountains, Oregon. Oregon Dept. Geol. and Mineral Indus., Bull.12, 64p.

Snavely, P.D., and Baldwin, E.M., 1948. Siletz River volcanic series, northwestern Oregon. American Assoc. Petroleum Geol., Bull.,v.32, pp.806-812.

---MacLeod, N.S., and Rau, W.W., 1969. Geology of the Newport area, Oregon. Ore Bin, v.31, no.2, pp.25-47.

---Rau, W.W., and Wagner, H.C., 1964. Miocene stratigraphy of the Yaquina Bay area, Newport, Oregon. Ore Bin, v.26, no.8, pp.133-151.

---et al., 1975. Alsea Formation; an Oligocene marine sedimentary sequence in the Oregon Coast Range. U.S. Geol. Survey, Bull.1395-F, 21p.

Sorauf, J.E., 1972. Middle Devonian coral faunas (rugose) from Washington and Oregon. Journal of Paleontology, v.46, no.3, pp.426-439.

Squires, R.L., 1989. Pteropods (Molluscs: Gastropoda) from Tertiary formations of Washington and Oregon. Journal of Paleontology, v.63, no.4, pp.443-448.

Stanley, G.D., 1986. Late Triassic coelenterate faunas of western Idaho and northeastern Oregon: implications for biostratigraphy and paleogeography. *In*: Vallier, T.L., and Brooks, H.C., eds., Geology of the Blue Mountains Region of Oregon, Idaho, and Washington. U.S. Geol. Survey, Prof. Paper 1435, pp.23-35.

---and Beauvais, L., 1990. Middle Jurassic corals from the Wallowa terrane, west-central Idaho. Journal of Paleontology, v.64, no.3, pp.352-362.

---and Senowbari-Daryan, B., 1986. Upper Triassic, Dachstein-type, reef limestone from the Wallowa Mountains, Oregon: first reported occurrence in the United States. Palaios, v.1, pp.172-177.

---and Whalen, M.T., 1989. Triassic corals and spongimorphs from Hells Canyon, Wallowa terrane, Oregon. Journal of Paleo., v.63, no.6, pp.800-819.

Stearns, R.E.C., 1902. Fossil shells of the John Day region. Science, n.s., v.15, pp.153-154.

---1906. Fossil mollusca from the John Day and Mascall beds of Oregon. Univ. Calif. Publ. Geol. Sci., v.5, no.3, pp.67-70.

Steere, M., 1955. Fossil localities in the Coos Bay area, Oregon. Ore Bin, v.17, no.6, pp.39-43.

---1958. Fossil localities of the Eugene area, Oregon. Ore Bin, v.20, no.6, pp.51-59.

---1959. Fossil localities of the Salem-Dallas area, Oregon. Ore Bin, v. 21, no.6, pp.51-58.

Sternberg, C., 1909. Life of a fossil hunter. New York, Holt Publ., 286p.

Stevens, C.H., and Rycerski, B.A., 1983. Permian colonial rugose corals in the western Americas - aids in positioning of suspect terranes. *In*: Stevens, C.H., ed., PreJurassic rocks in western North American suspect terranes. Society Economic Paleont. and Mineralogists, Pacific Section, pp.23-33.

---Miller, M.M., and Nestell, M., 1987. A new Permian Waagenophyllid coral from the Klamath Mountains, California. Journal of Paleo., v.61, no.4, pp.690-699.

Stewart, R.E., 1956. Stratigraphic implications of some Cenozoic foraminifera from western Oregon. Ore Bin, v.18, no.1, pp.1-6.

---and Stewart, K., 1951. Oligocene shale in Astoria, Oregon. Ore Bin, v.13, no.11, p.74.

Stirton, R.A., 1940. Phylogeny of North American Equidae. Univ. of California Publ. Geol. Sciences, v.25, no.4, pp.165-198.

---1944. A rhinoceros tooth from the Clarno Eocene of Oregon. Journal of Paleo., v.18, no.3, pp.65-67.

---and Rensberger, J.M., 1964. Occurrence of the insectivore genus *Micropternodus* in the John Day Formation of central Oregon. Southern Calif. Acad. Scences., Bull., v.63, pt.2, pp.57-80.

Stock, C., 1930. Carnivora new to the Mascall Miocene fauna of eastern Oregon. Carnegie Inst., Contributions to Paleo., Publication 404, pp.43-48.

---1946. Oregon's wonderland of the past, the John Day. Science Monthly, v.63, pp.57-65.

---and Furlong, E.L., 1922. A marsupial from the John Day Oligocene of Logan Butte, eastern Oregon. Univ. Calif. Dept. Geol. Sci., Bull., v.13, no.8, pp.311-317.

Storer, R.W., 1989. The Pleistocene western grebe *Aechmophorus* (Aves, Podicipedidae) from Fossil Lake, Oregon: a comparison with recent material. Univ. of Michigan, Museum of Paleo., Contrib. from the Museum of Paleontology, v.27, pp.321-326.

Stricker, L., and Taylor, D.G., 1989. A new marine crocodile (Mesosuchia: Metriorhynchidae) from the Snowshoe Formation (Jurassic) Oregon. Journal of Vertebrate Paleo., v.9, Suppl. to No.3, p.40A.

Sudworth, G.B., 1908. Forest trees of the Pacific slope. U.S. Dept. of Agriculture, 441p.

Taggart, R., 1990. The vanished forests of Succor Creek. Natural Science, v.4, no.1, pp.15-18.

---and Cross, A.T., 1990. Plant successions and interpretations in Miocene volcanic deposits, Pacific Northwest. Geol. Society of America, Special Paper 244, pp.57-68.

Taylor, D.G., 1980. Jurassic shallow marine invertebrate depth zones, with exemplification from the Snowshow Formation, Oregon. Oregon Geology, v.44, no.5, pp.51-56.

---1988. Middle Jurassic (late Aalenian and early Bajocian) ammonite biochronology of the Snowshoe Formation, Oregon. Oregon Geology, v.50, no.11-12, pp.123-138.

Taylor, D.W., 1960. Distribution of the freshwater clam *Pisidium ultramonanum* ; a zoogeographic inquiry. American Journal of Science, Bradley Vol., v.258-A, pp.325-334.

---1963. Mollusks of the Black Butte local fauna. Amer. Philos. Soc., Trans., v.53, pt.1, pp.35-40.

Tedford, R.H., Barnes, L.G., and Ray, C.E., 1994. Early Miocene littoral ursoid carnivoran *Kolponomos*: systematics and mode of life. *In*: Berta, A., and Demere, T.A., Contributions in marine mammal paleontology ... Proc. San Diego Society Natural History, v.29, pp.19-32.

Thompson, G.C., Yett, J.R., and Green, K.E., 1984. Subsurface stratigraphy of the Ochoco Basin, Oregon. Oregon, Dept. Geol. and Mineral Indus., Oil and Gas Investig. 8, 22p.

Thoms, R.E., 1965. Biostratigraphy of the Umpqua Formation, southwest Oregon. Univ. Calif., PhD.

---and Smith, H.C., 1973. Fossil bighorn sheep from Lake County, Oregon. Ore Bin, v.35, no.8, pp.125-134.

Thorpe, M.R., 1921. Two new fossil carnivora. American Journal of Science, ser.5, v.1, pp.477-483.

---1922. *Araeocyon*, a probable old world migrant. American Journal of Sci., ser.5, v.3, pp.371-377.

---1925. A new species of extinct peccary from Oregon. Amer. Jour. Science, ser.5, v.7, pp.393-397.

Tidwell, W.D., 1975. Common fossil plants of western North America. Brigham Young University Press, Provo, Utah, 197p.

Toohey, L., 1959. The species of *Nimravus* [Carnivora, Felidae]. America Museum of Natural History, Bull., v.118, art.2, pp.75-112.

Turner, F.E., 1938. Stratigraphy and mollusca of the Eocene of western Oregon. Geol. Soc. America, Special Paper 10, 130p.

Uyeno, T., and Miller, R.R., 1963. Summary of late Cenozoic freshwater fish records for North America. Univ. Mich. Mus. Zool., Occasional Papers, no.631, 34p.

Vallier, T.L., and Brooks, H.C., eds., 1986. Geology of the Blue Mountains region of Oregon, Idaho, and Washington. U.S. Geol. Survey, Prof. Paper 1435, 93p.

Vanderhof, V.L., 1937. A study of the Miocene sirenian *Desmostylus*. Univ. Calif. Publ. Geol. Sci., v.42, pp.169-262.

VanFrank, R., 1955. *Palaeotaricha oligocenica*, new genus and species; an Oligocene salamander from Oregon. Brevoria, no.45, p.1-12.

VanLandingham, S.L., 1990. Observations on the biostratigraphy of Pliocene and Pleistocene diatomites from the Terrebonne district, Deschutes County, Oregon. Micropaleontology, v.36, no.2, pp.182-196.

Vokes, H.E., Norbisrath, H., and Snavely, P.D., 1949. Geology of the Newport-Waldport area, Lincoln County, Oregon. U.S. Geol. Survey, Oil and Gas Inv. Map, OM88.

---Snavely, P.D., and Myers, D.A., 1951. Geology of the southern and southwestern border areas, Willamette Valley, Oregon. U.S. Geological Survey, Oil and Gas Inv. Map OM-110.

Wallace, R.E., 1946. A Miocene mammalian fauna from Beatty (Beatys) Buttes, Oregon. Carnegie Inst., Wash., Publ.551, pp.113-134.

Wang, X., and Tedford, R.H., 1992. The status of genus *Nothocyon* Matthew, 1899 (Carnivora): an arctoid not a canid. Journal of Vertebrate Paleo., v.12, no.2, pp.223-229.

Wardlaw, B.R., Nestell, M., and Dutro, J.T., 1982. Biostratigraphy and structural setting of the Permian Coyote Butte Formation of central Oregon. Geology, v.10, pp.13-16.

Warren, W.C., and Norbisrath, H., 1946. Stratigraphy of upper Nehalem River basin, northwestern Oregon. American Assoc. Petroleum Geol., Bull., v.30, no.2, pp.213-237.

---Norbisrath, H., and Grivetti, R.M., 1945. Geology of northwestern Oregon, west of the Willamette River and north of latitude 45 15'. U.S. Geol. Survey, Oil and Gas Inv. Map, OM 42.

Washburne, C.W., 1914. Reconnaissance of the geology and oil prospects of northwestern Oregon. U.S. Geol. Survey, Bull.590, 111p.

Weaver, C.E., 1942. Paleontology of the marine Tertiary formations of Oregon and Washington. Univ. of Wash., Publ. in Geology, v.5, pt.I, II, III, 790p.

Welton, B.J., 1972. Fossil sharks in Oregon. Ore Bin, v.34, no.10, pp.161-170.

Whalen, M.T., 1988. Depositional history of an upper Triassic drowned carbonate platform sequence: Wallowa terrane, Oregon and Idaho. Geological Society of America, Bull., v.100, pp.1097-1110.

White, C.A., 1885. On invertebrate fossils from the Pacific Coast. U.S. Geol. Survey, Bull.51, pp.28-32.

White, J.D.L., 1994. Intra-arc basin deposits within the Wallowa terrane, Pittsburg Landing area, Oregon and Idaho. *In:* Vallier, T., and Brooks, H., Geology of the Blue Mountains region of Oregon, Idaho, and Washington. U.S. Geol. Survey, Prof. Paper 1439, pp.75-89.

---et al., 1992. Middle Jurassic strata link Wallowa, Old Ferry, and Izee terranes in the accreted Blue Mountains island arc, northeast Oregon. Geology, v.20, no.8, pp.729-732.

Wolfe, J.A., 1954. The Collawash flora of the upper Clackamas River basin, Oregon. Geol. Society of Oregon Country, Newsletter, v.20, no.10, pp.89-94.

---1960. Early Miocene floras of northwest Oregon. Univ. of Calif. PhD.

---1969. Neogene floristic and vegetational history of the Pacific Northwest. Madrono, v.20, pp.83-110.

---1981. Paleoclimatic significance of the Oligocene and Neogene floras of the northwestern United States. *In*: Niklas, K.J., Paleobotany, paleoecology, and evolution, v.2, New York, Prager, pp.79-101.

---and Hopkins, D..M., 1967. Climatic changes recorded by Tertiary land floras in northwestern North America. *In*: Hatai, K., ed., Tertiary correlations and climatic changes in the Pacific. Pacific Science Cong. ll, Tokyo, 1966, pp.67-76.

Woodburne, M.O., and Robinson, P.T., 1977. A new late Hemingfordian mammal fauna from the John Day Formation, Oregon, and its stratigraphic implications. Journal of Paleontology, v.51, no.4, pp.740-757.

Wortman, J.L., and Matthew, W.D., 1899. The ancestry of certain members of the Canidae, the Viverridae, and Procyonidae. Amer. Museum of Natural History, Bull.12, pp.109-138.

Zullo, V.A., 1964. The echinoid genus *Salenia* in the eastern Pacific. Paleontology, v.7, pt.2, pp.331-349.

---1969. A late Pleistocene marine invertebrate fauna from Bandon, Oregon. Calif. Academy of Sciences, Proc., 4th ser., v.39, no.12, pp.346-361.

---1969. Pleistocene symbiosis, pinnotherid crabs in pelecypods from Cape Blanco, Oregon. Veliger, v.12, no.1, pp.72-73.

Whitlock, C., 1992. Vegetational and climatic history of the Pacific Northwest during the last 20,000 years. The Northwest Environmental Journal, v.8, pp.5-28.

Worona, M., and Whitlock, C., 1995. Late Quaternary vegetation and climate history near Little Lake, central Coast Range, Oregon. Geological Society America, Bull., v.107, pp.867-876.

Zittel, Karl von, 1913. Text-book of paleontology. London, Macmillan, v.1.

INDEX

Dalzell, Bonnie, 246, 260
Daonella 97-98
Dating 79-81, 267
David, Lore R. 237-238
Davis, Leander 285-286, 290, 312, 316
Day, William 290
Days Creek Fm. 114, 197
Deer 302-303
Deer Butte Fm. 330
Denning Spring Flora 16-17
Dennstaedtia 32
Dentalium 153
Derbya 92
Deschutes County 63-66, 242-243
Deschutes Fm. 63-66, 242
Desmatophoca 249-250
Desmostylus 258-260
Detling, Mildred 136-137
Diatoms 54-55, 65-66, 170
Dibunophyllum 90
Diceratherium 307
Dickinson, William 105-106
Dicksonia 14
Diller, Joseph 113-114, 129, 154
Dinictis 298
Dinosaur 214
Diploclisia 27
Discocyclina 133
Distichophyllia 100
Distillation 2
Dodds, Betty 160
Dogs *see* Canidae
Donovan Fm. 111
Dosinia 168
Dothan Fm. 118
Dott, Robert 115, 118-119, 135
Douglas County 11-12, 132-134, 197
Downing, Ken 329
Downs, Theodore 311-313
Drake, Ellen 283-284
Drake, John 120, 279
Drewsey Fm. 324-327
Dromomeryx 312
Dryopteris 17
Duncan, George 225, 342
Dyticonastis 210
Eagle Creek Flora 60-61
Eaton, George 282
Ehlen, Judi 170

Ekgmowechashala 297-298
Elk River Fm. 172-173, 246
Elk terrane 118
Elkhorn Ridge Argillite 102
Elkton Fm. 134-135
Emlong, Douglas 251, 253-254, 259, 305
Empire Fm. 166-170, 250, 257
Enaliarctos 247-248
Enhydra 246
Entoptychine rodents 309
Epigondonella 117
Epiphragmophora 176
Epitonium 132
Eugene Fm. 147-151, 195
Eumetopias 250
Exogyra 121
Extinctions 96-97, 229, 348
Fecal preservation 323
Feldmann, Rodney 196-198
Felidae 298-299
Ficus 29, 32, 39, 43
Fish, bony 236-238
Fish, freshwater 238-245
Fish scales 237
Fisher, Richard 34
Fisher Fm. 30-31, 206
Flat clams 98
Floras Lake Sandstone 169, 171
Fluminicola 176
Follo, Michael, 99-100
Fontaine, William 11, 15
Foraminifera 93, 132-137, 140, 159
Fossil Lake *see* Lake County
Fossil soils *see* Paleosols
Fraser, Edward 241
Fremd, Ted 292
Fryberger, Jake 254
Fulgurofusus 143
Furlong, Eustace 318
Fusulinids 92-93
Gabb, William 76
Galeodea 132
Galice Fm. 117-118
Gari 132
George, John 336
Gervillia 101
Gibbs, George 161, 256, 336
Gidley, James 334
Gilmore, Charles 211, 213, 215, 334